Engineering
Complex Systems
with Models and Objects

Other McGraw-Hill Books of Interest

ISBN	AUTHOR	TITLE
0-07-000748-9	Aiken	*Data Reverse Engineering: Untying the Legacy Knot*
0-07-001974-6	Andriole	*Managing Systems Requirements: Methods, Tools, and Cases*
0-07-015840-1	Davis	*201 Principles of Software Development*
0-07-032826-9	Jones	*Applied Software Measurement: Assuring Productivity and Quality*
0-07-036929-1	Leach	*Software Reuse: Methods, Models, and Costs*
0-07-039400-8	Lyu	*The Handbook of Software Reliability Engineering*
0-07-042948-0	Modell	*A Professional's Guide to Systems Analysis, 2/e*
0-07-052229-4	Pressman	*A Manager's Guide to Software Engineering*
0-07-059574-7	Sodhi/Sodhi	*Object-Oriented Methods for Software Development*
0-07-061719-8	Stone	*Developing Software Applications in a Changing IT Environment*

To order or receive additional information on these or any other McGraw-Hill titles, in the United States please call 1-800-722-4726. In other countries, contact your local McGraw-Hill representative.

Engineering Complex Systems with Models and Objects

David W. Oliver

Timothy P. Kelliher

James G. Keegan, Jr.

McGraw-Hill

New York   San Francisco   Washington, D.C.   Auckland   Bogotá
Caracas   Lisbon   London   Madrid   Mexico City   Milan
Montreal   New Delhi   San Juan   Singapore
Sydney   Tokyo   Toronto

Library of Congress Cataloging-in-Publication Data

Oliver, David W.
  Engineering complex systems with models and objects / David W.
Oliver, Timothy P. Kelliher, James G. Keegan, Jr.
      p.   cm.
  Includes bibliographical references and index.
  ISBN 0-07-048188-1
  1. Systems engineering. 2. Systems analysis. I. Kelliher,
Timothy P. II. Keegan, James G. III. Title.
TA168.055   1997
620'.001'1—dc21   97-4055
                                                            CIP

McGraw-Hill

A Division of The McGraw·Hill Companies

1 2 3 4 5 6 7 8 9 0   FGR/FGR   9 0 2 1 0 9 8 7

ISBN 0-07-048188-1

*The sponsoring editor for this book was John Wyzalek, the editing
supervisor was Paul R. Sobel, and the production supervisor was
Suzanne W. B. Rapcavage. It was set in Century Schoolbook by Ron
Painter of McGraw-Hill's Professional Book Group composition unit.*

Printed and bound by Quebecor/Fairfield.

McGraw-Hill books are available at special quantity discounts to use
as premiums and sales promotions, or for use in corporate training programs. For more information, please write to the Director of Special
Sales, McGraw-Hill, 11 West 19th Street, New York, NY 10011. Or contact your local bookstore.

 This book is printed on recycled, acid-free paper containing a
minimum of 50% recycled, de-inked fiber.

To Diane
—dwo

To Margaret, Katherine, and Colleen
—tpk

To May and Jennifer
—jgk

Contents

Preface

Origins of the Book

This book began as a result of experiences at a meeting in London in December 1992. This was one of the formative meetings of the IEEE Technical Committee on Engineering of Computer-Based Systems. A group of senior systems engineers from around the world met to share their experiences and discuss engineering of computer-based systems as a profession. There was an effusive sharing of how work was done in different institutions.

After a day or so it became apparent that it was difficult to share how work was being done by the institutions represented because the same words had different meanings for many of the participants and a common perspective was missing. The group began to describe their ideas and experience to one another using graphic models being developed in the U.S. and in Europe to describe systems. An acceptable temporary notation was chosen to create initial draft models. Discussion and alteration of the models began to generate consensus on some issues and to identify and clearly state issues which were unresolved. It worked to apply the same modeling techniques to describe both systems and the engineering process for designing and specifying systems. This book was inspired by the London experience and it draws on the publications and tutorials developed by the authors over the last decade.

Goals of the Book

This book is an attempted to describe the best practices of systems engineering. The same modeling techniques is used to describe the systems engineering process and to describe complex systems themselves. The first goal is to describe the basic abstractions needed to do the work independently of any particular methodology or notation. The approach is to define the work steps of the process and to develop an information model for each of the major steps. The result is a metaprocess description which can be tailored to organization culture, particular methodologies, and tools. A second goal of the book is to clarify the choices that exist in organizing the information into useful views or subsets of the complete system description. The models are organized such that they support trade-offs to find a near optimal solution to system problems. The third goal of this book is to demonstrate the fact that complex systems are really systems of systems and that the same basic engineering process can be applied to the larger systems and the smaller ones from which they are composed. The models are organized such that they support analysis at the industry and business levels, through the systems level and on down to the subsystem level by applying a single repeated technical core process at all levels.

Our final goal of the book is to provide sufficient examples and exercises that clarify the basic abstractions used, the process used, and the work done in defining a system.

Audience

The authors intend that this book be useful for several audiences: managers, engineers, students, and developers of tools to support engineering of complex systems. The text is intended to serve both as an introduction to modeling and the application of modern object-oriented techniques and as a reference for more experienced users. In this role engineers can use the text to improve their core competencies and to refer back to during daily work. Graduate and undergraduate students who have mastered several areas of engineering may find it a useful instruction text in how to define systems using models and objects.

Engineers in particular design disciplines, such as mechanical, electrical, software, database, human factors, and logistics engineering may find that it helps them understand the basic information captured in systems development. It may help them understand how that information can be transformed to give them additional insights they need for their work, in the notations and models of their choice. It may help them to request information that they need and to supply the information needed in the system development. It will help participants from a variety of disciplines to participate in integrated product teams.

Managers need to understand information representing numerous aspects of a system in order to develop a business strategy and direct the engineering organization. The choices they make must advance the business competitively by meeting user needs and wants. Management and engineering need to exchange information so that the systems developed will be optimized to achieve the business strategy and so that management can understand and track engineering progress and issues. This book describes a process in which this exchange and tracking can happen. The same process applies whether for new product introduction, or for developing the next generation of a product, or for improving the quality of an existing product. It is a goal of this book to describe the abstractions and models needed to bridge the management-engineer interface so that both groups have the information they need in the form they find most useful.

Also, the authors intend that the information models in this book be useful to the developers of tools and environments for automating the engineering of complex systems. The infrastructure needed to capture the description of complex systems-of-systems and to transform that information as needed by a variety of disciplines is described within the text. These tools are produced by tool and environment developers who usually have a strong software and database development background. The process behavior models and information models of this book will be useful in their work.

David W. Oliver
Timothy P. Kelliher
James G. Keegan, Jr.

Acknowledgments

We're indebted to those who helped us through the arduous process of completing this book.

Margaret Kelliher helped greatly with our organization and, without her, we wouldn't have completed the first chapter.

Dr. Julian Holtzman reviewed drafts of the manuscript and provided thoughtful insight.

The support, encouragement, and patience of our wives; Diane, Margaret, and Mary has been invaluable.

The INCOSE tools working group, especially Dr. Brain McCay and Rick Steiner, has provided a valuable arena for developing the concepts of the book. The IEEE Technical Committee on Engineering of Computer-Based Systems, ECBS, has been an invaluable resource for evaluating information models, especially the contributions from Ken Jackson. We are indebted to the leadership of Dr. Jonah Z. Lavi and Dr. Stephanie White in sustaining the IEEE Technical Committee. We thank Dr. Harry E. Crisp II and Dr. Phillip Q. Hwang for the Naval Surface Warfare Center support to develop a process model for ECBS. These organizations have provided the means to develop, discuss, and publish the concepts discussed in this book. The concepts are not formally endorsed by these organizations.

We are indebted to people and places that have shaped our careers. For Dave, this includes the technical and management experience provided by GE Corporate Research and Development Center, training at the GE Crotonville Institute, and the practices and example set by exemplary managers, particularly Hubbard Horn, John Eshbach, Virgil Stout, and William Chu. For Tim, whose career is also at GE's Corporate Research Center, this includes Dave McGonagle who gave him a chance to get started and a direction to head. It also includes many others that he has met at GE and elsewhere along the way. For Jim, William Premerlani and Will Schroeder offered their personal experiences which helped complete the book.

Engineering
Complex Systems
with Models and Objects

1

Introduction

1.1 The Engineering of Complex Systems Based on Models

People as toolmakers have developed systems for thousands of years and have developed techniques for coordination of large efforts. In a timespan shorter than a single career, the complexity of systems and the pervasiveness of computers and software have increased so much that production of modern systems demands the application of a wide range of engineering and manufacturing disciplines. The many engineering and manufacturing specialties that must cooperate on a project no longer understand the other specialties. They often use different names, notations, and views of information even when describing the same concept. Yet, the products of the many disciplines must work together to meet the needs of users and buyers of systems. They must perform as desired when all the components are integrated and operated.

1.1.1 This book

This book describes how to combine text descriptions and rigorous modeling to analyze and describe large or small complex systems. The systems engineering work begins with the needs of users, owners, and operators and with the realities of the marketplace. The systems engineering work transforms these needs into a description of a system architecture and design that specifies the components to be designed, implemented, and integrated. The fundamental process for the engineering of systems is an optimization process. That process finds a near-optimal solution for the system out of a multitude of possible solutions. The process produces rigorous descriptions of the near-optimal solution by defining what the components are, what they must do, and how they interact to perform as a system. This book focuses on the technical engineering work of transforming needs to a near-optimal system solution for complex systems that require multiple engineering disciplines to do the work. The approach is a synthesis of proven systems engineering best practices with the rigor of information transformations. The basic abstractions and processes required are described. The resulting metaprocess description for systems engineering work is highly tailorable to organization need and culture.

To develop any complex system, a team of engineers, working at the system level, must analyze the needs of the users, operators, and owners. The systems team must give to the many design, engineering, and manufacturing disciplines a rigorous description and specification of the system and the components that are to be produced. These descriptions must be provided in the representations, terminology, and notations used by the different design disciplines. They must also be unambiguous, complete, and mutually consistent such that the components will integrate to provide the desired emergent behavior for the system. When the product is completed and offered for sale, its emergent behavior must match the needs of customers so well that they will choose to buy and use it.

The systems team must also describe the emerging system to the interested stakeholders: management, marketing, users, owners, operators, and acquisition authorities. These stakeholders are the decision makers for funding development and for purchase of product or service. The system descriptions must effectively address the concerns of the stakeholders in form, language, and level of detail useful to them. These system descriptions will be less detailed than those provided to design, engineering, and manufacturing disciplines.

One thesis of this book is that modeling results in higher-quality systems, designed and produced at lower cost and in a shorter time, with a better fit to the market. A second thesis of the book is that with modeling the system specification can be executed to show what will occur and can be transformed efficiently and rigorously into the several different languages and forms useful to both the system stakeholders and to the design, engineering, and manufacturing disciplines. A third thesis of the book is that with the same modeling applied to systems engineering itself, you get a well-defined discipline, improved capability to train, and essential definitions needed for building automation and infrastructure for efficient and creative systems engineering. These definitions are consistent with the best practices and standards developed over many years and augment them with executable models.

There is a management role in the engineering of systems to provide a systems view for scheduling and management of resources, and a systems view for the resolution of the technical issues that arise. This book discusses these management tasks to separate them clearly from the technical tasks of systems engineers. The major focus of the book, however, is on the technical work and how to accomplish this rigorously. Systems engineering management is described in detail in the selected references (Blanchard and Fabrycky, 1990; Defense Systems Management College, 1990).

1.1.2 Systems engineering as a discipline

The development of modern complex systems requires engineers from several disciplines and also engineering generalists. In some industries, such as aerospace, the engineers focusing on the front-end definition of the system are called *systems engineers*. This job function is taught as a separate discipline in a growing number of universities. In other businesses engineers with these front-end responsibilities are referred to by many different terms and their work may or may not be recognized as a distinct discipline. Recognized or not, it is critically important because it

- Matches the product to the marketplace

- Defines the components to enable the designers to design and build them

- Determines most of the design choices affecting system cost and performance

- Ensures that the components will integrate successfully and perform together as required

- Provides specifications free of errors, since errors are very expensive to correct in the latter stages of design and production

It must, therefore, accurately reflect a total system design that is both feasible and effective in component design. In addition, the system design must be not only correct but also unambiguous; if not, then the components will not integrate correctly and the desired emergent behavior will be compromised. Failure to do this work, up front, causes the system to cost more than was budgeted, miss its market window, and have an increased chance of marketplace product failure.

Where does systems engineering end? Design of the components is the responsibility of the engineering experts in the disciplines: mechanical engineering, software engineering, database engineering, civil engineering, and the like. Implementation of these components is the responsibility of manufacturing, building construction, and others. Design of the total package of components, including their interrelationships, is the domain of the systems engineer. Of course, what one company considers to be a component, another treats as a system.

This book describes a process for combining rigorous modeling with text descriptions to analyze and describe

1. User needs

2. The system to meet those needs

3. The components to be designed and built

Following this process leads to a near-optimal system solution. This fundamental process for the engineering of complex systems is an optimization process. It finds a near-optimal solution out of a plethora of possible solutions. It produces rigorous descriptions of the near-optimal solution by defining what the components are, what they must do, and how they interact as a system. The process draws on the best practices of systems engineers and combines these with modern modeling techniques. Together these produce a rigorous method by which to design complex systems.

1.2   Importance of Engineering Complex Systems

There are economic and technical changes sweeping the world that make systems engineering critically important to the industrialized nations and their peoples. There is also a deadlock, an impasse, which the art of systems engineering faces and which presently limits its contributions.

1.2.1   Global economic and technical change

In earlier times, goods and payments passed across regulated national borders, but production facilities, knowledge, and culture remained within those borders as a national competitive advantage. At present there is an almost instantaneous movement of ideas, information, key people, and capital across national borders. Productive capacity can be quickly established anywhere there is an economic advantage. It is possible to have high technology, high productivity, high quality, and *low wages* (Schwab and Smadja, 1994). This is a transnational phenomenon. It is occurring across nations where regions are working together to define markets and make investment by international companies most attractive (Thurow, 1992; Krugman, 1994). Europe is moving toward a trading block. Hong Kong has embraced Shenzen and the Zhu River delta of China. Malaysia has become a world-leading producer of semiconductors and is now discouraging labor-intensive industry. Indonesia, Malaysia, and Thailand are linking their cities of Medan, Penang, and Phuket. Taiwan, Japan, and Korea are moving productive capacity to China and Vietnam. The United States and India are producing software cooperatively.

To remain competitive, global companies are relocating design and production wherever it is advantageous to produce goods and to maintain relationships for selling goods (Krugman, 1994; Ohmae, 1995). Major global companies are increasingly opening their top management and boards of directors to candidates from all nations (Reich, 1991). This is beginning to occur even in nationalistic Japanese companies and family-oriented Chinese companies. Global businesses which do not follow these economic imperatives are likely to wither. This is the information age, and technology has shortened the time to cross oceans.

Span of national control and investment in national advantage. The advanced industrialized nations can no more prevent the movement of design and production capability to other regions of the world than could the Luddites of England prevent replacement of their hand loom cottage industry in the early 1800s by punch-card-automated looms.

Nations and blocks of nations have the capacity to create an environment that encourages investment. Singapore provides an excellent example of investment strategy, but not of individual freedoms (Sisodia, 1992). The investment policies in the United States are less strategic (Porter, 1992). One of the most critical investments for any nation is in the skills and industrial culture of its people (Reich, 1990). The people—unlike capital, information, patents, laboratories, design organizations, and production facilities—remain located in the nation. The skill of the workforce is a major attraction to investment. Investment produces the jobs for the people.

Some investments by a company or nation give it a unique advantage which establishes and maintains profitability even in the face of aggressive low-cost competitors. Such advantages have been called *disequilibrium advantages* (Thurow, 1996). Educating and infrastructure for systems engineering for the definition of complex systems provide such a disequilibrium advantage.

Importance of systems engineering. The development of new large complex systems with world sales potential is a major contribution to any economy. No nation can keep the production of parts within its borders if there is an economic advantage elsewhere. However, industrialized nations can keep the development of new complex systems within their borders if they have a preeminently qualified workforce and infrastructure for defining competitive systems efficiently. Some parts will be sourced worldwide and help open global markets. Most parts manufacture, assembly, and integration can be kept within borders by the organization that creates the system. A few examples from just one industry are the Boeing 777, the stealth bomber, the replacement American Airlines ticket reservation system, and the FAA flight-control system. Some of these examples were successes and some were failures (Gibbs, 1994). The successes provide downstream employment and job training experience for thousands of workers. The failures waste capital and human resource. Existing experience with successful complex systems, professional systems engineering skill, and systems engineering infrastructure have tremendous positive downstream leverage on an economy.

However, there is a gap, a roadblock in attaining state-of-the-art systems engineering skill levels and infrastructure.

1.3   The Gap

The information which is critical to a modern system definition comes from users, operators, owners, marketing organizations, and procurement organizations. This information is often available only in informal, natural language, such as English. The language expresses needs to be met without referring to engineering concepts and terms. This is the systems engineering input.

The output from systems engineering is a set of specifications. These are disseminated to a wide variety of engineering disciplines which need specific information in their own notations and views, available to them in their own computer-based tools. Systems engineering information needs to be rigorously transformed to the multiple different models, notations, and views of the downstream engineers who create designs.

The *gap* is the void between needs expressed in informal, natural language and component specifications described in the multiple engineering notations. To date this gap has been bridged by good systems engineering practices and by hard work. This work results in huge text documents detailing the component specifications for designers. Engineers in each downstream discipline must read and interpret the text, transform it into their own models and terminology, and then enter it into their computer tools. They must remove the ambiguity and inconsistencies between what has been written and what they know will work correctly. Clearly, this process is time-consuming and error-prone.

1.3.1   Closing the gap

Modeling can fill the gap. Modern technology now gives us desktop access to powerful computers and software which can provide modeling to fill the gap, reduce the effort to cross from needs to specifications, and increase rigor and correctness.

Capture of the modeling information for modern complex systems is important both for productivity in the engineering work and for checking information for inconsistencies, omissions, and errors.

Prior experience in other disciplines.   Similar gaps have existed in other fields, including mechanical engineering, integrated-circuit chip design, and software engineering. In some cases these gaps have been closed. Mechanical engineering is a good example of the evolutionary approach to filling the gap. Mechanical engineering is one of the oldest engineering disciplines and has addressed many of the problems now faced by the systems engineering. One of the major tasks of mechanical engineers is to specify the geometry of parts which are to be manufactured and assembled. These geometries are then analyzed to ensure that they will perform according to the requirements and that they can be manufactured efficiently.

The traditional mechanical engineering technique to describe a part's geometry was to use physical drawings. In the 1960s computers and software tools began to be used to capture mechanical geometry information. However, these tools belonged exclusively to the mechanical engineers. The computerized drawings still had to be read and translated separately by other engineers performing analysis and simulation because their computer tools used for analysis could not exchange information with the mechanical design tools.

The geometric specification of mechanical systems is now rigorously transmitted and transformed among computer tools for design, analysis, and manufacturing. The numerous tools were originally developed independently with different assumptions about nature of geometry information. Integration of the tools was not possible until a language was developed which unambiguously described the required geometry. The Express language was chosen. It is semantically well defined and spans the application of geometry. In addition, standards have been developed and used to implement the seamless translation and transfer of information among tools for mechanical design, analysis, and manufacture. The STEP/PEDES standards for representing geometry is one such standard, the value of which was demonstrated by projects such as the Boeing 777 aircraft (Norris, 1995).

When transistor design was first begun a single engineer could understand a circuit in its entirety. A gap developed as the circuits grew in complexity and then moved from discrete components into integrated-circuit chips. The same level of attention to detailed design was needed as in the older component designs, but it grew beyond the scope of individual comprehension. To close the gap, a new generation of design and analysis tools had to be built and a methodology for effective tool use had to be developed. Integrated-circuit chips are now designed and simulated using VHSIC (hardware definition language) or schematic capture and are transformed into geometric mask features for manufacture using standardized intermediate forms for the information. Well-established design rule standards define exactly how manufacturing foundries can accommodate the design and the circuit layout (Mead and Conway, 1980).

Software engineering has closed a similar gap, only to have the gap reappear at a higher level. Assemblers and compilers were developed to close the initial gap between programmers and the computers with which they worked. This not only helped to ensure correct operation of their programs, but also took much of the drudgery of programming out of the hands of humans and put it into the computer. This sufficiently closed the initial gap. It reappeared, however, at a higher level. As computers grew more powerful and correspondingly software became more complex, the compilers and languages they supported were no longer sufficient to ensure correct operation. A new generation of tools have been developed to help close the new gap. In these tools software algorithms and structure are designed graphically and in higher-level languages. These are compiled by rigorous transformation to the machine language needed by specific computer architectures. Data relationships are captured in information models which can be represented graphically or in symbolic language. The database schema can be generated from the models (Premerlani and Blaha, 1993, 1994).

Closing the gap in the engineering of complex systems.   The gap for the engineering of systems can be filled by extending the modeling techniques that are applicable to the definition of systems described in this book.

Rigorous, executable models of behavior (what things do) and structure (how things are built) means the capture of system requirements and specifications in models that are computer-executable and unambiguous. It is possible to use automatic transformations of the system models into exactly the views and notations needed by the supporting engineering disciplines. This rigor cannot be obtained with nonexecutable specifications written in natural-language text alone. That is not to say that text is unimportant. It is used to accompany the models and provide explanations of them.

The tools for this work, however, as was the case for mechanical engineering, have been created by different laboratories and vendors, and cannot exchange information with one another. There is at present no agreed-on, computer-executable description of the work to be done in systems engineering and of the information to be captured and transformed. Such standardized computer-executable descriptions are essential for creation of an integrated tool environment.

The same modeling techniques that are applicable to system requirements and specifications can be used to define the systems engineering work to be done and the information to be captured and transformed at each step of the work. It is possible for the systems engineering profession to carefully define the process it uses, rigorously defining its accumulated best practices as a behavior for engineers. An executable metaprocess model provides a framework for this definition. The information captured and transformed at each step of the metaprocess can be represented in an executable information model which captures the structure of data relationships. We will show how to use this metaprocess, not to drive engineers to perform their work in exactly the same way, but rather to tailor the methodologies, notations, and views of choice by individual businesses and organizations.

Purposes of modeling.   Modeling is used to reduce the time and effort expended by engineers in shortening the design cycle time. It is used to check the information for consistency and completeness, reducing the error rate. It is used to preserve the current engineering results for use during later maintenance, product upgrade, or product replacement efforts. It is used to describe, unambiguously, every symbol and number such that each has one and only one meaning. The models ensure that at the end of the process all necessary information is available and correct.

Modeling in no way substitutes for creative engineering thinking and problem solving. Creativity and new solutions come from the engineers. Modeling reduces their manual work and improves accuracy.

1.4   Definitions

Terms such as *science, engineering, system, context, structure,* and *behavior* are widely used and understood. The specific interpretation of each word varies with the context in which it appears, according to the person seeing it and the disciplines using it. A few definitions are given to clarify these terms for their use in this book.

1.4.1 Science

"Science is the branch of study that is concerned with the establishment or strictly with the quantifiable formulation of verifiable general laws chiefly by induction and hypothesis". (Merriam Webster, 1981.)

Science carefully observes the behavior of things and creates quantitative laws that describe what things do under defined conditions. These laws are executable quantitative models. They can be evaluated by people or computers to obtain numbers that describe things and what the things do.

1.4.2 Engineering

In *The New Encyclopedia Britannica* (1980) definition "Engineering is the professional art of applying science to the optimum conversion of the resources of nature to benefit man," the words *engine* and *ingenious* are derived from the same Latin root, *ingenerare,* meaning to create. Also

> Engineering is an art requiring the judgement necessary to adapt knowledge to practical purposes, the imagination to conceive original solutions to problems, and the ability to predict performance and cost of new devices or processes.
>
> Unlike the scientist the engineer is not free to select the problem that interests him; he must solve problems as they arise; his solutions must satisfy conflicting requirements. Usually efficiency costs money; safety adds to complexity; improved performance adds to weight. The engineering solution is the optimum solution, the end result that, taking many factors into account, is most desirable. (*The New Encyclopedia Britannica,* 1980.)

Engineers solve real problems using the laws of science, executable models, to predict quantitatively the performance of alternative solutions to real problems in order to create new things that benefit people. It is a creative art to find better systems that better meet people's needs. Quantitative modeling taken from the results of science is the aid that engineers use.

1.4.3 Model

Merriam Webster, (1981) defines a *model* as "a pattern of something to be made."

A model describes the essential nature of a process or thing. It is not the thing itself. Models are validated only when they have been verified by observation and measurement under controlled conditions. Models are unambiguous; they use mathematics, graphics, or symbolic languages that have only one meaning for the symbols used.

Natural languages such as English do not qualify for modeling. The natural languages are essential for written explanations of the models.

1.4.4 System

"A system is a complex unity formed of many often diverse parts subject to a common plan or serving a common purpose" (Merriam Webster, 1981).

A *system* is a thing built from many other things, or components, which interact for a common purpose. To define a system an engineer must describe its context, behavior or purpose, and structure.

1.4.5 Behavior

According to Merriam Webster (1981), *behavior* is "the way in which an organism, organ, or substance acts, especially in response to a stimulus."

When we describe the behavior of a system, we consider scenarios of its use under a variety of conditions and the system's response to the scenarios. The engineer must describe the system response to the external things under all possible conditions.

1.4.6 Structure

The Merriam Webster (1981) definition of structure is an "arrangement of parts, or of constituent particles, in a substance or body."

The structure of a system is the parts that it comprises and the relationships among them. The engineers must describe the structure of the system:

- A list of all the system's components
- How the components are interconnected
- What portion of the total system behavior is carried out by each component

1.4.7 Context

"A context is the interrelated conditions in which something exists or occurs" (Merriam Webster, 1981).

A significant misconception about context is that it is given in a particular problem and does not need to be analyzed in the art of finding a near-optimal solution to the problem. Very often the most important aspects of the problem involve looking at alternatives in the context and evaluating them.

1.4.8 Optimization

Merriam Webster (1981) defines *optimum* as "the best or most favorable degree, quantity, number."

It follows, then, that optimization is the process to achieve the most favorable degree. In systems design we need to consider optimization at two levels: context and system.

Context optimization

- Analysis of alternatives in the context of the system
- Choice of a near optimal context for the problem

System optimization

- Analysis of alternatives in the structure of the system; what components may be used and what each component may do.
- Choice of a near-optimal set of components and their individual behaviors; a design of the system

1.5 Basic Abstractions

We use a set of common abstractions to simplify the world around us. They are so familiar that we seldom consciously think about them as we use them and do not distinguish among them clearly as we speak or write about them. These are the same basic abstractions that are needed for modeling in the engineering of complex systems. However, in modeling it is necessary to clearly define the abstractions and use symbols for them to avoid ambiguity of meaning.

Because these abstractions are basic, they appear in the many engineering disciplines and in languages used for software engineering (Liskov and Guttag, 1985). Unfortunately, the basic abstractions are called by different names, represented with different symbols, and combined in different ways by the engineering disciplines and in the supporting tools. These abstractions and their meanings or semantics are the basis for both modeling in systems engineering and for automated translation of that information into the notations and views of other engineering disciplines.

1.5.1 Basic abstractions used with structure

Things or objects. The concept of distinguishable objects is one of the most fundamental notions of humanity. Several aspects of objects are used to describe or specify them:

1. Name of the object

2. All the properties of the object that are important for the problem of current interest

3. All the tasks, actions, or functions that are to be performed by the object for the problem of current interest

4. All the inputs that the object accepts and the outputs it generates

5. How to connect to the object (its interfaces)

Parts tree or aggregation.   Systems are often composed from other systems. Objects are built from objects. *Aggregation* allows us to consider the object as a unit, ignoring its parts, a vast simplification in thought. Alternatively, it allows us to consider an object as an assembly of parts, to think about how it is built. A parts tree captures this information. When all the parts are properly assembled, the object is produced.

Interconnection.   Since things (or objects) are built from things, we must have a way to express how things relate to each other. We must be able to show which parts in an assembly are connected and which are not. *Interconnection* shows this and defines additional information about how the connection takes place and what interfaces are used.

Number.   From infancy children are taught the abstraction of numbers and how to count. If we have many of a thing, a number lets us express how many in a rigorous way. When we learn arithmetic, we have a set of rigorous logical rules that we can use to execute this abstraction and transform the information as needed.

Classification.   Classification deals with the kinds of things that exist. It is a grouping abstraction based on shared properties. Classes can be broken down into subclasses and the subclasses into subsubclasses The abstraction of class and classification tree is distinctly different from that of parts and parts tree.

- The abstraction of parts describes how something is decomposed or assembled.

- The abstraction of class shows common properties or behavior of things. It represents alternatives that may be chosen and provides a means to find or index things.

One may wish to select a pet by choosing among birds, fish, dogs, or cats. If the choice is a dog, is the dog a poodle, a Labrador retriever, or a terrier? These are class choices. The pet shop will probably be arranged with animals of any one class in a particular area. One finds a Labrador by going to the dog section.

The distinction between parts of things and classes is often blurred in speech and in writing. Both abstractions are important and useful, and they need to be distinguished in any notation used to model systems.

Association.   The abstractions *aggregation, interconnection,* and *classification* are all referred to more generally as *associations.*

1.5.2   Basic abstractions used with behavior

The basic abstractions used with behavior are function, their ordering, and their inputs and outputs. While these may sound unfamiliar, they are commonly used by most people. A simple example will illustrate these abstractions. We will look at a behavior and then pull it apart into its basic components.

Consider the behavior of "Put out the milk for dinner" as though it were not intuitively obvious and had to be explained in detail. For example, imagine explaining it from the standpoint of a young child who does not know what to do or from that of a person from a primitive area who had never seen a modern kitchen.

"Put out the milk for dinner" is *composed* of other behaviors such as "Get glasses from the cupboard," "Get milk bottle from the refrigerator," "Pour milk into glasses," "Return milk bottle to the refrigerator," and "Put glasses on the table."

Each of these behaviors involves one or more actions taking place. These actions are variously called *work steps, methods, functions,* or *activities.* Different words have been used to describe this abstraction, which refers to work that transforms things. In this discussion, we use *function* for this abstraction. The basis of this abstraction is the description of work which transforms things.

In more formal language, a function is described in terms of inputs, outputs, and a transform relating output to input. The function "Pour milk" has as inputs a bottle of milk and empty glasses. It has as outputs glasses filled with milk and a bottle from which milk has been removed.

Functions, taken by themselves, are not sufficient to describe behavior. There is an ordering to the functions. Some ordering is intrinsic; it is imposed by the reality of the world. In other cases the choice of order may not affect the desired transformation and can be chosen for convenience. It is often desirable to leave some of these alternative choices to designers.

In our example, "Get glasses" and "Get milk bottle" may be done in any order. "Get glasses" and "Get milk bottle" must both be completed before "Pour milk" can be done. "Get glasses" must precede "Put glasses." "Pour milk" must precede "Return milk bottle." "Pour milk" and "Put glasses" may be done in any order.

Textual descriptions of ordering and timing relationships become very confusing for behaviors of even modest complexity. Various diagramming techniques have been developed to simplify these descriptions. Functional flow block diagrams are one such technique (Blanchard and Fabrycky, 1990; MIL-STD-499, 1968).

In summary, the abstractions of behavior are

- Functions

- Inputs and outputs to the functions

- Ordering of the functions, including how inputs may trigger functions and how inputs may establish conditions for selecting alternative paths in a complex behavior

1.6   Organization of This Book

This book describes both the principles of modeling complex systems and the process of engineering complex systems. It provides a coherent example of modeling a system to demonstrate how modeling is employed.

1.6.1   Principles of modeling

In Chaps. 1 through 10, the principles of modeling are developed from primary concepts and abstractions and a core engineering process is presented. These primary concepts and abstractions are familiar to everyday life. They correspond to basic concepts used in the many engineering disciplines from software engineering through mechanical and electrical engineering. Because of their generic nature, they form a foundation that can be used in the transformation of models from systems engineering specifications to the notations and views needed by the design engineering disciplines.

The primary concepts are used to build the modeling principles and a description of the core technical systems engineering process. The core process is shown to apply to the several phases of development: concept phase, domain analysis phase, and system design phase. The generic applicability of the core process is a simplification in training, project execution, and tool development and procurement.

The modeling concepts and techniques are described using both text and graphic models. A variety of notations can be used for the graphic models. Although enthusiasts argue that particular notations are superior, for our purposes it is sufficient that the graphic notation

1. Is sufficiently complete to capture the information used in systems engineering

2. Is computer-executable

3. Has been published and is in use

4. Is easy to learn and to use

Unfortunately, there is no single existing notation which satisfies all four requirements. We do in this book what is commonly done in practice, that is, to marry two different methodologies, each with its own strength. For the capture of information about structure of things, a variant of the *object modeling technique* (OMT) notation from software engineering has been chosen, (Rumbaugh, et al., 1991). For the capture of information about behavior, the notation of the *functional flow block diagram* (FFBD) has been chosen from systems engineering (MIL-STD-499, 1968). These diagrams are not computer-executable and have been augmented with input/output information. They are closely related to Alford's behavior diagrams (Alford, 1977, 1992).

Small examples are used to explain and clarify the concepts. An information model is provided for each of the major systems engineering work steps to show the information handled in that step and the relationships among the information items. These models illustrate the information to be collected and transformed in each work step. They show how the pieces of information are interrelated. They also give basic information for tool development and integration.

1.6.2 An example of modeling

Without examples, the descriptions of concepts and abstractions become an intellectual activity with little feeling of how to use them in real-world development projects. In Chaps. 11 through 14 we examine a real-world problem. Any real-world development of a complex system, however, is too large to capture in a portion of a book because there is too much detail.

As a compromise, this part of the book describes a single small example problem modeled with the process and concepts described in the first part of the book. Great emphasis is placed on the transition of knowledge from the system analysis and design to design engineering. Handoff to software and database engineering is used as an example. This emphasis has been selected for two reasons: there is increasing pervasiveness of software and database development in modern complex systems and there is a shorter tradition of systems engineers communicating with these disciplines.

The example problem is selected because it is familiar to most readers. It is an *automated teller machine* (ATM) system. The treatment takes the problem from needs and concept analysis through specification of components. It considers the effects on bank structure that adding ATM may introduce. In this respect this ATM example is both different and more comprehensive than similar examples used elsewhere.

1.7 Summary

The book concludes with a discussion of engineering of complex systems as it is done today. The ability to engineer complex systems efficiently and with rigor is an important asset for businesses and for nations. Presently there are excellent engineering best practices for the development of large complex systems that have been proved over time. These practices, however, are largely unsupported by automation and tool environments. Parts of the process are automated, but the existing tools are not integrated. A major reason for this is the extensive use of natural language to express most of the design information. Natural language is ambiguous and, therefore, not executable by people or computers.

Modeling, used efficiently, is the solution to rigorous and efficient engineering of complex systems. Coupled with development of standards for information exchange, it can also address the problems of creating tool environments.

Systems engineering can draw on experience gained in other disciplines. Other engineering disciples have closed their gaps by using executable models to perform their work. They have created the foundations for tool environments by employing models to define the information they use and how they transform that information.

The basic abstractions needed for modeling in the engineering of complex systems are common to everyday experience. To proceed with modeling, these abstractions need to be defined, represented uniquely in a modeling notation, and applied. A number of symbolic languages and graphic languages exist that can be used for these purposes.

1.8 Exercises

1. Refer to the "Put out the milk for dinner" example in Sec. 1.5.2. Create your own graphic notation to express your solutions to the following:

    a. Create and draw a picture of an object (thing) with a place to record the object name, the object properties, and the object functions.

  b. Create a picture of the context of the person, as an object and as the system to be described, who will put out the milk. Consider which objects are external things in the context and which objects will be inputs or outputs in the behavior.
  c. Create a picture for each of the functions "Get glasses," "Get milk bottle," "Pour milk," "Return milk bottle," and "Put glasses."
  d. Show how the above functions are ordered in a graphic picture. Consider the required order. Consider any additional ordering you may wish to impose.
  e. Create a picture of how inputs and outputs are related to the functions.
  f. Combine the pictures of exercises d and e to capture in one view the functions and their inputs and outputs and ordering.
  g. What different kinds of milk might you get from the refrigerator? Create a class tree for these choices.

2. What problems arise is using the graphic notation developed in question 1?
3. What gaps, other than the modeling gap, exist in the process of engineering complex systems?
4. What degree of formality and rigor is required in executable models?
5. In what ways can modeling speed development of a complex system?

1.9 References

Alford, M., 1977: A requirements engineering methodology for real time systems, *IEEE Transactions on Software Engineering,* vol. SE-3, no. 1, 60–69.

Alford, M., 1992: Strengthening the systems/software interface for real time systems, *Proceedings of the Second International Symposium of the National Council on Systems Engineering,* vol. 1. 411, Seattle, Wash.

Blanchard, B. F. and W. Fabrycky, 1990: *Systems Engineering and Analysis,* 2d ed. Englewood Cliffs, N.J.: Prentice-Hall.

Defense Systems Management College, 1990: *Defense Systems Engineering Management Guide.* Washington D.C.: U.S. Government Printing Office, 000802001202-5.

Gibbs, W. W., 1994: Software's chronic crisis. *Sci. Am.* (Sept.) p. 86.

Kronlof, K., 1993: *Method Integration: Concepts and Case Studies.* Chichester (U.K.): Wiley.

Krugman, P., 1994: Does third world growth hurt first world prosperity? *Harvard Bus. Rev.,* **72**(July–Aug.), 113–121.

Liskov, B. et. al., 1981: CLU Reference Manual, *Lecture Notes in Computer Science.* G. Goos and J. Hartmanis, eds. Springer-Verlag.

Liskov, B., and J. Guttag, 1986: *Abstraction and Specification in Program Development,* Cambridge, MA: MIT Press.

Mead, C. and L. Conway, 1980: *Introduction to VLSI Systems,* Menlo Park, CA.: Addison Wesley.

Merriam Webster, 1981: *Webster's Third New International Dictionary,* Philip Babcock Gove, ed. Springfield, Mass.: Merriam-Webster Inc.

MIL-STD-499, 1968: *Functional Flow Diagrams,* AFSCP 375-5, USAF, DI-S-3604/S-126-1, Form DD 1664.

Norris, G., 1995: Boeing's seventh wonder. *IEEE Spectrum* (Oct.), 20–23.

Ohmae, K., 1995: Putting global logic first. *Harvard Bus. Rev.* **73**(Jan.–Feb.), 119–125.

Porter, M. E., 1992: Capital disadvantage: America's failing capital investment system. *Harvard Bus. Rev.* **70**(Sept.–Oct.) 65–82.

Premerlani, W. J. and M. R. Blaha, 1993: Object-Oriented Re-Engineering of Legacy Databases, *Fifth Annual Software Technology Conference, April 1993, Salt Lake City, Utah.*

Premerlani, W. J. and M. R. Blaha, An approach for reverse engineering of relational databases. *Comm. of the ACM,* vol. 37, 5, May 1994.

Reich, R. B., 1990: Who is us? *Harvard Bus. Rev.* **68**(Jan.–Feb.) 53–64.

Reich, R. B., 1991: Who is them? *Harvard Bus. Rev.* **69**(March–April), 77–88.

Rumbaugh, J., M. Blaha, W. J. Premerlani, F. Eddy, and W. Lorensen, 1991: *Object-Oriented Modeling and Design.* Englewood Cliffs, N.J.: Prentice-Hall.

Schwab, C., and C. Smadja, 1994: *Harvard Bus. Rev.* **72**(Nov.–Dec.) 40–50.

Sisodia, R. S., 1992: Singapore invests in the nation corporation. *Harvard Bus. Rev.* **70**(May–June) 40–50.

The New Encyclopedia Britannica, 1980, 15th ed., vol. 6, p. 860.

Thurow, L., 1992: *Head to Head: The Coming Economic Battle among Japan, Europe, and America.* New York: Morrow.

Thurow, L., 1996: *Head to Head: The Future of Capitalism.* New York: Morrow.

2

Basics of Structure

2.1 Introduction to Structure

This chapter focuses on structure and the primary ideas, or abstractions, which are essential to its modeling. These abstractions are already familiar from everyday life. The words we use in everyday speech, however, and the ideas they convey are ambiguous. This chapter clarifies the abstractions for representing structure and shows how the ambiguity is resolved (Liskov and Guttag, 1986). It also presents the basis for producing executable structure models which can be transformed into alternative views and verified by computer. We use the graphic notation of object modeling technique (OMT) (Rumbaugh et al., 1991) because it is simple, readily understood, widely used, and supported by tools. While this book focuses on the abstractions needed for the engineering work, other notations can be used if they span the needed abstractions.

2.1.1 Structure and behavior

Before delving into the semantic makeup of structure and how to model it, we first describe the importance of separating structure from behavior. Figure 2.1 shows this relationship between these two concepts.

These two components, structure and behavior, are the essential views of any system description. Behavior is the *what it does* part of the system description, and structure is the *how it is built* part. These two views, with a mapping of behavior onto structure, form a system description. If the desired behavior is defined separately from a structure, then alternative structures can be readily identified and the desired behavior can be mapped onto each of them, so that each exhibits that behavior. A trade-off analysis can then be performed to pick the

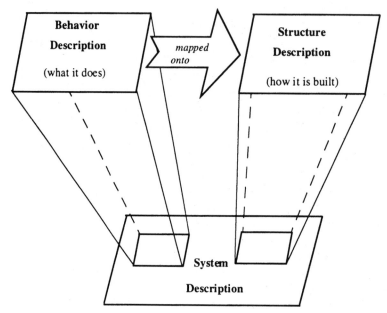

Figure 2.1 Behavior and structure.

best solution. This is a critical best practice in the engineering of systems because it finds a near-optimal solution while guaranteeing that the desired behavior emerges from the system design.

Not all engineering disciplines place strong emphasis on trade-off among alternatives to find a near-optimal solution. Some of those disciplines mix behavior and structure together in the views they use of their systems or components. That mixing works for those disciplines, but it makes trade-off more difficult because there is no independent description of what the system is to do.

2.1.2 Basic views of structure

The key views of information used to express structure are things or objects, their internal attributes, and the associations among them. Figure 2.2 depicts the relationships among these basic views and their relationships to the description of a system's structure.

Object classes are the primary building blocks for all structure models. They model the elemental pieces of a system's structure. The primary associations among object classes are

- *Classification trees,* which represent categories of things and the relationships between the categories

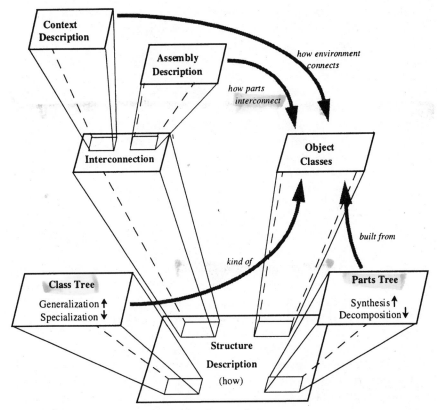

Figure 2.2   Description of structure: the elemental views.

- *Interconnection,* which represents the connections among things and between the environment and the system
- *Parts trees,* which describe how things are composed to make bigger things

These views are all discussed in more detail later in this chapter along with the OMT notation for them. The concepts and notations are illustrated with an example.

2.1.3   Executable models of structure

Executable models can be executed either by a computer or manually by an engineer to interpret the models, check for accuracy, check for completeness, or translate them into notations used by other disciplines. Each kind of item in the model has a single meaning and is represented by a unique symbol. The information in the models is sufficient to fully describe the engineering work at hand.

When nonexecutable models are used with computer tools, the models can be read and interpreted by trained engineers. There is some ambiguity in the models, and the interpretations by different engineers may vary somewhat. The computer cannot be used to interpret the models, check for accuracy, check for completeness, or translate them into notations used by other disciplines.

An executable parts tree can show the breakdown of a system into its assemblies, its least-replaceable units, and its smallest parts. Such a tree can be executed to generate the list of parts needed at any stage of assembly or the list of parts required for field service of the system. If properties of the parts are associated with their object class descriptions, then the parts tree can be executed to calculate properties such as cost or weight for the entire system, for subassemblies, or for least-replaceable units.

An executable interconnection diagram can be used to ensure that every part, or object class, has at least one interconnection. When a system is developed hierarchically with several levels in its parts tree, the interconnection diagrams can be checked to ensure that the multitude of interfaces at the lower levels are consistent with the interfaces defined at higher levels. If the interconnection diagram represents the wiring list for electronic components, then the computer can do automated layout of the components by referring to a library which contains a physical description of the electronic components and the design rules that apply.

An executable classification tree represents the kinds of parts that may be chosen for a system. It can be used as the taxonomy for a browsing facility to search a library of parts for the kind of part that is needed. It can be used as the basis for the menus of a human-machine interface. It can be used in software with an appropriate compiler to generate the message passing among software objects. It provides the basic information needed for reuse.

Consider a scenario of electronic circuit design. An electrical engineer designs a circuit for implementation on a circuit board. The circuit elements are chosen from a classification of types of circuit elements. This choice produces a parts tree. The circuit is defined by establishing the interconnections among the circuit elements. Because the behavior of each element is known, the electronic behavior of the circuit can be calculated. The parts which can be used for these circuit elements are chosen from a classification that organizes the parts library. The part pin connections can now be related to the circuit element interconnections, and the physical properties of the parts can be obtained from the parts library. Since the geometry of the parts is now known, the parts can be automatically laid out on a circuit board according to design rules using the interconnection data which has been preserved and transformed through these steps. Now that the physical interconnection detail has been added, the resistance and capacitance of the interconnections can be extracted and combined with the electrical properties to compute actual timing conditions in the circuit. When timing is satisfactory, the information can be transformed into masks for forming the circuit board, drill tapes for automatically drilling the part mounting holes, and the instructions for automatic insertion machines to insert parts into the boards. Throughout this scenario the three fundamental associations of classification trees, parts trees, and interconnection are executed repeatedly, with additional information added at each step, and with information transformations applied for application to particular implementation capabilities.

In a different engineering domain we can see the same need for development of executable structural models. Modern software engineering practice calls for software engineers and database designers to determine the interactions between their respective parts of the system before committing to any particular implementation. The way data is stored and partitioned, the structure of the database, has a profound effect on the system's speed, performance, and behavior. The tools used to capture the structure information contain generators which generate the code declarations and the database schema from the models. These declarations and schema can then be executed and used in trade-off and optimization decision-making. Once final trade-off decisions have been made, the resulting generated code and schema become part of the system's implementation.

As the examples demonstrate, when professionals decide to use executable models and choose one, or a few, semantically well-defined graphic or symbolic languages for their work, automation can be introduced into the process. This type of automation aids the designer in choosing the best design. It produces magnitudes of quality and productivity improvement. The rigorous transformations of information make sure that the final product implements the design faithfully. With the addition of executable behavior information (discussed in Chap. 3) to the structure information, simulations of performance can be performed at many stages of design and implementation to ensure that the first implementation works as desired.

Examples of graphic languages are

- Buhr (1984) or Booch (1983) diagrams for designing Ada software
- Electrical schematic diagrams

- Control engineering block diagrams
- Object modeling technique (OMT) diagrams for software and data-bases

Examples of semantically well defined symbolic languages are

- COBOL, or C++, software design languages
- VHDL, a hardware description language
- Express (which was used to define geometry standards)

Unless systems engineers capture their requirements and specifications of behavior and structure in a precise and executable language, their requirements and specifications will remain ambiguous and error-prone. While this status quo persists, each downstream engineering discipline will have to continue interpreting natural-language specifications instead of receiving data in their particular notation. These manual interpretation efforts are not only costly and error-prone; they waste a valuable resource, skilled engineers' time, which would be better spent designing and solving real engineering problems. When the systems information is described precisely, automated tools will ensure that the correct information is provided to the component engineers quickly, accurately, and unambiguously.

There are a large number of notations suitable for systems engineering concepts. Criteria for evaluating the various notations are ease of training, ease of use, match with organization culture, and adequacy of tool support. In performing this evaluation it is essential to understand the underlying semantic constructs required to do systems engineering. Once the base concepts are understood, then the tools, views, and representations of information that can help the systems engineer can be judged. In this book we have chosen to use the OMT notation, with minor adaptations to better represent the systems engineering structure information.

The remainder of this chapter introduces the semantics and OMT notation for structure and illustrates it by modeling the structure of a pocket knife. The semantics and notation for modeling behavior will be considered in Chap. 3.

2.2   Example: Modeling a Pocket Knife

In order to introduce OMT notation for structure and to make clear what is meant by the written descriptions, we will walk through the steps taken to model a well-known physical object. We have chosen a pocket knife as our subject. The particular knife we are modeling, shown in Fig. 2.3, has two blades, a can opener/small screwdriver, a

Figure 2.3   Ordinary pocket knife.

bottle opener/large screwdriver, an awl, a corkscrew, and a key chain. All of these parts of the knife and the relationships among them need to be captured, unambiguously, in our model.

2.3   Objects and Classes

The next several sections introduce the various object modeling concepts and give an example of each concept as applied to the pocket knife. We also give a brief overview of the OMT notation for each concept and note where our usage departs from the general practice. [See Rumbaugh et al. (1981) for a more complete treatment.] This formal method, when coupled with other modeling techniques described elsewhere in this book, forms an executable model of the entire system. This model can then be tested and verified for correctness. We begin with objects.

2.3.1   Definition

What are objects? In general, they are things, physical or logical things. Looking around a room, you can see many objects: chairs, tables, and carpets. These are all obvious examples. There are also some less obvious objects: openings, color, and airflow. Choosing the *right* set of objects to model for a particular problem or to include in a system design is an art. There can be many potential *right* sets of objects. Trade-off analysis performed after the mapping of behavior onto the object structure guides the final choice of objects to include in the system implementation.

When we speak about objects, we talk of classes of objects and instances of objects. *Classes* define a category of things, where all the members share certain structural and behavioral traits. Trucks, cars, and planes are all examples of classes. All trucks share certain properties, as do all planes. *Instances* define a specific object such as "Bill's red truck." They are members of a class and as such share the common behavior and properties, but they also have a distinct identity apart from the class.

Classes can be general such as "vehicles," which would include cars, planes, tricycles, and all sorts of other types. Classes can also be very specific such as "internal-combustion, four-wheeled, two-passenger automobiles." In developing an object model, trade-offs need to be made about the amount of detail that is included in a class definition. The more specific it is, the easier it may be to use in a particular implementation. This weighs against the portability and reusability of the object design. It may be hard to adapt to an alternate architecture if the structure model is too narrowly defined.

2.3.2   Modeling objects in OMT

Object models are used to identify and capture the information pertaining to an object class and to define the associations between object classes. The information captured includes

- Class name
- Attributes (properties)
- Functions (methods, operations) performed by an object class

By using object models, a systems engineer can formally express the composition of an object class and its associations with the other object classes in the system. The model of the class then embodies the specification and requirements for the systems structure. As the class model is developed, it is important to record the rationale for design decisions along with the model.

Figure 2.4 shows how the class definition is depicted using OMT.

Class name.   The class name is the primary identifier by which the existence and purpose of the class are conveyed from the designer to

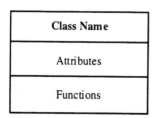

Figure 2.4   Class definition box.

potential users of the class. The only semantic rule associated with a class name is that it be unique. This ensures that the class is distinguishable from all other classes. Practicality, however, dictates that a name appropriate for its associated structure and functionality be chosen. As with choosing which classes to use in a system, the choice of a name is not an exact science. The name should be broad enough to cover most of the potential uses of the classes, yet narrow enough not to overstate the capabilities of the class. There are a variety of naming conventions in use, all equally valid (Young, 1990). One convention should be adopted to all objects within a system.

Class attributes.   Class attributes are the properties shared by each instance of the class. The list of attributes for a class must include all of the properties of the class that are needed for the engineering problem at hand. For a class that models a physical thing such as a car, the attribute list will include items such as weight, acceleration, fuel consumption, and turning radius. The attributes are the kind of information typically found on a spec (specifications) sheet.

Attributes are used in two ways. They can model calculated information or local information. For the class *car*, the attribute *acceleration* will be a function of attributes of parts used to build the car, such as weight, engine torque, transmission ratio, and tire diameter. In order to calculate acceleration for the car, values must be known for these attributes. The system engineers may have an established goal for acceleration if it is important to customer needs and wants. In this case, they must budget-design targets for weight and engine torque to the designers of the components. They must monitor the actual values achieved in design, and finally validate acceleration on the implemented product. The other attribute usage is for local information. These attributes store the rest of the information that must be known about an individual instance. In the case of the class *car*, fuel type is such an attribute. One instance may have the value *gasoline* for its fuel type, and another may have the value *diesel*.

An attribute is more than just a name. Type information is generally included in addition to the name. They may also have default values which are used to initialize instances. These defaults persist in the instance until a better value has been established.

Choosing which attributes to include in a class definition is part of the art of object modeling. Only the highly relevant attributes needed by engineers for the problems and questions they must answer should be included as part of the object class. Other, secondary attributes are often better left to other parts of the structure. If, while defining classes, one class is found to contain a collection of weakly related attributes, then the structure as modeled is probably lacking and needs to be reworked.

Class functions. A class can be passive, having no functions, or it can be active, having a variety of functions. The functions detail what behavior the instances of the classes can perform. Physical objects that are active generally have an energy source that fuels their activity. A variety of terms are used synonymously with function: *method, operation,* and *activity.* In the parlance of object-oriented structure design, *method* is most commonly used.

As with attributes, choosing which functions are part of a class is a mixture of science and art. Some functions naturally belong as part of a class. Others are not so obvious. Class *car* would be likely to have start, stop, accelerate, and turn functions among others. Our pocket knife might have open-tool, close-tool, cut, and sharpen methods. Modeling refines the choice of method.

It is only as a class is viewed in relation to the rest of the system and in relation to the desired behavior (functional requirements) for the system that judgments can be made about which functions should be included or excluded. Some functions for a class are discovered when the desired behavior for the system is mapped or allocated to the object classes from which the system is to be built. For the pocket knife example, the function cut may not be a part of the class pocket knife at all; it may be part of the class *blade* or even class *person.*

The assignment of functions to a class define its interfaces with the rest of the parts in a system. They serve to hide all of the internal structure and behavior details of the class. This leads to a great degree of flexibility and reuse potential. Mechanical engineers have embraced this black-box encapsulation since Joseph Bramah designed and manufactured his locks in England in 1784 using interchangeable parts (*The New Encyclopedia Britannica,* 1980, vol. 11, p. 11). Independently Eli Whitney designed and mass-produced muskets with interchangeable parts for the U.S. government in 1801 (*The New Encyclopedia Britannica,* 1980, vol. 19, p. 822). The rise of object-oriented software design has led software designers to adopt a similar approach. In the modern development of large systems, industry standards, referred to as *protocols,* are often defined for interfaces so that many vendors can supply parts of the system yet maintain proprietary designs for the interior structure and performance of the parts they supply.

Instances. Instance diagrams are similar to class diagrams with the exception that they describe actual objects or things and not just type

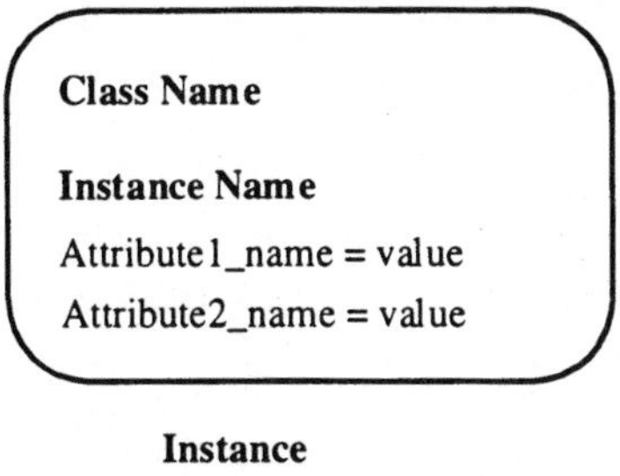

Class Name

Instance Name
Attribute1_name = value
Attribute2_name = value

Figure 2.5 Instance diagram.

Instance

definitions. Figure 2.5 shows the graphic notation used for an instance diagram in OMT.

An instance diagram has rounded edges on its outline and shows the instance's name and class along with the attributes and the instance's value for the attribute. In an instance diagram you can have many instances with the same class.

2.3.3 Example: pocket knife, object class definition

Figure 2.6 shows a first-pass design for the pocket knife class.

Since we are modeling a pocket knife, that is the name we will give to our class definition. As our understanding of the design evolves, so may the name. From examining the knife we are modeling, six attributes are chosen to characterize it. The attributes *number of blades, number of tools,* and *tool types* are all used to characterize the ele-

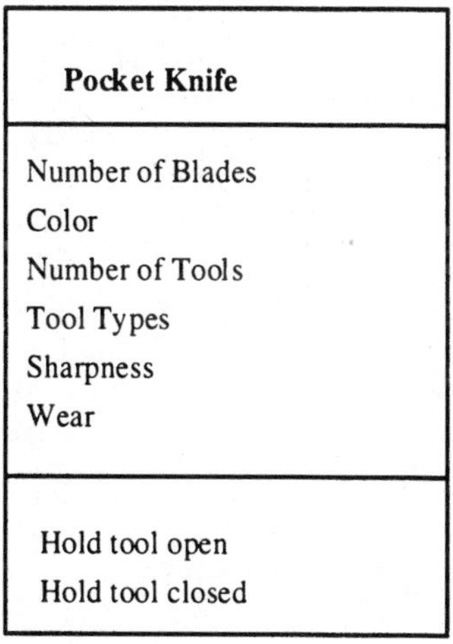

Pocket Knife

Number of Blades
Color
Number of Tools
Tool Types
Sharpness
Wear

Hold tool open
Hold tool closed

Figure 2.6 Initial class definition for pocket knife.

ments that are part of the pocket knife. *Sharpness* and *wear* characterize the performance of the pocket knife in use in its environment. *Color* is an appearance attribute. Later we will consider whether all of these attributes are appropriate to this class, or whether some of them are more appropriate to some of the classes from which they are built or to which they relate. Other attributes may also need to be added such as *strength* or *corrosion resistance*.

The functions (methods) for pocket knife will be considered thoroughly in Chap. 3. In this chapter a few of the ideas concerning assignment of functions to objects are developed, particularly where structure considerations contribute to the understanding of behavior and the assignment of functions to objects. The functions for pocket knife involve holding the tools open or holding them closed. This is not obvious because one might initially associate cut, turn, carve, whittle, and similar functions with pocket knife. However, what distinguishes a pocket knife as a whole is that it holds the tools closed in the handle, and then holds tools open when they are in use. There is a physical mechanism which stores and releases energy to do this: a spring. These two functions are not a result of any one part, like the spring, but are the result of the assembly of the parts into the whole with interfaces among the parts which have been carefully designed to give the assembly this emergent behavior which is a result of several parts working together.

In contrast, functions such as cut or turn are the result of the application of a particular tool to a workpiece with which it interfaces properly. A can opener cuts open a can, and a Phillips head screwdriver tool turns a Phillips head screw. Similarly, functions such as carve or whittle are appropriately assigned to the person who is manipulating the pocket knife against the workpiece because these functions refer to the purpose and control of the overall activity. The important point to understand is that the full description of an object includes the identification of the functions that object performs, and that the analysis needed to make such an assignment involves study of both structure and behavior.

2.3.4 Example: pocket knife instances

Having defined the pocket knife object class, we can now look at instances of the class. To do this, we use an instance diagram. Figure 2.7 shows how this looks. The four instances shown are all pocket knives, but they are distinct from one another.

The same functions can be performed by each of the instances since they are the same class.

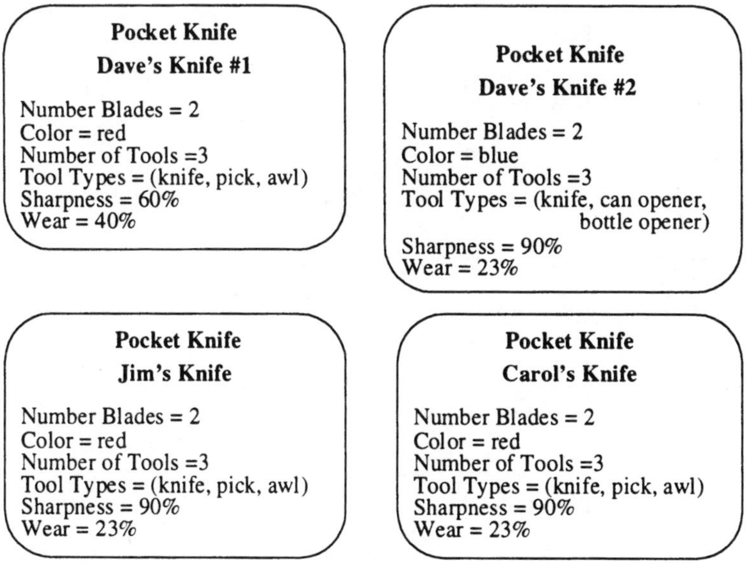

```
 ┌─────────────────────────┐   ┌───────────────────────────┐
 │   Pocket Knife          │   │    Pocket Knife           │
 │   Dave's Knife #1       │   │    Dave's Knife #2        │
 │                         │   │                           │
 │ Number Blades = 2       │   │ Number Blades = 2         │
 │ Color = red             │   │ Color = blue              │
 │ Number of Tools =3      │   │ Number of Tools =3        │
 │ Tool Types = (knife,    │   │ Tool Types = (knife, can  │
 │   pick, awl)            │   │         opener,           │
 │ Sharpness = 60%         │   │         bottle opener)    │
 │ Wear = 40%              │   │ Sharpness = 90%           │
 └─────────────────────────┘   │ Wear = 23%                │
                               └───────────────────────────┘

 ┌─────────────────────────┐   ┌───────────────────────────┐
 │   Pocket Knife          │   │    Pocket Knife           │
 │   Jim's Knife           │   │    Carol's Knife          │
 │                         │   │                           │
 │ Number Blades = 2       │   │ Number Blades = 2         │
 │ Color = red             │   │ Color = red               │
 │ Number of Tools =3      │   │ Number of Tools =3        │
 │ Tool Types = (knife,    │   │ Tool Types = (knife, pick,│
 │   pick, awl)            │   │   awl)                    │
 │ Sharpness = 90%         │   │ Sharpness = 90%           │
 │ Wear = 23%              │   │ Wear = 23%                │
 └─────────────────────────┘   └───────────────────────────┘
```

Figure 2.7 Several instances of pocket knife.

2.4 Aggregation

Most things in the world are built from other things; certainly this is true of complex systems. *Aggregation,* or a parts tree, is the abstraction used to represent the parts which constitute a bigger thing. This powerful abstraction allows us to think about the whole thing, think about the set of its parts, or focus on one of the parts that is used to build it. When our thought process goes from the whole to its parts, the process is considered to be *decomposition* or *partitioning.* When our thought process goes from the parts to the whole, the process is considered to be *synthesis* or *composition.* Aggregation represents the tree of parts. Engineers can work top–down, bottom–up, or middle–out.

2.4.1 Modeling aggregation in OMT

Figure 2.8 shows how the aggregation association is depicted graphically in OMT. In this case, the universe is at the top of the aggregation hierarchy, with each tier in the tree representing a finer granularity of parts, until the very bottom, which models the fundamental particle class. The diamond on the lines connecting a class to its constituents denotes the association as being one of aggregation. This type of tree is called an *AND tree.*

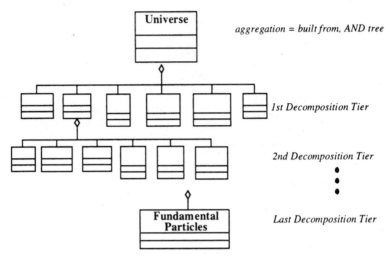

Figure 2.8   Aggregation used to model the structure of the universe.

Aggregation has been used to represent two useful but inconsistent concepts:

1. To mean *built from,* a whole assembled from its parts and requiring all parts to be present.
2. To mean *contains a,* a whole containing the indicated parts, but existing in the absence of the parts.

Aggregation drawn with an open-diamond symbol is used to represent *built from.* In this text we will use a solid black diamond for the abstraction *contains a.* This is an extension beyond traditional OMT.

The diagram in Fig. 2.8 depicts aggregation as a tree. In the real world there are many aggregation trees; there are also many aggregations that are networks rather than trees. Consider if the universe diagram were to be fleshed out. Every class on the penultimate tier has an aggregation relation (made up of) with fundamental particle. They also would have other aggregation relations with higher-order classes (is part of). Thus aggregation relations can become a network of relations among the existing classes. The system of interest may be anywhere within this vast network. The engineer uses only that small portion of the network needed for the problem. The same modeling abstractions are used for all tiers.

2.4.2   Example: pocket knife with aggregation

Aggregation in object models provides a means for representing the relationship between classes. The pocket knife was shown in Fig. 2.3.

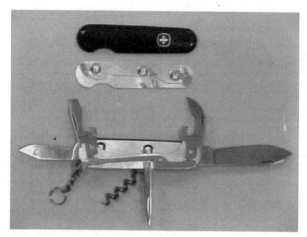

Figure 2.9 Pocket knife disassembled.

An expanded view of it is shown in Fig. 2.9. From this view we can see that the knife is built from two plastic side panels, a metal case built from plates, springs and rivets, six tools, and a key chain. This is the structure that we should model if we are to end up with a flexible and broadly useful design. We will use aggregation to describe it.

The metal case is secured with a rivet, and three rivets are used for hinges for the tools. In system design it is important to determine how the parts are related to subassemblies until the final object is assembled. The parts tree, however, can be drawn in several different ways, each with its own use. If one only needs to collect all the parts, it is sufficient to go from pocket knife to all the parts in one tier. For our use in modeling the structure of the pocket knife, we choose to show all the aggregate levels of structure. This is shown in Fig. 2.10.

The new design mirrors the observation we made looking at the picture of the disassembled knife. The plates, springs, and rivets constitute the metal knife case. This, in turn along with the tools and the key chain, make up the metal knife assembly. Finally, this assembly and the plastic side panel aggregate to form the pocket knife. At each of the diamonds, there is an assembly.

Figure 2.10 uses a view of the classes different from that which we saw in the previous section. In it we have chosen not to show all the attributes and methods of the classes. To proceed further with the design, this level of detail should now be added. We will do some of that investigation but leave the complete design as an exercise for the reader.

Taking the attributes first, consider color. We find that this attribute no longer belongs to pocket knife but rather should be moved to the plastic side panel class. Additionally, this class needs to be augmented with an attribute that deals with the logo. If we look at a dif-

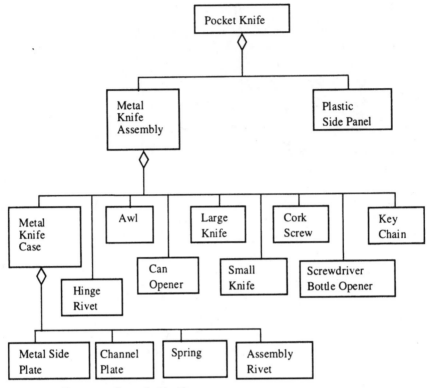

Figure 2.10   Parts tree for pocket knife.

ferent attribute of the original class, number of blades, we find that it
is no longer necessary. The aggregation structure clearly shows how
many blades the knife has. It is eliminated. The remainder of the
original attributes must be similarly considered.

Now consider the methods from the original design. Tool-specific
functionality such as "cut" and "open can" need to be moved out of the
pocket knife and into the appropriate tool classes. With this change
we begin to see an improved, more flexible design. Changing which
tools are included with the knife is now just a matter of aggregating a
different set. The methods of the knife class are not affected by the
change. In the original design, all the methods of pocket knife would
need to be updated to accommodate this change.

We should revisit the name of our class at this point. We have explicitly modeled the tools that make up this knife. This has actually
reduced the scope of the pocket knife class somewhat. The model, as
it stands, is more appropriately named *six-tool pocket knife*. Later on
we will show how to model a more flexible design that covers a wide

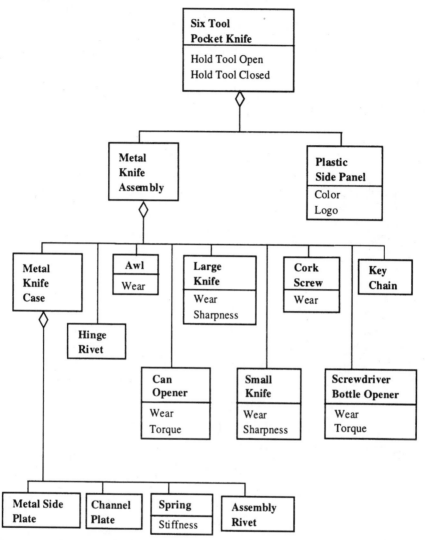

Figure 2.11   Parts tree for six-tool pocket knife.

range of tooling options without needing to change the aggregation relations. Figure 2.11 shows the design as it currently stands, with the attributes redistributed as discussed above.

The aggregation used here is more general than a one-tier picture that goes immediately to all the parts. One can change the kind of pocket knife by substituting different kinds of tools among the six that can go in the tool. One can make the knife bigger and able to accommodate three more tools by adding an additional spring and channel plate to the metal knife case. This type of design and style of showing aggregation promotes reuse, which has been called *family-of-parts* for many years in mechanical systems. Many different knives can be assembled from the same set of parts by varying the number of channel plates and springs, and by selecting among tools that can be used.

Aggregation is modeled as a relationship between classes. Thus the six-tool pocket knife class is associated with the metal knife assembly class. Instances share in this association as they share in all other aspects with their class definition. Thus Dave's six-tool pocket knife will be associated with Dave's metal knife assembly and Dave's plastic case and instances of all the other classes with which the six-tool pocket knife has an aggregation relationship.

2.5   Cardinality or Number

It is very desirable to have another abstraction to show the choices and constraints one has in selecting among objects. The aggregation tree is an AND tree that shows that a class is built from part 1 and part 2, and part 3. It is not sufficiently detailed to capture binary information noting the existence or nonexistence of connections in these trees. Each of the situations below merits further description within the structural model to capture what would otherwise be expressed in hard-to-digest prose or, more probably, never be explicitly stated:

- Exactly one instance is a part of a class which aggregates it.
- Potentially many instances are included as parts.
- The part may or may not be included.
- An exact number of parts is required.
- A range of parts is required.

2.5.1   Cardinality in OMT

Figure 2.12 shows how each of these are depicted within the graphics of the OMT methodology. Symbols are used for the frequent cases of many and optional. The association is annotated numerically for other cases.

2.5.2   Example

With the additional flexibility given by the introduction of the cardinality abstraction, we can be more specific in our model of the six-tool pocket knife. Several facts about the knife have been left out of the model so far. These involve the number of each part that is required. Figure 2.13 shows the updated model with this information added.

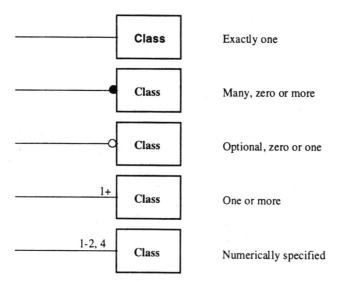

Figure 2.12 Cardinality and conditions expressed in OMT.

2.6 Classification of Objects

The next major abstraction for describing structure which we will discuss is classification. Put simply, *classification* is a way of grouping similar things. Classifying is one of the earliest skills developed by children. They learn to understand the world around them by developing categories for all that they experience: fun things, hot things, things that get me in trouble. Given that this skill is developed early and continues to be reinforced throughout life, it would be foolish not to exploit classification for understanding and designing systems. It has been employed for centuries in various ways:

- Library catalogs
- Layout of items in a store
- Grouping of financial items in accounting
- Providing products that can be customized
- Designing with a family of parts

Depending on which direction you look at it, classification can be seen as generalization or specialization. In *generalization* we look at a collection of objects and use common attributes (properties) or behavior to group things together. Sneakers, boots, and slippers can all be generalized as shoes. In *specialization* we take the opposite view. We break down a general class into smaller ones which share the attributes of

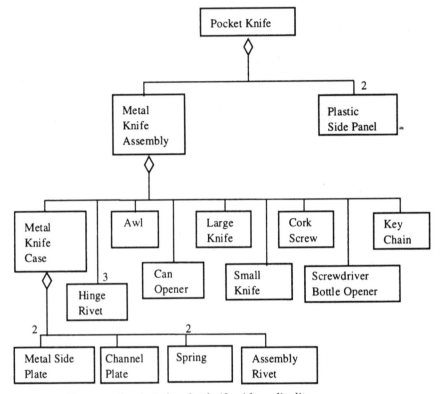

Figure 2.13 Parts tree for six-tool pocket knife with cardinality.

the general class but have different attributes which distinguish one from another. Shoes are specialized as sneakers, boots, and slippers.

The groupings, classes, are used to discuss, store, or locate a group of things. The difference between finding something in a department store or in a flea market is that the merchandise in the department store has been classified and arranged geographically according to well-understood classes. To get sneakers, one goes to the shoe department of the department store or to a shoe store.

The attributes and functions of a general class are all present in the more specific classes that are descendent from the general class.

2.6.1 Classification in OMT

As with the other elements of structure, it is useful to have a graphic notation for classification to augment text. Figure 2.14 shows how OMT represents classification with a triangle. In OMT the class at

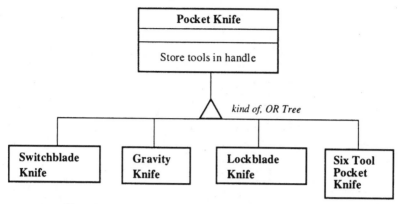

Figure 2.14 Classification tree for pocket knife.

the root of the tree is known as a *superclass,* while those at the bottom of the tree are called *subclasses.*

2.6.2   Example: classification of tools

Going back to our example, we note that there are more kinds of pocket knives than we have considered so far. The six-tool pocket knife is only one of these. Others include

- *Switchblade knives,* which open and lock the blade on depression of a release.

- *Gravity knives,* which open the knife by gravity and lock it on depression of a release.

- *Lockblade knives,* which are opened by the user but lock open.

- *Multitool pocket knives,* which are opened and closed by the user. The knife holds the tool open or closed, but does not lock it in position.

Figure 2.14 classifies pocket knives according to how they are opened and held open. Each of the subclasses inherits common features from the parent class. In this case they all inherit the function "Store the tools in handle." Each of these subclasses has unique functions and attributes which distinguish it from the other subclass members. The four subclasses differ in the manner in which tools are opened and held open.

In our example, we have designed a six-tool pocket knife. We noted, however, that perhaps there is a better way to model this design. Classification can be used to this effect. Figure 2.15 gives a classification of 16 possible tools to use in a multitool pocket knife. They all are tools and as such share whatever common attributes are modeled as

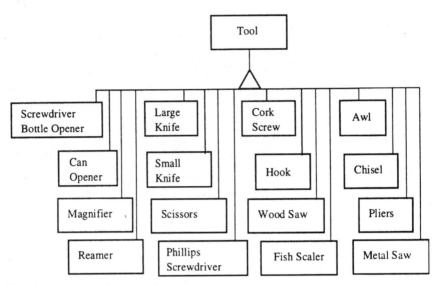

Figure 2.15   Types of tools for class *tool.*

part of the tool class. For this example, that would probably include *size* and *attachment point* since all the tools are required to fit within the storage space provided in the handle of the pocket knife.

The tool class introduced above can now be inserted into the aggregation tree for the six-tool pocket knife in place of the direct aggregation of the individual tools. We have now succeeded in extending our design from a very specific six-tool pocket knife that required a change in the structure model to change the tools which were included to a family of six-tool pocket knives where 8008 distinct six-tool designs are possible without requiring a change to the structure model.

By combining the new tool class with a change in the cardinality constraints on the design, we can generalize the model even further. The simple abstractions used to describe structure are powerful enough to describe a product family that extends beyond six-tool pocket knives. Analysis of the structure model shows that one can build knives with 3, 6, 9, or 12 tools by adding springs and channel plates. Knives for a variety of purposes can be composed by choosing among the 16 tool types. As we make this change, we will need, once again, to update the name of the class. This time we move to a more general name *multitool pocket knife*. The model of this multitool shows a variable n used for cardinality. In this case n can be any integer value from 1 to 5. Figure 2.16 shows the resulting design.

It is apparent that one can use aggregation and classification to represent just the collection of parts needed to make a specific knife,

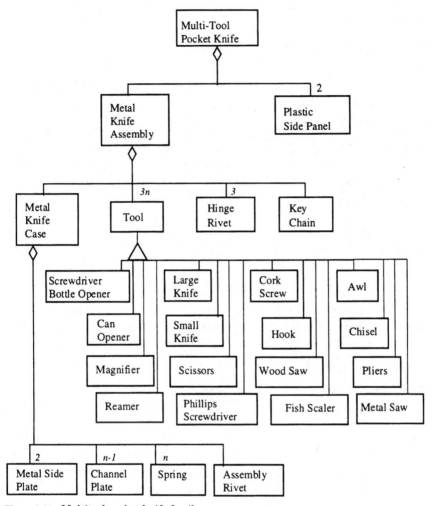

Figure 2.16 Multitool pocket knife family.

the assembly of a particular knife, or an entire family of knives and their assembly. No one of these alternatives is better than another. It is efficient to use the simplest description that captures all the information needed for the problem at hand.

2.7 Interconnection of Objects

Objects do not stand alone. They work together in a cooperative manner to achieve the goals of the designer. *Interconnection* is the abstraction we use to think about how things (systems and objects) interrelate physically or logically.

2.7.1 Definition

Objects interact with some but not all the other objects in their environment. Each of the interactions is modeled as an interconnection. Each interconnection has a number of properties that also need to be modeled. Chief among these properties are the role that the interconnection models and the input/output transfer which takes place at the interconnection. Interconnections between a system and its environment describe its context. Interconnections internal to a system describe its assembly.

Roles and interconnection.   Every interconnection has a role associated with it. Roles define the reason for two classes to have an interconnection. Understanding of the roles used in interconnection is key to understanding the corporate behavior of the classes. Roles are by their nature symmetrical; that is, if class A has a role association with class B, then class B has a corresponding role association with class A. In some cases as we will see later the role is secondary to the information being transferred. The following are some examples of role associations:

- A person holds a knife/the knife is held by a person.
- A generator powers a motor/a motor loads a generator.
- A parent supports a child in college/a child in college is supported by a parent.
- Requirements trace to functions/functions trace to requirements.

Input/output and interconnection.   Input and output along an interconnection describe the flow of information, material, or energy among the objects. Although every interconnection has a role associated with it, the same is not true of input/output. Only active objects which encapsulate functions that transform information, material, or energy send something which is output from one object and input to another. Interconnections exist between passive objects, but they have no associated I/O. From the standpoint of developing an executable model, capturing the I/O information is critical. The I/O definition contains information detailing the type and quantity of stuff being generated and consumed. This, along with numbering and conditional markers, makes the model executable.

Some examples of input/output associated with interconnections are

- A person applies force to a knife, measured in newtons.

- A telephone caller speaks to a callee/the callee speaks to the caller, measured in information content.

- A generator delivers current to a motor, measured in amperes.

- A parent gives money to a child in college, measured in dollars.

Input/output has directionality and may flow in one direction between objects, or in both directions.

Not every interconnection has input/output associated with it. For derived requirements and the parent requirements from which they are derived, there is a logical reason for interconnection, but there is no input/output associated because requirements are passive objects, and do not generate outputs or consume inputs.

Some engineering disciplines, like electrical engineering, consider primarily interconnection and input/output. Others, such as database engineering, deal primarily with passive objects (information items) and consider primarily interconnection and roles. In systems engineering, both are needed.

2.7.2 Interconnection in OMT

In OMT interconnection is represented graphically as a line between the objects involved. The line is annotated with the reason for the interconnection and sometimes the inputs and outputs. Cardinality and conditionality are also represented on interconnections. The same cardinality notation is used for these that is used with aggregation. Figure 2.12 summarizes this notation. In OMT interconnections are called *associations*. The aggregation and classification relations are also called *associations* in OMT.

2.7.3 Example: multitool pocket knife context

Classes have an environment in which to operate. This environment is called the *context* of the object. By modeling the context, we will gain additional insight into the working of the object we are designing. Interconnection establishes the boundary between the thing and the context in which it is used. In software terms, it defines the *application-program interface* (API). In the physical realm, it is the boundary definition for differential equations or the physical coupling to other objects.

One way to approach development of the context of a system is to think through its use or operation in its environment. When written in text in narrative form this information is often called an *operations concept*. A simple narrative for a pocket knife follows:

> She reached into her right pocket and took out the pocket knife. She opened the large blade and grasped the knife firmly. She picked up the

workpiece in her other hand and whittled it to the desired shape. She put down the workpiece, closed the knife, and put it back into her pocket.

Note that the only actions as written are performed by the person. The knife blade is acting as a pressure transformer which receives 10 or 15 lb of force on the handle and transforms that to tens of thousands of pounds per square inch of pressure where the blade edge pushes against the workpiece surface. But there are actions performed by the knife that were not written down. Here is the same operations concept, augmented with the knife's actions.

She reached into her right pocket and took out the pocket knife. She opened the large blade *with her thumbnail against the closing force of the knife and the knife held the blade open.* She grasped the knife firmly. She picked up the workpiece in her other hand and whittled, *by applying force to the knife which transferred the force to the workpiece,* it to the desired shape. She put down the workpiece, closed the knife *against the holding force of the knife (and the knife held the blade closed),* and she put it back into her pocket.

To model the context, we must first identify the objects involved. The objects in the environment with which the knife interconnects are the person, the pocket, and the workpiece. Figure 2.17 shows these interconnections. If not needed for clarity, the line between person and pocket and the line between person and workpiece can be eliminated because they do not show interconnections directly to pocket knife and are not essential for understanding its context.

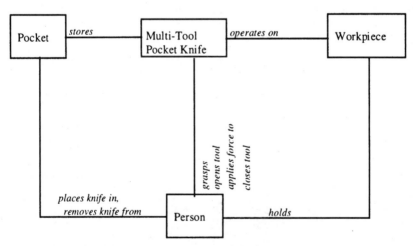

Figure 2.17   A multitool pocket knife context.

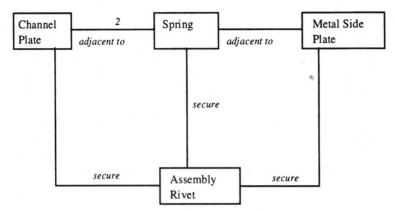

Figure 2.18 Assembly interconnections for metal knife case.

2.7.4 Example: multitool assembly interconnection

In addition to relating to things in their context, things are also built out of other things. Certain of the parts interconnect or are associated to assemble the thing. Interconnection shows how to assemble an object from its parts. For each aggregation, or assembly point, in the aggregation for the multitool pocket knife, there is an assembly of parts, an interconnection. Figure 2.18 shows the assembly interconnections for the metal knife case.

The channel plate, spring, and metal side plate are secured by the assembly rivet. The channel plate is adjacent to two springs. Dimensioned mechanical drawings convey more information about physical objects than do the object diagrams, but that is the work of mechanical engineers doing detail design. The object diagrams for structure capture the parts, the choices among parts, and how the parts are to assemble, without designing the parts.

2.8 Roles

We have described the abstractions needed to describe structure and a notation for these abstractions. These abstractions are all static in nature; that is, they capture the structure of the system at one instant and in one context. Real systems are more complex than this. A single object may have several roles in the system depending on when in the life cycle it is viewed and what problem is being considered by what group of people. Possible roles a thing (object) may have in systems engineering include

- *Subject system,* the thing being defined
- *External system,* something in the context of the thing being defined
- *Component,* a part of the thing being defined
- *Input/output,* something consumed or produced by the thing being defined

In our pocket knife example the knife as we have studied it is the subject system. From the standpoint of a carver, however, it is just one of many tools in the carver's environment. Consider all the roles an automobile engine might have:

- The subject system by the engine design team
- An external system by the transmission design team
- A component by the automobile design team or by a buyer considering engine options
- An output by the engine manufacturing facility
- An input by the automobile assembly plant
- An input and output by the just-in-time logistics group that delivers parts to the automobile assembly plant

It is important to know what roles an object participates in when viewing it to understand its place in the total structure. It is also important to maintain consistency in the object's design between its use in different roles. The structure modeling capability described captures these associations rigorously, enabling all designers to develop a shared understanding. Roles and their effect on structure will be discussed in detail in later chapters.

2.9   Allocation of Functions to Objects

Now that some structural analysis has been performed, the knife is understood in terms of several structure models:

1. A classification tree which shows the parts that can be selected
2. A parts list or aggregation which shows the parts selected and the parts needed for assemblies of parts
3. An interconnection diagram that defines the context
4. Interconnection diagrams that show the interfaces in the assemblies and subassemblies

These structure models help with the assignment of functions to the objects in the models, although behavior analysis, described in Chap. 3, is needed to fully develop alternatives in assigning functions to the objects. From the context it is seen that functions such as whittle or carve or fasten with screw are appropriate to assign to the person who will manipulate the workpiece and the pocket knife and select an appropriate tool. Functions such as turn Phillips head screw or cut open can are appropriate to assign to specific tools. When this understanding is augmented with executable models of the behaviors involved, the problem and proposed solution are described rigorously.

2.10   Summary

The semantics for static structure have been defined. The semantic abstractions defining objects are

Object classes having

- Name
- Attributes
- Functions

Object instances inheriting

- Attributes and having attribute values
- Functions

The semantic abstractions defining associations among objects are

Parts tree (aggregation)

Interconnection applied to

- Context
- Assembly

Classification

Cardinality

These abstractions have been demonstrated with the modeling of a real product:

The models can be detailed and applied narrowly to a specific product.

The models can be generalized to model a product family and the reuse options.

The models of structure are computer-executable.

A notation, OMT, has been described for this modeling; any other notation may be used that covers these abstractions. The notation can be selected or tailored to organization culture and preferences.

2.11   Exercises

1. Create a class diagram for a person using a pocket knife. Include important attributes and functions.
2. Look at Fig. 2.6 and examine the attributes. Do any of the attributes belong more appropriately with the parts of the knife? Are there important attributes missing? Consider your fingernails in opening such a knife. Consider limits in turning screws or prying open paint cans with a screwdriver tool. Redraw the class diagram for multitool pocket knife and create one for *tool*. Identify the appropriate attributes and initial functions for both classes.
3. Create assembly diagrams for multitool pocket knife and for metal knife assembly.
4. The multitool pocket knife stores tools in channels, which are not parts, but are regions defined by a set of parts. Define channels using OMT models.
5. More than one type of tool is available to use in making pocket knives. How does the type of tool affect the model of channels?
6. Observe your surroundings.
   a. Create class definitions for six things in your environment.
   b. Create assembly or interconnection diagrams for these six things.
   c. Choose two of the classes and show how they are related using classification.

2.12   References

Booch, G., 1983: *Software Engineering with Ada.* Menlo Park, Calif.: Benjamin/ Cummings.

Buhr, R. J. A., 1984: *System Design with Ada.* Englewood Cliffs, N.J.: Prentice-Hall.

Liskov, B., et al., 1981: CLU Reference Manual, *Lecture Notes in Computer Science,* G. Goos and J. Hartmanis, eds., Springer-Verlag.

Liskov, B., and J. Guttag, 1986: *Abstraction and Specification in Program Development,* MA: MIT Press.

The New Encyclopedia Britannica, 1980, 15th ed.

Rumbaugh, J., M. Blaha, W. J. Premerlani, F. Eddy, and W. Lorensen, 1991: *Object-Oriented Modeling and Design.* Englewood Cliffs, N.J.: Prentice-Hall.

Young, D. A., 1990: *The X Window System: Programming and Applications with Xt.* Englewood Cliffs, N.J.: Prentice-Hall.

Basics of Behavior

3.1 Introduction to Behavior

In Chap. 2 we described the elements of structure and a notation for those elements. In this chapter we explore the same issues for behavior. *Behavior* is what a thing or object does, or what one wants a thing to do. Behavior for a system describes *what* the system is to do, independent of *how* the system will do it. A full description or model of behavior contains sufficient information to enable a person or a computer to execute the model and observe the desired behavior. When behavior is expressed with such a description, it is referred to as an *executable behavior.* Such descriptions have been developed to enable engineers to develop timelines for the performance of systems, and to execute time-dependent simulations and probabilistic calculations. When behavior is captured in executable form, it may be checked for correctness. In this way conditions such as starvation, where one part of a system never receives the inputs it needs, or deadlock, where separate parts of the system are stuck waiting for each other, can be uncovered and corrected during system design.

Many methods of describing behavior have been developed over the years. The methods vary in formality and in the degree of detail which they capture.

This chapter looks at details which must be captured in order to have an executable behavior, and compares this information to some popular methods for describing behavior or partial views of behavior using text alone or graphic notations.

3.1.1   Elements of behavior

In order to create a complete description of a behavior a number of modeling elements are required. The necessary set of semantic elements includes

- Functions, which accept inputs and transform them to outputs
- Inputs and outputs, of various types
- Control operators, which define the ordering of functions

These modeling elements must be defined using a precise definition language, expressing these elements with a notation which is unambiguous. The particular set of symbols and notation used is unimportant as long as they are understood and consistent. Any notation which has all of these characteristic elements can be made executable.

Despite the precision and range of expression afforded by use of a behavior notation, text cannot be eliminated. Except at the lowest level, a text description is required to accompany the behavior model. The text provides a description that can quickly give consumers of the model an intuitive feel for the model. The details can then be quickly found by looking at the model. As with all other parts of system design, several conventions have been developed for these text descriptions. The most common are:

- Definitions for a data dictionary.
- Imperative statements, often containing the word *shall,* which constitute a list of what the system, object, or thing is to do. These are particularly useful for contract and acquisition purposes. This list is termed the *specification* by the organization producing it, which becomes the customer. In current practice, it often forms the basis for the contract to build a system, requiring a supplier to produce something according to the list. From the supplier's viewpoint, this list is called the *system requirements.*
- Narrative statements which can be joined together to provide a text description of what the object is intended to do. A narrative of this type is called an *operations concept.* It is useful for communication with users, owners, operators, management, marketing, and other disciplines which do not need or wish to deal with all the engineering detail.

It is important to note that these text descriptions are not sufficient to fully describe a system, just as the model does not stand on its own. Only by blending the two sets of information do they become a complete picture.

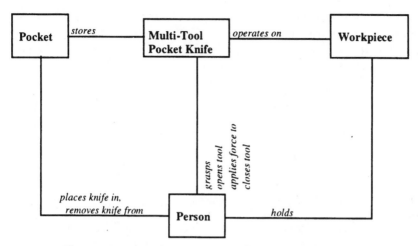

Figure 3.1 Structural context of multitool pocket knife.

3.1.2 Behavior in the systems context

The static description of context establishes what elements in the environment interact with the system. The static model of context defines the system by establishing what external systems interact with the subject system and by listing what excitations, functions, the external systems perform to which the subject system must respond. Figure 3.1 shows the final context model for the pocket knife example as developed in the previous chapter. Throughout the development of the structure model definition of the functions associated with the classes was left vague. The interconnections in the context diagram suggest some of the necessary functions. To go further with function definition, however, we need to take a step back from the structural model and develop a model of the desired behavior. Once this is defined, we can then partition the behavior and map it onto the structural elements.

3.1.3 This chapter

The static model is lacking two major elements required to rigorously describe behavior:

- The ordering of the functions
- The inputs and outputs to each function

In this chapter we will explain these concepts in detail and introduce appropriate graphic modeling notation for modeling them. We will continue illustrating the modeling concepts and notation with our multitool pocket knife.

After these descriptions and illustrations, we will use OMT to precisely define an information model for behavior. The chapter concludes with a discussion of how these models and concepts relate to requirements and specifications.

3.2 Modeling of Behavior

The first questions to be considered in modeling behavior are

- What happens?
- In what order?
- What inputs and outputs are involved?

Modeling of functions is the way we address the first of these basic questions. The second question is addressed by the ordering of a collection of functions in a system. For ordering, a number of concepts need to be represented:

- *Sequencing,* which indicates which functions must precede or succeed others
- *Concurrency,* describing functions which can occur simultaneously
- *Selection,* capturing choices which must be made between functions
- *Iteration,* indicating which functions are repeated as a block

For the third question inputs and outputs to the functions are modeled.
For large complex systems it is always necessary to break the system structure and behavior into parts, using aggregation, in order to manage the complexity. The behavior view can be simplified in another way, by using partial views of the behavior which together constitute the behavior. Some examples of partial views are

- *Functional flow block diagrams* (FFBDs), for functions and ordering of functions
- *Data-flow diagrams* (DFDs) (Martin and McClure, 1985; Yourdon, 1989) and *N-squared charts*, for functions and input/output

3.3 Functional Flow Block Diagrams

Functional flow block diagrams were developed in the late 1950s by TRW Corp. to help describe ballistic missile behaviors which were found to be too complex to be adequately described in text. Further work at TRW enhanced the descriptions to make them executable (Alford, 1977, 1992). We will introduce first the basic FFBD and then

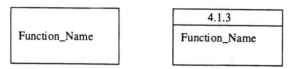

Figure 3.2 FFBD notation for functions.

discuss the necessary extensions to make the diagrams executable. FFBDs are discussed in detail in a number of other reference works (Blanchard and Fabrycky, 1990; MIL-STD-499, 1968; Kockler et al., 1990). The primary views of behavior modeled with FFBDs are functions, their ordering, and their composition.

3.3.1 Functions

In FFBDs functions are represented as blocks or rectangles labeled with the function name. Often a number is assigned to the function and displayed as a banner across the top of the block. This number tracks the function location within the hierarchy. (We will discuss hierarchy later.) Figure 3.2 shows this notation.

3.3.2 Ordering

Ordering of functions is shown by lines connecting the blocks.

Sequence. A simple sequence is shown by an arrow coming out of the right side of the predecessor and into the left side of the successor. Time in FFBDs flows from left to right. Of course, limitations such as page size sometimes cause the diagram to wrap back to the left side of the page. This is shown in Fig. 3.3.

Concurrency. Concurrency is represented by an AND relationship. The AND shows that all the branches coming from it can happen at the same time. This is not to say that all the branches have to be performed in parallel, only that they can. In the diagram the AND is shown as a circle with the word *AND* written inside. All the concurrent

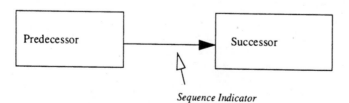

Sequence Indicator

Figure 3.3 FFBD depiction of sequence.

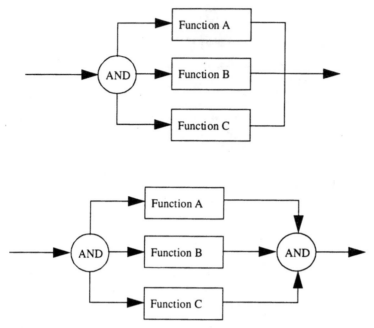

Figure 3.4 Representations of concurrency in FFBDs.

branches emanate from the circle. The branches for the concurrency join back together with the main sequence arrows when the concurrency is completed. Optionally, the concurrency can be completed with a second circle with *AND* inscribed and the branches merging into the circle. Choice of which form to use is left to the designer or dictated by the use of a particular support tool. Figure 3.4 shows both forms.

Selection. Selection is represented by an OR relationship. Selection represents two or more alternative paths through the functions which can be taken. The FFBD diagram representation is similar to concurrency with the word *AND* replaced by the word *OR*. A third shorthand form is also used for selection. When a binary choice is made, the selection can be shown by two arrows leaving a function block, each labeled with a selection criterion. Figure 3.5 shows the various forms.

Iteration. Iteration is the last of the major ordering operations that is used to model behavior. In FFBDs iteration is depicted similarly to the third form used for selection. Iteration is shown as an arrow coming out of a decision block which loops backward over a set of functions. The backward arrow is labeled with a completion criterion. This is shown in Fig. 3.6.

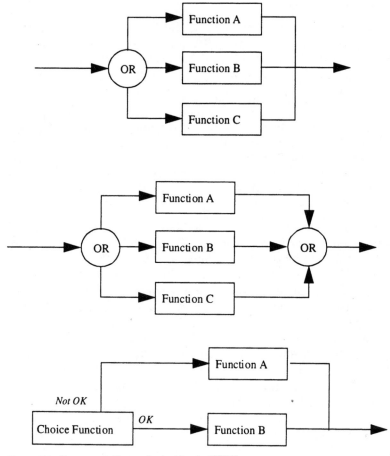

Figure 3.5   Representations of selection in FFBDs.

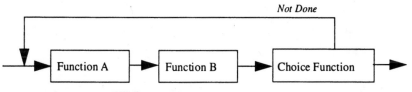

Figure 3.6   Iteration in FFBDs.

3.3.3 Example: pocket knife

The FFBD notations introduced so far—function, sequence, selection, concurrency, and iteration—are sufficient to begin modeling the behavior of the pocket knife. We begin the modeling by referring to the same usage scenario used in modeling the static context.

> She reached into her right pocket and took out the pocket knife. She opened the large blade with her thumbnail against the closing force of the knife, and the knife held the blade open. She grasped the knife firmly. She picked up the workpiece in her other hand and whittled it to the desired shape by applying force to the knife, which transferred the force to the workpiece. She put down the workpiece and closed the knife against the holding force of the knife, and the knife held the blade closed. She put it back into her pocket.

In considering the static context, we focused primarily on the objects that are involved in the scenario. From the behavior standpoint we focus on the actions that are performed. After both models are developed we will map from the behavior onto the structure. Figure 3.7 shows the FFBD model of the actions performed in this scenario.

This model shows a view of the *intrinsic* behavior of the *person,* the behavior as limited by physical reality. The knife is removed from the pocket before it is opened. The tool is opened before the work is held because it takes two hands to open the knife. The work must be held at the same time as it is operated on. The work is released before the tool is closed in order to have a hand free to close it. The tool is closed before placing it in the pocket. The iterative loop allows for the possibility that a different tool or different workpieces will be operated on in the same session.

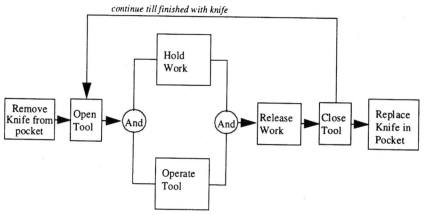

Figure 3.7 FFBD for person using pocket knife.

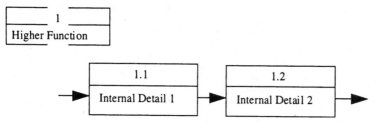

Figure 3.8 Hierarchy representation in FFBDs.

3.3.4 Hierarchy

If we were to attempt to model every function with all the associated details in one diagram, it would quickly become too large and unwieldy. To overcome this limitation, hierarchy is used. Hierarchy of functional design provides convenient encapsulations of detail. At the higher levels the function blocks represent complex functions, as the design proceeds and the lower levels are reached, the functions are increasingly atomic. The numbers which label the function blocks track the level and placement of blocks within the hierarchy. At each level a new level of numbering is used. Each block within the hierarchy then has a unique number which specifies its location. Figure 3.8 shows the FFBD representation of hierarchy.

Example: behavior hierarchy. In one of the functions in Fig. 3.7, *open tool,* there is a selection among alternative tools to open. Rather than put that detail into the same FFBD, we will use hierarchy to show that information in a separate diagram. A lower-level FFBD is drawn for open tool as shown in Fig. 3.9. The FFBD uses an *OR* construction to show selection.

The original FFBD model, developed by examining the scenario, is not sufficient to capture all the required behavior. The scenario examined the knife in its context. To make a complete model, we need to expand to include the behavior of the knife as well. Figure 3.10 shows the simple cyclic ordering of the functions. The knife holds a tool closed, then holds a tool open, and can then hold the tool closed.

3.3.5 Input and output

The ordering of functions requires the capture of their sequence, concurrency, selection, and iteration. The functional flow block diagram is one graphic notation that records this information. This information is only a partial view of behavior because none of the functions' inputs and outputs are described. Inputs/outputs must be included in the model because they are the entities transformed by the functions, be-

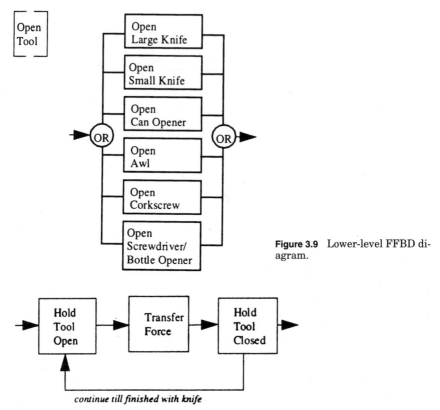

Figure 3.9   Lower-level FFBD diagram.

Figure 3.10   FFBD diagram for pocket knife.

cause they trigger some functions, and because they provide the information about the path to take at some of the selection points among functions. Understanding these interactions is essential to understanding the full behavior. In addition, the input and output models are required to execute the model and verify their correct operation.

Behavior diagrams.   When input/output information is added to an FFBD or equivalent diagram, one obtains a behavior diagram. Behavior diagrams of this general type were developed by Alford (1977, 1992). The Alford diagrams are rotated 90° so that the time flow is vertical and down instead of horizontal, left to right. The Alford diagrams are designed to distinguish among several kinds of concurrency and incorporate symbols for each type. In this form they are supported by the RDD-100 tool (Ascent Logic Corp.). In a horizontal format behavior is supported by the Core tool (Vitech Corp.). There are differences in the notations supported by different tools, but the capture of

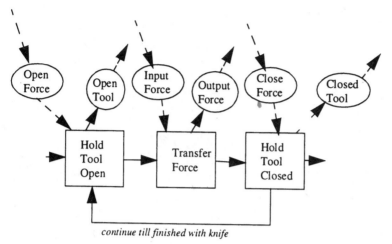

continue till finished with knife

Figure 3.11   Behavior diagram for pocket knife.

functions, the ordering of functions, and the capture of input/outputs is common to the different implementations of executable behavior. A related representation is that of statecharts (Harel, 1987), which will be discussed later. This is the usual situation: a plethora of competing notations and tools to capture the same abstractions without tool support to transform among the notations and tools.

For use within this book, the input/outputs are depicted as ovals, and the dashed arrows show the direction of flow of the inputs/outputs. Such a diagram is shown in Fig. 3.11.

In this simple example the inputs come from the context and outputs return to the context. The behavior of the person in the context results in a more complex behavior diagram as shown in Fig. 3.12.

It provides an executable description of what the person does. The process begins with a pocket knife in a pocket and a piece of work. It ends with the pocket knife back in the pocket and a modified piece of work. The excitations to which our subject system pocket knife must respond are the input open force from the function open tool, the input force from the function operate tool, and the input close force from the function close tool. The response from the pocket knife to open force is an open pocket knife with the selected tool held open. The response from the pocket knife to the force is to transfer the force to the workpiece in the form of cutting or screwing or however the selected tool applies its force. The response of the pocket knife to close force is a closed pocket knife with the tool held closed. Taken together, the two behavior diagrams can be put together to form a single behavior of the pocket knife in its context. Figure 3.13 shows this single diagram.

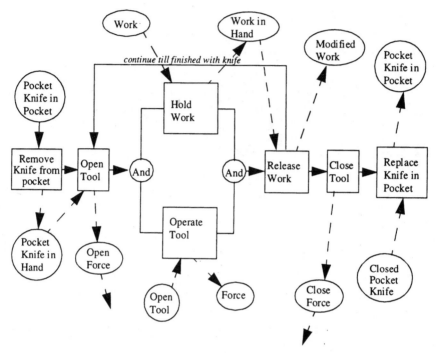

Figure 3.12 Behavior diagram for person using pocket knife.

3.4   Data-Flow Diagrams

As noted earlier, functional flow block diagrams are a useful partial view of behavior which suppresses all input/output information. The behavior diagrams just discussed added in the input/output information. If we subtract the sequencing information from the behavior diagrams, what is left are the elements of a data-flow diagram. The data-flow diagram and N-squared chart are useful partial views of behavior which are captured in two different notational styles and which suppress the information of ordering of functions.

Figure 3.14 shows the behavior diagram with the sequencing information suppressed. The notation differs from DFD notation. In DFD notation the functions are in ovals, not in rectangles. The inputs/outputs are annotations on arrows that go from one function to another. Data store are shown as the name of the data store with a line above and below the name. Figure 3.15 shows the input output diagram of Fig. 3.14 recast as a data-flow diagram. The diagram consists of four disconnected elements since the diagram does not include the pocket knife itself.

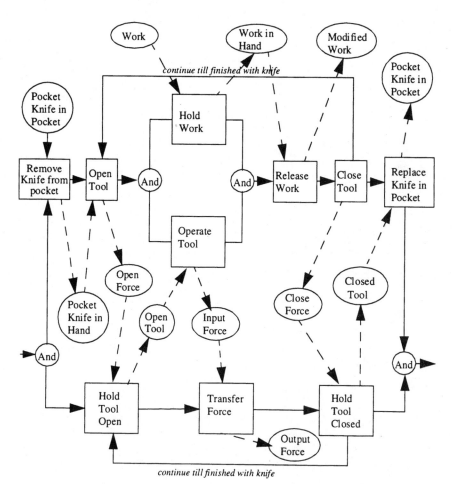

Figure 3.13 Behavior diagram for pocket knife in its context.

3.5   Representation of Behavior as State

Another view of behavior which has gained usage in recent years is state modeling. This provides a powerful and convenient method to capture the pattern of activity for a given structure. A number of diagraming techniques are used for modeling behavior with state representation. Chief among these are statecharts and state transition diagrams. These diagrams are very useful for generating implementations at leaf level where complex trade-off is not needed. When trade-off is yet to be performed, however, state representations can obscure the possibilities for trade-off or become unmanageably large.

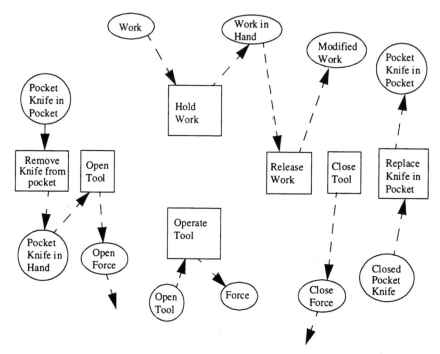

Figure 3.14   Input/output diagram for person.

Two different formalisms are used for representing state. In the first, known as the *Mealy machine,* the functions, or activities, are modeled as taking place during the transitions between states (Mealy, 1955). In the second, the functions are modeled as taking place while the machine is in the state. These are known as *Moore machines* (Moore, 1956). The two representation are interchangeable in terms of their ability to model a problem (Hopcroft and Ullman, 1979). It is important, however, to understand which approach is being used when interpreting a state diagram.

For any given FFBD, a state diagram can be constructed which models the same set of functions. To see that this is the case, consider the transformations necessary to get from an FFBD to a state model. They are the same transformations used to change a nondeterministic finite automaton into a deterministic automaton. Assuming that the state representation will be a Moore machine, the transformations are as follows:

- For each function in the FFBD, create a state. Assign the function as the activity to be performed while in the state.

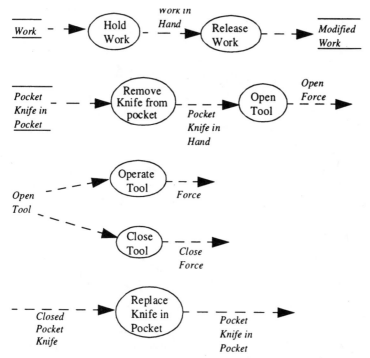

Figure 3.15 Data-flow elements for pocket knife context.

- For each sequence block in the FFBD, construct a transition be-tween the states representing the functions on either end of the se-quence. These transitions are labeled as *default,* or *epsilon,* transi-tions.

- For each selection in the FFBD, create a transition to each of the selection choices. Label each transition with the value which corre-sponds to the selection criteria.

- For each concurrency in the FFBD, create new states for each of the possible combinations of concurrency; that is, create a new state for each permutation of functions that may be activated con-currently. Replicate all transitions from the original states to each of the new states. Add transitions to each of the new states from the state(s) representing the function(s) which preceded the concurrency in the FFDB.

This process, of course, can lead to a very large state model if concur-rency was used in the FFBD model. Statecharts (Harel, 1987) were developed to overcome this exponential expansion problem.

State Name

entry / entry-action
do: Activity - A
event-1 / action 1
event-2 / action 2

...

exit / exit-action

Figure 3.16 States in statecharts.

Statecharts. Statecharts have the advantages of being hierarchical, having a well-defined relationship with functions, and defining AND states to represent concurrency. The AND states that are used with statecharts are really composite states which group together several substates into a single entity. Statecharts represent states as shown in Fig. 3.16.

Statecharts in OMT use the Moore formalism, which implies that the functions and activities occur within the state. In the statechart diagram the states are shown as rounded contours with transitions appearing as arrows. Within the contour for a state the actions of the state are written. Each state can have an entry action; a *do:* action, which is the main function of the state; a list of actions to perform when triggered by events; and an exit action. The various actions are all called *activities.* Functions in FFBDs correspond to activities in statecharts. Sequence in FFBDs results in sequential states in statecharts. A selection in FFBDs corresponds to transition to states with corresponding activities in statecharts. Concurrency in FFBDs, AND, corresponds to AND states in statecharts.

Figure 3.17 gives an example of a statechart diagram.

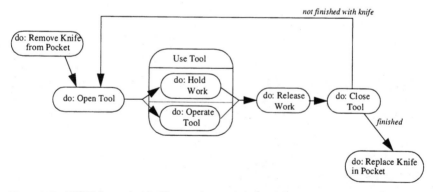

Figure 3.17 FFBD for pocket knife recast as a statechart.

Statecharts and FFBDs handle hierarchy similarly. Each of the state bubbles can be decomposed into a finer level of granularity. This is the same mechanism FFBDs employ. In contrast to FFBDs, however, the transitions in statecharts can also be refined in statecharts at lower levels.

From a modeling standpoint we have shown that statecharts work fairly similarly to FFBDs for capture of behavior. A problem arises, however, when the time for trade-off analysis and mapping to structure occurs. The statechart approach assumes that there will be one piece of structure which is implementing and, therefore, responsible for maintaining the state information. This tying of behavior model to a predetermined system structure places strong limitations on trade-off.

3.6   Pocket Knife Example, Summary

Together, Figs. 3.1 and 3.7 define the static associations of the pocket knife and the dynamic interactions. They define the interconnections of the pocket knife with its environment. They define what that environment does to which the pocket knife must respond (the excitations), and they define the response of the pocket knife. They are computer-executable. In the aggregated form they can be used to make simulated estimates of system performance.

Although the static and dynamic models of context fully define the system (pocket knife) environment, they contain no information about the internal structure of the pocket knife. They capture what the subject system must do in response to the external systems, not how the subject system is to be built. A final step is necessary to go from the design as it stands to a complete system definition. The behavior must be mapped onto the static structure. This is discussed in detail later in this book.

3.7   Information Model for Behavior

Behavior will now be described with a more formal approach using an information model. We will use the OMT notation to describe the structure of the information needed to describe behavior. Figure 3.18 is an information model which defines behavior. Each association it presents is described.

3.7.1   Behavior

The key element of this information model is the *behavior* object. By understanding it and its associations, readers will come to understand what is meant by behavior.

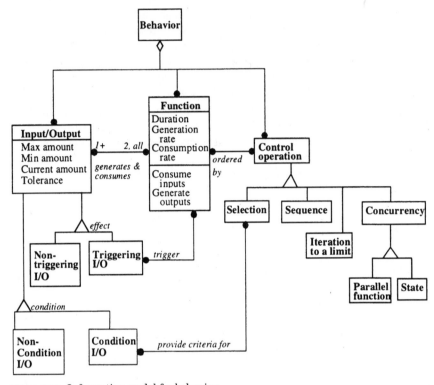

Figure 3.18 Information model for behavior.

As shown by the aggregation, behavior is built from input/output items, functions, and control operations. The cardinality shows that the behavior is not made of just one of each item but is a multiplicity of each, as many as are required to define the behavior. Furthermore, there is a relationship between function and input/output and between function and control operations which describes how many of each exist within the behavior.

3.7.2 Input/output

Input/output items are passive objects. For the behavior model view, we need to capture the attributes that characterize the input/output. These includes a range of size of the item and tolerance information. Each input/output is associated with at least one function. Most input/outputs are associated with at least two functions: one which generates it and another that consumes it. An input/output can be broadcast to all functions.

Each function is associated with two or more input/output items.

There are two important independent classifications that define subclasses of input/output relating to behavior. The subclass classified by *effect* designates nontriggering and triggering items. The subclass classified by *condition* designates input/output items that do not define criteria for decision and those that do define criteria for decision.

Input/output triggering items turn functions on and off. There can be more than one triggering item for a function, and more than a single function can be triggered by a single triggering item.

Condition items contribute to the order of functions by providing the criteria for selecting among alternative paths in a behavior.

3.7.3 Function

Function is the other major constituent of behavior. For the behavior model we need to capture information about the function relevant to providing a simulation of the behavior. This information includes

- *Duration:* how long this function takes to execute as a time or probability estimate
- *Generation rate:* the speed at which it generates outputs
- *Consumption rate:* the speed at which it consumes inputs

In addition, functions have two operations: consume inputs and produce outputs.

Function is interconnected with the control operation class marked with an *ordered by.* From this we learn that a function can be ordered by many control operations and that a control operation can order many functions.

3.7.4 Control operations

Control operations determine the order in which multiple functions are activated. They are any one of four types. The simplest is *sequence*; as the name implies, this says that one function comes after another function. *Selection* is the basic conditional operation. On the basis of some input/output item to which it is associated, the selection control operation determines which of several possible functions to perform next. *Iteration* to a limit is a special case of sequence and selection. It is such a common case, however, that it is elevated to a control operation of its own. In essence it is the looping operator. *Concurrency* describes the reality that more than one function is active at the same time.

The expression of concurrency is critically important. Early in the analysis of a system there are often many functions which are known to be important and are known to be concurrent. If the concurrency of the functions is captured in the behavior model, independent of structure, then the concurrent functions can be allocated to objects (resources) in different ways to provide major design alternatives.

As seen from the information model, concurrency can be represented two ways: as parallel function and as state. The allocation of the concurrent functions to objects defines the state structure for those objects. A different allocation will result in a different state picture for the objects. For this reason it is useful to capture behavior with the functional representations when developing requirements and to add state views as the allocation to objects is established.

The set of control operations shown in here is a minimal set. More complex control operations can be constructed from this simple, minimal set.

3.7.5   In summary

In total, the information model defines a behavior as a collection of inputs and outputs together with some functions. These functions are ordered by a set of standard control operations. The functions consume the inputs and produce the outputs. The inputs provide the key values for triggering the functions and controlling the selection decision making. Behavior and these elements are made hierarchical by the structure associations.

3.8   Information Model for Input/Output

There are several additional classifications of input/output which are important to the engineering of systems and were not included in the discussion of behavior. These additional classifications deal with issues such as the physical nature of the input/output and its longevity whether it is consumed promptly or is stored. These additional classifications are important in some applications and are unimportant in others. They are shown in Fig. 3.19.

Classification by condition and classification by effect have already been discussed. Classification by physical nature is important to the general case of systems. The input/output may be a material thing, it may be energy in one of its many forms, or it may be *information*. Software engineering and software engineering methodologies often assume that all input/output is of the class information. This viewpoint needs to be generalized to include material objects and energy when these techniques are applied to systems.

Input/output of the class *triggering I/O* has two subclasses depending on whether the I/O has content. The content may be information, a physical thing, or energy. Very often in the physical world the trig-

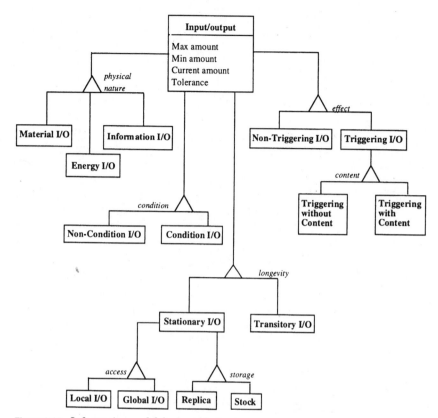

Figure 3.19 Information model for input/output.

gering and the physical content are intimately associated. This is the case when a person or animal steps into a bear trap with a foot or when smoke sets off a smoke alarm. Methodologies or notations that insist that triggering be disconnected from content in their basic abstractions need to allow for association of content with triggering to represent systems in which that association is a reality.

An equally important concept is that of how long an input/output persists: its longevity. Is it *stationary,* persisting in the system for some time before being consumed, or is it *transitory,* consumed as rapidly as it is produced. Data in software may belong in either of these subclasses. In the worlds of chemistry and biology some substances are produced as intermediate products and have only a transitory existence. Others may remain for long periods of time even when that is undesirable as in the case of PCB contamination. It is important in many applications to deal with the stationary or transitory aspects of input/output because of the practical implications. The assignment of input/output to these two subclasses is very dependent on the application and on the critical issues and time scale important to the application.

For input/output that is persistent, there are two further important subclasses. One of these is based on the concept of access. The access to the persistent things may be available to all, *global I/O*, or it may be restricted to a particular group, *local I/O*.

A final classification is based on the manner in which input/output is stored, *storage*. Some things are themselves stored physically as stock. They are placed in a warehouse of some kind, and one can only take out as many or as much as was put in because of the physical laws of conservation of mass and energy. Examples are TV sets in a warehouse, or the potential energy in the water behind Hoover dam.

In many modern instances the physical item itself is not stored at all. What is stored is a replica of the object in association with a machine which can use the replica to rapidly make as many of the objects as desired. For many applications people speak of this situation as though the actual object were stored, and they abstract away all the details of creating and storing the replica and creating copies of the original object. For their practical purposes they have no need for this detail, so they treat the situation as though the object were stored and consider the time to create the object as an access time. This is the way data storage is considered in software engineering. It is not data that is stored on a magnetic disk, but tiny regions of magnetization. This detail can be neglected by many, but not by those who design and manufacture the magnetic storage devices. There are many examples in the physical world such as negatives of photographs or dies for plastic injection-molding machines. The unique characteristic of this subclass is that one stores an object once, really the replica, and can get as many copies of it as desired.

3.9   Relationship between Behavior and Structure

Behavior and structure, as we have discussed, can be viewed in many ways by depicting part or all of the information. The two must be modeled separately for the sake of finding alternative solutions and performing trade-off analysis. This does not say, however, that there is no relationship between them. Obviously, there must be. This relationship is modeled in Fig. 3.20.

3.9.1   Structure models

Classification, interconnection, and aggregation are the three major modeling abstractions. They can be used in diagrams separately or in

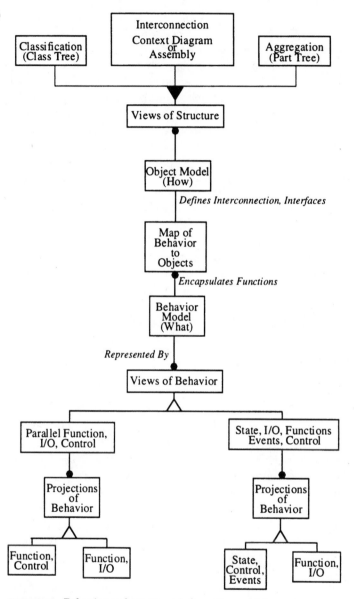

Figure 3.20 Behavior-and-structure information model.

combination. Consequently, the classification is shown as inclusive (the dark triangle) in Fig. 3.20.

Because the behavior is mapped to structure, the behavior and structure models are not completely independent. The central part of the figure shows a mapping of behavior onto the objects which will provide the behavior. This mapping encapsulates the behavior in the objects. The list of functions or methods in the class definition box representing objects must be consistent with the mapping of behavior. Because the behavior includes all inputs and outputs, the mapping of behavior to objects establishes which active objects intercommunicate via inputs and outputs. The mapping establishes the interconnections between active objects that support input/output. The structural interconnection association must be consistent with the results of the mapping or allocating behavior to objects.

It is very important to realize that one cannot predict the emergent behavior of a system from the properties of the parts alone. How the parts interact is critical. In the simple case of the pocket knife, the "hold tool open" behavior cannot be realized until the knife case, the tools, and the spring are riveted together. It is the dynamic interaction of the parts which allows a tool to be opened or closed easily, yet held in place firmly. This is the reason for allocation of behavior onto objects such that the interaction of the objects will produce that desired behavior.

3.9.2   Behavior models

At the bottom of Fig. 3.20, two ways of representing concurrency are shown. In one type concurrency is represented using state; and in the other, using parallel functions.

A complete view of behavior using parallel functions requires capture of functions, I/O, and control operations. Behavior diagrams are this type of view of behavior. There are two partial views. The first is of function and control—functional flow block diagrams provide this type of partial view of behavior; the second partial view is of function and input/output. Data-flow diagrams, N-squared charts, and IDEF0 charts provide this type of partial view of behavior.

A complete view of behavior using state requires capture of state, functions, input/output, events, and control operations. No single diagram capturing all this information is known to the authors. Rather, two partial views are used to model the behavior. The first is of state, control, and events. Statecharts provide this type of partial view of behavior. The second partial view is of function and input/output. Data-flow diagrams, N-squared charts, and IDEF0 charts provide this type of partial view of behavior. The literature describing statecharts refers to functions with the word activities. The activities are modeled in a partial view of the executable behavior and can be allocated to objects in the same manner as when using behavior diagrams.

3.10 Models and Text for Requirements/Specifications

Models and text capture the same basic information for requirements and specifications. Often requirements/specifications are written as "The system shall do some described task." In this form it is an incomplete description for the implementer. To be complete, a requirement/specification in text needs to include

- The name of the external system causing the excitation
- What the external system does
  - The outputs from the external system to the subject system
  - All pertinent conditions
- What the subject system does in response
  - All quantitative aspects of the response, how fast or how much
  - The outputs from the subject system
  - All pertinent conditions
- The names of the external systems which receive those outputs

Such a complete statement is the equivalent to a behavior model for the external system linked to the response from the subject system.

A similar close relationship exists between behavior models and the operations concept in text. The operations concept describes in narrative form what the external systems do and what the subject system does in response. They are written from the standpoint of how one would experience the system rather than as a list. If one executes, either mentally or by computer, a linked behavior model of external system and subject system, such as that shown in Fig. 3.13, then a text description of what happens in the model is the operations concept.

This redundancy is not wasteful. The requirements/specifications in list form are very useful for contractual purposes because they provide a checklist of what the implementer must deliver. The operations concept in narrative form provides a story form of exactly what the system is supposed to do. It is very valuable for those who are not going to immerse themselves in modeling. These text descriptions, however, cannot be computer-interpreted because they are in natural-language text. They will remain ambiguous because natural language is not precise. The use of models augments the text forms by providing computer-executable and transformable information that is free from ambiguity and needed by the engineers who will design according to the specifications. The art of engineering is to apply all these descriptions in text and models to the problem at hand with precision and without wasting engineering effort. It is an art.

3.11   Summary for Behavior

This chapter has described behavior with an informal approach and a formal approach. We conclude with a textual definition of good practice in modeling.

Behavior is a rigorous description of what a system is to do. It includes the functions to be performed, the sequencing control of those functions, and the inputs and outputs from the functions. A good modeling approach for behavior keeps the behavior information separate from the structure information. It also captures the behavior information with enough rigor to allow the behavior to be executed and analyzed.

3.12   Exercises

1. Examine Fig. 3.7.
   a. Why are "hold work" and "operate tool" concurrent?
   b. If we add additional objects to the context, what other objects beside *person* could be used for one or the other of these functions?
   c. Would the behavior model need to change because of the added objects? Why?
2. Model a person as your subject system in the context of getting dishes from the cupboard, food from the refrigerator, or cooked food from the stove and placing these items on the dinner table.
   a. Create the object descriptions for each of the major objects. Include attributes and functions in each object description.
   b. Create a static context model for the person.
   c. Create a functional flow block diagram for the person. Keep the functions concurrent if reality does not require a sequence.
   d. Create a behavior diagram for the person.
   e. Assign time estimates for each of the functions and make timeline estimates for the concurrent sets of functions.
   f. Assign the work among three people to finish in minimum time.
3. Develop a behavior model for baking chocolate-chip cookies.
4. Physically, it is possible to use pocket knifes in ways for which that they are not designed.

a. What exceptions were not accounted for in the design?
b. How does the model need to change to reflect the exceptions?
c. Do the changes improve the usefulness of the model?

3.13 References

Alford, M., 1977: A requirements engineering methodology for real-time systems. *IEEE Transact. Software Eng.,* **SE-3**(1) 60–69.

Alford, M., 1992: Strengthening the systems/software interface for real-time systems. *Proceedings of the Second International Symposium of the National Council on Systems Engineering,* vol. 1. 411, Seattle, Wash.

Ascent Logic Corp. (Product of Ascent Logic Corp., 180 Rose Orchard Way, San Jose, CA 95134).

Blanchard, B. F., and W. Fabrycky, 1990: *Systems Engineering and Analysis,* 2d ed. Englewood Cliffs, N.J.: Prentice-Hall.

Harel, D., 1987: Statecharts: A visual formalism for complex systems. *Sci. Comput. Program.* **8,** 231–274.

Hopcroft, J. E., and J. D. Ullman, 1979: Introduction to Automata Theory, Languages, and Computation. Reading, Mass.: Addison-Wesley.

Kockler, F. R., et al. 1990: (Defense Systems Management College) *Systems Engineering Management Guide.* U.S. Government Printing Office, 000802001202-5.

Martin, J., and C. McClure, 1985: *Diagramming Techniques for Analysts and Programmers.* Englewood Cliffs, N.J: Prentice-Hall.

Mealy, G. H., 1955: A method for synthesizing sequential circuits. *Bell Syst. Tech. J.* **34**(5) 1045–1079.

MIL-STD-499, 1968: *Functional Flow Diagrams,* AFSCP 375-5 MIL-STD-499, USAF, DI-S-3604/S-126-1, Form DD 1664, June 1968.

Moore, E. F., 1956: Gedanken experiments on sequential machines. In *Automata Studies,* edited by C. E. Shannon and J. McCarthy, pp. 129–153. Princeton, N.J.: Princeton University Press.

Vitech Corp. (product of Vitech Corp. 2070 Chain Bridge Road, Vienna, VA 22182-2536).

Yourdon, E., 1989: *Modern Structured Analysis.* Englewood Cliffs, N.J: Yourdon Press.

4

Core Technical Process

4.1 Process

A *process* is the sequence of actions done by people and machines. What engineers do when they define a complex system is the *systems engineering process*. The engineering process applied to complex systems has been described using text in books and standards. This chapter solidifies these ideas and makes them explicit and rigorous with models of behavior and views of behavior. The models separate and distinguish several different processes that are described in the field of complex systems:

- *The product life cycle:* the sequential phases of development and use through which any product evolves.

- *The systems engineering process:* the ordered set of engineering steps that engineers use to go from user needs to specifications for all the components to be designed or procured. Two subprocesses are considered: a systems engineering management process and a systems engineering technical process.

- *The acquisition process:* the set of tasks required of the product engineers and manufacturers to assure those in authority that the project is meeting all goals. There are numerous acquisition processes in use.

- *The design engineering process:* the ordered set of engineering steps that engineers in the many design disciplines, such as mechanical, digital, and software engineering, use to design their components.

- *The manufacturing process:* the ordered set of implementation steps that manufacturing engineers use to implement the manufacturing facility and to produce the product.

Models can explain these processes in detail, show their relationships, and help engineers follow the processes. Words such as *process* and *methodology* are used with very different meanings in different organizations and disciplines. They are defined here in a way that is useful in discussing engineering activities.

The technical work of systems engineers, the technical process, is the focus of this chapter. It will be described with a simple core process with a few major steps that are applied repeatedly as the system specification develops. The repeated use of a single core process is powerful in practice, and it simplifies both training and tool content.

4.1.1   Process, methodology, and tools

1. Definition of *process:* an ordered set of work steps, done by people and machines, that are utilized to produce a set of outputs from a set of inputs. It can be executed by people, machines, computers, or a combination of these. A complete description of the process includes naming the steps, describing how the steps are ordered, and describing the inputs and outputs among all of the steps.

   - The description uses executable models of behavior.
   - The models can be expressed in any graphic or text language that spans the abstractions needed and that is executable.
   - This process as defined here is called *metaprocess* in some disciplines, where *meta* means "a higher form of."
   - The metaprocess model captures the inherent concurrency of steps that may be performed in parallel and do not have to be performed in a particular sequence.

2. Definition of *methodology:* a particular implementation of a process. The steps in the process are specified in great detail, and alternatives in the ordering of the work steps or in notation and views of information are removed and standardized. A methodology ensures that a large number of workers performing the same process will do each step in the same way. On large projects this is essential for intercommunication among the people and ability to perform the work reproducibly.

3. Definition of *tools:* a thing used by people to automate their work. Many tools are developed to automate a part of a single methodology. Some tools are developed to automate a metaprocess and may be used interchangeably with a number of different methodologies.

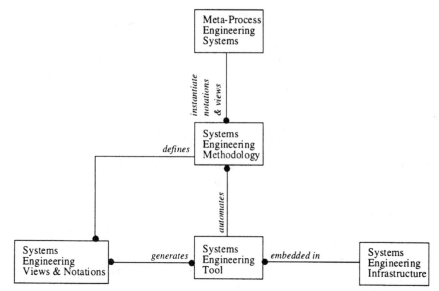

Figure 4.1 Associations between metaprocess, methodology, tools, and infrastructure.

Figure 4.1 shows the associations among metaprocess, methodology, tools, and infrastructure for engineering complex systems. There are many systems engineering methodologies which particularize, tailor, and instantiate the single systems engineering metaprocess. The figure shows that each systems engineering methodology defines a set of views and notations that will be used as a standard by all the workers following that methodology.

The tools are embedded in the systems engineering infrastructure of businesses and customers.

Investment in *training in methodology and tool use* is required to make the infrastructure effective, and this is usually *the most expensive investment.* A plethora of methodologies, views, and notations exists at present. How they differ or are equivalent is difficult to see by comparing them unless one can refer to a metaprocess. At present there exists a plethora of tools which automate parts of the many methodologies, and the tools do not intercommunicate. Often a set of methodologies are chosen that span the work, and the available tools are interconnected with custom interfaces (Kronlof, 1993, pp. 11–12). For N tools there are $N(N-1)/2$ interfaces, and the tools must treat data with consistent meanings (semantics) and functionality. A new release of any tool can affect $(N-1)$ interfaces.

By learning what systems engineers do at the metaprocess level, it is possible to understand what are the possible useful views of information and how the methodologies are similar and different. In Chap. 3, we described the possible views of information. Tool integration requires that the same piece of information always be used with the same meaning by all the tools. A well-defined process description is a prerequisite for integration.

4.1.2 Product life cycle, acquisition, and systems engineering process

The systems engineering process describes the engineering work steps. It is applied at many of the phases of the product life cycle which describes the phases or steps through which a product evolves. There is often a blurring of the distinction between the systems engineering process and the product life-cycle phases.

It is helpful to decompose the systems engineering process into two subprocesses—a management process and a technical process—which can be discussed separately. Figure 4.2 shows one level of this decomposition.

The acquisition process is the process used by government or a company to acquire product from a supplier. The systems engineering process generates the documents required by the acquisition process. Often the engineering steps executed are driven by the need to produce documents. Best practice dictates generating the documents required by the acquisition process from the needed engineering steps.

The basic relationships among product life cycle, acquisition process, and systems engineering process are clarified in Fig. 4.3.

Figure 4.3 asserts that there is a single product life cycle that is used by both government and business. Although different industries name the parts of the product life cycle differently and have different degrees of emphasis on different phases, products go through the following phases:

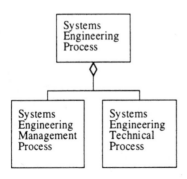

Figure 4.2 Parts list for systems engineering process.

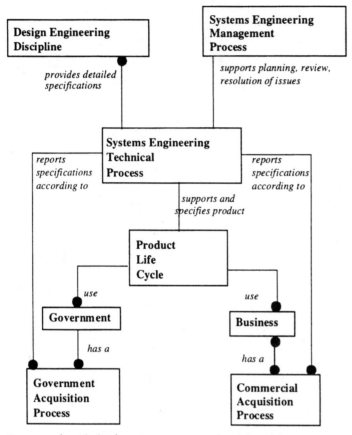

Figure 4.3 Association between process, product life cycle, and acquisition.

1. *Domain analysis phase:* domain analysis to define a product line and reusability strategies for products or product components.

2. *Concept phase:* concept analysis to define a business strategy or a product concept and establish its value to users.

3. *System phase:* system analysis to define and specify the components, cost, and performance of the product.

4. *Feasibility phase:* detailed component design, implementation, and integration for an engineering model, a prototype, or partial prototypes sufficient to show performance and manufacturing feasibility.

5. *Initial manufacture phase:* low-volume manufacture in preproduction volumes with release of product to customers (perhaps selected customers). In the commercial world this is the first point at which customer response can be measured and product success

can be estimated on the basis of actual response. It is the first point for revenue payback on the development investment for businesses which define and market their own products.

6. *Full-scale manufacture phase:* full-scale manufacture and shipping of product to customers. It includes field support and product enhancement.

7. *Field support phase:* customers are notified that manufacture has stopped and that field support with spare parts continues.

8. *Product removal phase:* product is removed from the marketplace, perhaps with incentives to customers. It is often replaced with a more advanced product which is in phase 5. Product disposal occurs, sometimes in an ecologically sound manner.

The product life cycle is used by the government and by many commercial businesses. It is a process, a time-ordered set of phases, a behavior.

The *systems engineering technical process* is the engineering work that supports and specifies the product in all phases of the product life cycle—specification, cost, and performance from domain to concept through product removal. The core steps in the technical systems engineering process are performed repeatedly and are concentrated in the early product life-cycle phases: (1) domain analysis phase, (2) concept phase, and (3) system phase. If there are changes or problems during later phases, this technical work will have to be revisited during the later phases.

The many different acquisition processes, both commercial and government, require reports of technical progress to assure those with authority that the project is progressing satisfactorily. These documents are not the systems engineering technical work. They are generated from the information produced by the systems engineering technical process. They vary tremendously in content, level of detail, and format.

The systems engineering management process supports the systems engineering technical process with planning, review, and coordination of issue resolution. It makes it work.

The systems engineering technical process delivers all its detailed technical engineering specifications to the many different design engineering disciplines which will perform the detailed design of the mechanical, electrical, digital, software, and people components for the system. The specifications need to be complete and correct. They need to be delivered in the set of views and notations of the designers.

In going from user needs to the specifications to the designers, any large complex system is decomposed into a set of parts, a tree of several tiers of decomposition. A core set of engineering steps are applied repeatedly to the subsystems and components at each of these tiers.

4.1.3   The systems engineering process model

Any process, whether used for systems engineering, for semiconductor chip manufacture, for business marketing, or for cooking food, can be described as a behavior. This involves the steps that are taken, the inputs and outputs for each step, and the ordering of the steps. In order to clarify the systems engineering process yet keep the figures simple, the process will be described with a FFBD view that shows the steps and their ordering.

The systems engineering management process is broken into three pieces: project planning, review and replanning, and change control. Correspondingly, there are a set of six modeling steps, core steps, in the systems engineering technical process that define it. They are used repeatedly as the system is decomposed into subsystems and then subsubsystems. Figure 4.4 shows these associations as a parts list.

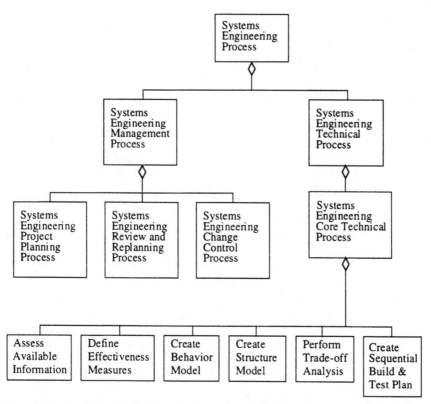

Figure 4.4 Extended parts list for systems engineering process.

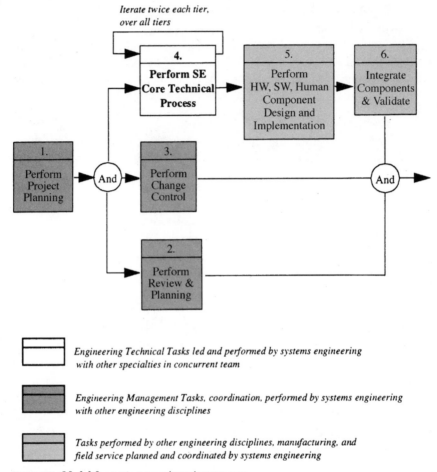

Figure 4.5 Model for systems engineering process.

Systems engineering management tasks. The systems engineering management process is built from three major sub-subprocesses which are ordered as shown in Fig. 4.5. These three sub-subprocesses are

1. Project planning process

    This process creates an initial systems engineering management plan (SEMP) for the project defining tasks, resources, resource assignments, milestones, costs, and schedule at each milestone.

    The SEMP is a high-level plan which requires additional detail as the project evolves.

The SEMP schedules the deliverable items required by the acquisition process.

The SEMP must be modified as the market changes, customers change what they want, and engineers and others discover issues which require a change in the plan to resolve the issues. The next two processes address these changes.

2. Project review and replanning process

This process monitors the planned forward tasks and team performance for the systems engineering technical work, the design, the implementation and integration of components, and the validation of the system.

This process provides the reviews as required by the evolving SEMP. The reviews are both frequent and fine-grain at the level of contributing engineers, and periodic and high-level for customers and management.

The purpose of review is to discover issues as early as possible so that they may be evaluated and corrected as early as possible to limit their cost and delay.

This process modifies the SEMP as the appropriate resolution of issues is discovered.

3. Change control process

This is a reverse process. It analyzes the impact of the issues discovered and establishes how resources must be redirected and to what extent work already completed must be revisited and modified.

Efforts as far along as step 6 in Fig. 4.5 (integrate components) may have to be redirected back to step 4 if requirements are altered late in the project.

Figure 4.5 is an FFBD view of behavior. The FFBD shows the steps of the systems engineering management process as dark (shaded) blocks, and the steps of the systems engineering technical process as a white (unshaded) block. There are design and implementation steps which are executed by other engineering and manufacturing disciplines. These steps are shown in blocks 5 and 6 of medium darkness. The systems engineering management process assists these two steps with resources, planning, and resolution of system-level issues.

Because of the existence of the issues and the change control process, there is a well-defined way to analyze the impact of any issue, and modify the engineering, manufacturing, and integration work. The changes are captured by replanning and adjusting reviews.

It is not possible to show all the possible feedback arrows from later efforts to earlier efforts because they may start anywhere and go back anywhere depending on the issue.

The steps of the systems engineering process are applied most intensively to the first five phases of the product life cycle: domain phase, and concept phase through initial manufacturing phase. Systems engineering management tasks or technical tasks may be required during the latter three phases of the product life cycle, full-scale manufacture through product removal, when system-level issues arise.

Systems engineering technical tasks.   The systems engineering core technical process is applied iteratively at each tier of the product decomposition. The core technical process is applied successively to the business using the product, to the product, to the product subsystems, and the product sub-subsystems until specifications are available for the components to be designed by the different engineering specialties. At each tier the process is applied twice: first to analyze the context of the subject under study and second to analyze the subject itself for decomposing it into components.

The systems engineering core technical process is composed of six major steps, which are discussed in detail in the next section.

4.2   The Core Technical Process

Figure 4.5 shows how the core technical process serves as one of the steps in the systems engineering process. It is applied repeatedly at all tiers of the system parts tree. It is applied twice each tier: once to the context and once to design the system in terms of its subsystems. From the viewpoint of the product life cycle, it is applied repeatedly from domain and concept analysis through definition of individual components.

Figure 4.6 shows the order of the six engineering modeling steps that make up the core technical process.

4.2.1   The six steps in the core technical process

The six steps accomplish the following tasks:

1. Evaluates and categorizes available information and obtains missing information.

2. Defines the criteria for optimization, the effectiveness measures. These are a small subset of all the requirements; perhaps 3 to 15

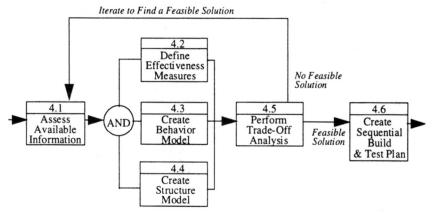

Figure 4.6 FFBD view for systems engineering core technical process.

in number even for large complex systems. They are the criteria that mean success or failure.

3. Defines the behavior that is desired with an executable model.

4. Defines executable structure models of the alternative sets of things, or objects, from which to build the system. In either step 4.3 or step 4.4 an allocation of behavior onto objects is made. Different sets of objects can be used to build the system, and for any of these sets the behavior can be partitioned among the objects in many different ways. These alternatives produce a number of alternative designs, or architectures.

5. Trade-off: selects among the alternative designs or architectures. Any design, to be feasible, must meet all the performance requirements at *system level*. The best feasible design is selected on the basis of the effectiveness measure values. This is the optimization process. It is a *key best practice* in the engineering of complex systems. One possible branch from step 5 is an iteration back to the beginning made necessary by no alternative design or architecture meeting the requirements. When this occurs, steps 1 to 5 are repeated to find feasible solutions, or requirements are relaxed so that a previous nonfeasible solution is accepted, or the project is terminated for budget and schedule overrun, or simple impossibility.

6. Creates a plan when a feasible and near-optimal design or architecture has been found. It provides an implementation plan for the selected design or architecture. The plan takes into account identified issues, successive product releases, risk remediation, partial

builds for early validation, time to market, budget, and available resources.

Steps 2, 3, and 4 are concurrent activities. They can be ordered, and some methodologies do this. In practice it is found that engineers move their attention among these three tasks. As understanding progresses in one of the tasks, it suggests changes in the other two.

These six core steps in the core technical process are not applied once for complex systems, but twice each tier over all tiers of the system parts tree. These core steps are described in more detail below. A chapter is devoted to each of them to define the subsets they contain and to illustrate the work with an example. Each chapter provides an information model (structure of the information item associations) for each of the steps.

Assess available information. The first step is to assess available information. That information may be in text form, in rigorous models, or in the minds of a collection of potential users of the system. This step involves collecting available information and categorizing it in terms of its source, its quality (what is wrong with it), and how it is to be used. Additional information is gathered if necessary. The information is upgraded and corrected as necessary. If prior work has been done thoroughly and rigorously with modeling, there is a minimum of activity in this step.

If the information is provided in the form of rigorous executable models, there will be a context model both static and dynamic for the system or components under consideration. These models will include the interfaces associated with assembly of the components to make a whole, the excitations of the system or components, the conditions under which this occurs, and the responses to those excitations.

When the available information has been assessed, the next steps in the core process are undertaken. The next three steps are interdependent, and they are carried out concurrently.

Define effectiveness measures. *Effectiveness measures* are the small subset of the requirements that are so important that the system will fail if they are not met and will be a huge success if they are met. They are the criteria used to make the tradeoff decisions of what to build. The design of a system is an ill-posed problem that has no solution without a set of criteria to guide choices. They correspond to the regularization functions used in optimal control or in calculus of variations.

The effectiveness measures are critically important because they are the criteria that drive the system solution that is found. They are critical because all the stakeholders—engineers, management, users, and operators—must agree on them, or there will be future problems. If these criteria are not both correct and agreed to, then the system development will be plagued with costly requirements changes and may miss its market. The effectiveness measure results are extremely useful in reviews with management, users, and operators who do not want to know all the technical engineering detail but do want to know about these critical system criteria.

Effectiveness measures are ranked by a set of priorities that can be established by statistically valid methods (Saaty, 1983). The effectiveness measure values are either computed from the properties of the system components and their behavior, or are established by group surveys which establish user preferences. The computations are based on mathematical models that use values of attributes.

Create behavior model. In systems engineering the system is described with separate views of behavior and structure so that alternative designs can be found by reallocating behavior among objects.

The behavior model captures what any thing, or object, is to do. It contains enough information to be executable. The model must capture all the steps or functions involved in the behavior, how the functions are ordered, and all the inputs and outputs of the functions. If the ordering of the functions allows alternative responses (paths), then the conditions for the alternative paths must be captured.

When the six core steps are applied to context, the behavior of the external systems which excite the subject system is captured. The response of the subject system to these excitations is also captured as a behavior. The excitations and responses constitute the functional requirements for the subject system.

When the six core steps are applied to the subject system, the behavior model refines the behavior of the subject system in greater detail. The level of detail must be sufficient to allow the subject system behavior to be partitioned among subsystems from which the subject system will be built.

It is the structure model that describes the structure of the context and the design of the subject system.

Create structure model. This core engineering step captures the static structure of the system context or of the subject system or of the components of the system. Static structure involves the description of things or objects and their associations. This information is recorded in text and graphically as described in Chap. 2.

Because large, complex systems are built from thousands or hundreds of thousands of parts, the structure model is developed hierarchically. The hierarchy is treated in the next section of this chapter.

At the system level, important performance characteristics are known for the system, such as acceleration for a car. The performance requirement of acceleration depends on the properties of components from which it is built, like engine horsepower, transmission ratios, and total car weight. All the attributes important to performance must be captured in the object descriptions of the parts, weight for all parts, horsepower for engine, etc. Budgeted values for these attributes must be supplied for designers to use as design targets.

This step usually produces alternative sets of objects which could be used and alternative ways of allocating the desired behavior, from step 4.3, among the objects. Alternative designs and architectures emerge from the completion of all three steps: 2, 3, and 4.

Perform trade-off analysis.   It is in trade-off analysis that the performance requirements and the effectiveness measures are evaluated at system level. The objective is not the optimization of individual components, but the optimization of the system. The attributes, properties of the components, are used to calculate the system-level performance and effectiveness for the alternatives that have been found in the previous steps.

Each component has a set of attributes such as cost, weight, reliability, power consumption, or heat dissipation. These attributes are the arguments of the equations for calculating both performance and effectiveness measures. During trade-off analysis values must be obtained for every attribute of every component. This is done with the following order of priority because of reliability of the values. It is done first by measurement of actual parts, second by simulation, and third by estimation. It is in this core step that physical simulation is performed to get at performance using the laws of physics, chemistry, logic, and biology. Simulation is performed to get the values needed for attributes that are part of the performance and effectiveness calculations. When the attribute values are available, performance is calculated at system level. It is important to optimize the system rather than the components. The alternative architectures or designs that do not meet performance requirements are discarded; they are not feasible. Those that meet performance requirements are feasible and one must select among them.

This selection is done by calculating the effectiveness measures and using them as the criteria for selecting a near-optimal architecture. When a near-optimal architecture is established, it is necessary to examine implementation issues. Implementation issues arise in applying the core steps to the system context and to the system itself. They occur at all tiers of development.

Iterate to find a feasible solution. Iteration may be performed for several reasons.

First, a feasible solution may not be found among the architectures that were established as alternatives in the earlier steps.

Second, the engineering work may be partitioned among several teams for a large system, and each team may iterate through the partial portions of the system for which it has responsibility as an intermediate engineering step to refine its own work to a modest number of alternatives. Unless the contributions of the several teams are combined and a system-level trade-off is done, this approach will lead to suboptimization of components rather than to system optimization.

Create implementation (sequential build-and-test) plan. This step controls prototyping, risk, and getting to market. It is created to account for a set of business realities.

There are several reasons for considering implementation. In some cases the resources available and the time to market dictate the partitioning of the system into several pieces that will be sequentially released to the marketplace as a set of products are a series of releases. In some cases the technical work uncovers business opportunities or a need for partnership with other businesses that must be examined in parallel with the technical development and incorporated in the overall planning.

In many cases certain portions of the development are high-risk. The plans for these portions need to be advanced in time with alternatives planned to accommodate the risks.

For large complex systems it is often an advantage to assemble partial builds of the system which can be used for early validation of critical threads through the system and for early use of parts of the system in protected and controlled circumstances.

The implementation plan is adjusted to encompass and compromise among all these needs. The *sequential build-and-test plan* provides the ordering of the build and the test of components, which may be built completely or partially. The components are assembled to create the system, and the responses of the system are measured to validate the implementation.

The sequential build-and-test plan is incorporated in the systems engineering management plan. The regular inclusion of this step in the core technical process forces a periodic updating of the SEMP at the time that the project develops new valid information.

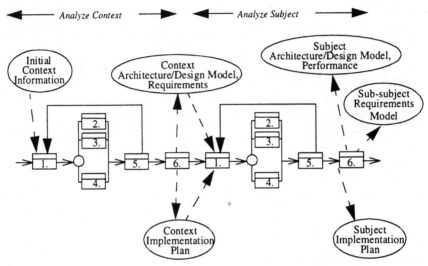

Figure 4.7   Sequential application of core technical process to context and subject.

4.2.2   Application at each tier

It is important to recognize that this optimizing process applies to both the system context and to the subject system itself. Some of the most important trade-off decisions for cost, performance, and market acceptance involve trades of what things belong in the system rather than outside the system and what behavior will be in the system rather than in an external system outside it.

The same core engineering steps are used for analyzing context and for analyzing the subject: system, subsystem, and sub-subsystem, as shown in Fig. 4.7. The sequential analysis of context and of subject are applied at each tier of engineering decomposition, for domain analysis, concept analysis, system requirements, synthesis, subsystem analysis, and so on.

4.3   Hierarchy

Systems engineering is inherently hierarchical. A hierarchy of parts is a fundamental abstraction that people use naturally to simplify their thinking about things. This abstraction allows us to think about a car as a whole, or to think about its parts, like the engine, or to think about subparts such as a fuel injector.

4.3.1 Small systems versus large systems

The development of small systems can be accomplished with a handful of engineers who can intercommunicate frequently and jointly track all the aspects of the development. The outputs, subject architecture/design model, subject performance, subject implementation plan, and sub-subject requirements model fully define the context of each of the sub-subjects.

In the development of large complex systems the core technical process needs to be applied twice in each tier, because of the expansion of parts and of engineering teams. The number of parts in a tier increases exponentially as the development moves from tier to tier. In large system developments there is a corresponding increase in the number of engineering teams applied. These teams receive context, behavior, and requirement information for their part of the system from other teams which developed the information at the tier above. It is important that the receiving team use the core technical process to thoroughly review the information received. It is important for them to correlate their information with that of other teams working on parts that interface with their part.

A small team developing a small system can track all the information and eliminate most of these reviews.

4.3.2 Tiers of hierarchy

Hierarchy is applied in a particularly useful way in systems engineering. At each level or tier of the hierarchy something different is studied, and both (1) context analysis and design and (2) system analysis and design are performed at each tier for large systems. It is necessary to use several tiers of context analysis and design and of system analysis and design because there are several different questions which need to be answered for any product. These questions must be answered by analyzing different things at different levels or tiers of the parts hierarchy: concept, system, subsystem, etc. The questions are

> *Concept tier:* core process applied to *the business using my product* to establish what my product should be to enhance the business.

- How does the business change when my product is incorporated?
- What *value* does my product have to the business or user for which it is being developed?
- Are there product segments which are *valuable to the customer* which had not been identified and that my product should address?

- Which are the *most valuable product segments to the customer,* and what is their value?
- In what sequence do the product segments have to be introduced to the customer to get the product installed? Low-value segments may have to be installed before high-value segments can be made to work.
- What is the emergent behavior (effectiveness measures) of my product, system, for *high value to user?*
- What things and behavior belong inside my product?
- With what does my product interface, its context?

System tier: core process applied to *my product.* Use to review context and requirements. Use to create product design.

- Review product context received from concept tier.
- Review the emergent behavior the product must exhibit (requirements) received from concept tier.
- The emergent behavior (requirements) is reviewed through the analysis of the system context, statically and dynamically using the core technical process.
- What is the product design?
- The product design defines the components (subsystems) which make up the product and the behavior (requirements) of each subsystem.

Subsystem tier: core process applied to *my product's subsystems.* Use to review context and requirements. Use to create product subsystem designs.

- Review product subsystems context received from system tier.
- Review the emergent behaviors the product subsystems must exhibit (requirements) received from system tier.
- The emergent behavior (requirements) is reviewed through the analysis of the subsystem context, statically and dynamically using the core technical process.
- What is the emergent behavior the product sub-subsystems must exhibit (requirements)?
- What are the product subsystem designs?
- The subsystem design defines the components (sub-subsystems) which constitute the subsystem and the behavior (requirements) of each sub-subsystem.

The hierarchy continues until it is possible to separate out the components that are hardware, software, and people—users and operators of the systems. So long as the components are composed of combinations of mechanical, electrical, digital, software things, and of people, it is not possible to provide requirements to the different engineering disciplines that do the detailed design and implementation.

When the requirements for hardware, software, and people components can be described separately, they are transmitted to the respective engineering design and implementation teams. Note that the systems engineering team needs to contain engineers who are expert in the relevant hardware, software, and people engineering disciplines. This description of hierarchy is summarized in tabular form in Table 4.1.

The table contains an additional tier, the *domain tier*, which is the tier of engineering work that develops a family of products rather

TABLE 4.1   Tiers

Tier	Subject system	External systems	Components	Output
Domain tier	Collection of customer businesses	Customer suppliers and customers' customers	Our product and product segments which can be reused	Dollar value, requirements for product line, or library of components
Concept tier	Customer business with our product in it	Customer suppliers and customers' customers	Our product and customer business segments	Dollar value to customer business and our product context and behavior
System tier	Our product	Customer business segments	Our product segments	Product segment requirements, system performance, cost targets
Subsystem tier	One of our product segments	Customer and our other segments	Our product subsegments	Subsegment specifications and system performance

Continue until hardware (HW), software (SW), and people components are separated

HW, SW, people requirements tier	One of our HW, SW, or people components	Other HW, SW, and people components	The subcomponents	HW, SW, and people component requirements and system performance

than single-point products. It produces design for reusability. The subject system under engineering analysis is a domain or set of businesses or users using our product. The businesses in the domain may be very different but able to profit from a common capability. The domain of businesses may be a single focused type of business studied at different points of time in its future evolution.

Domain tier: core technical process applied to model each business in the domain with my product in the business.

- What value does my product have to a collection of businesses or users which could benefit from it?
- Are there product segments which are valuable to multiple businesses or users?
- Which are the most valuable product segments to the multiple businesses or users, and what is their value?
- Am I designing my product so that it separates into segments that can be sold to multiple businesses?
- In what sequence do the product segments have to be introduced to the multiple businesses or users to get the product installed? Low-value segments may have to be installed before high-value segments can be made to work.
- Is my product family adaptable to meet a variety of price and performance targets?

The same core process is used at all tiers. What changes is what the process is applied to. At each tier there is a subject system to which the core technical process is applied. At each tier the subject system interfaces with external systems in its environment to establish its context. At each tier the subject system is decomposed into its parts, or, if working bottom up, the subject system is synthesized from its parts. At each tier there are some major questions to be resolved as summarized in the output column of Table 4.1.

4.3.3 Hierarchy, waterfall, and top–down development

The fact that systems engineering is inherently hierarchical does not imply that the work must proceed top–down or according to a "waterfall" model. The work is hierarchical because it focuses on questions and generates results that can be obtained only by analyzing different levels of detail: collection of businesses, a business, a product, segments of the product, subsegments, etc. Depending on the application, the work may proceed top–down or bottom–up, or top–down simultaneously with bottom–up, meeting in the middle and finishing.

Most development activities do not start with a clean sheet and a totally new product. Most developments are extensions of earlier systems or additions to an earlier system. In these cases the work is highly constrained to a few new or modified components and many of the existing interfaces must be maintained. Such projects are both top–down and bottom–up and may involve reengineering and reverse engineering if the existing system is not fully documented in its present state.

In all of these cases the systems engineers will very likely work at several different tiers of decomposition. They will need to apply both context analysis and design and system analysis and design at the various tiers unless there is complete existing information available to them.

4.4 Reengineering

Reengineering of large complex systems is often required because hardware components have become obsolete or unavailable, or because the software in the system has been made unmanageable in a cost-effective way. The most complex situations are those in which support information for the existing system is totally out of date with changes made to the system and yet the system must be kept functioning without downtime through the new system introduction and changeover. A major issue is the lack of correct higher-level documentation.

Under these conditions, the work shown in Fig. 4.5 proceeds as described earlier. It develops new specification from the current user needs. This provides information about how the system is used and about extensions which must be added to provide new capability. In parallel with this work it is necessary to reverse-engineer the existing system to replace the missing information. The reverse engineering does not need to replace the old documentation of structure of the existing system because that structure will be replaced in the new design. The reverse engineering needs to extract higher-level behavior from the available lower-level details.

This is a particularly difficult problem for many older software components. Many of them have been constructed with methodologies which distribute the high-level behavior widely through the software. Reverse engineering is a current topic of study, and tools to help with the issues are emerging. It can be accomplished manually by tracing responses through the system and extracting high-level logical units of behavior.

When the forward systems technical process results meet the reverse engineering results in the middle, then the work can continue systematically with a combination of new components and reverse-engineered components.

A major advantage of the systematic approach presented here is that it provides for thorough documentation in models. Domain analysis is included in the systematic approach to design in documented reusable products and components where the cost of the domain work is justified. With thorough documentation with models, the reverse engineering is avoided and reengineering is simplified and practical.

4.5 Behavior Model for the Core Technical Process

Figure 4.8 complements Fig. 4.6 by adding input and output to provide a behavior model for the core technical process.

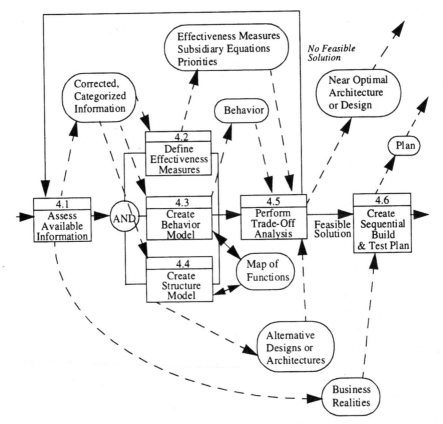

Figure 4.8 Behavior model for systems engineering core technical process.

4.6 Union of Best Practice with Modeling

Systems engineering best practices have been developing for hundreds of years and experienced rapid advance and codification in the 1950s and 1960s for complex systems. The best practices incorporate strong emphasis on optimization and trade-off for the system performance.

Other emerging disciplines, such as software engineering and mechanical engineering, have emphasized rigorous modeling and automated transformations of complex design information. Many of the methodologies applied to software engineering lack the engineering steps used for trade-off: definition of effectiveness measures, trade-off, and creation of a sequential build-and-test plan (Oliver, 1995). Some do not incorporate the capture of concurrency (Selic et al., 1994).

The model-based approach described here merges the best practices of the systems engineering of complex systems with the use of rigorous modeling and automated transformation of complex design information prevalent in other disciplines.

The following six chapters describe each of the modeling steps in the core process in more detail. In the course of these discussions it will be necessary to classify things like requirements to show how different types are captured in the models and associated with other information items.

4.7 Exercises

1. Apply the core technical process to the metal knife assembly of the six-blade pocket knife example. Use the examples of Chaps. 2 and 3 as available information. Reuse directly as much of the available information as possible.
   a. Assess the initial information available. Identify missing information. Classify the kinds of information.
   b. Create a static and dynamic context for the metal knife assembly.
   c. Create effectiveness measures for the knife which would help it dominate its market.
   d. Create a structure model for the metal knife assembly. Will this include an interconnection model of the parts?
   e. Create a behavior model for the metal knife assembly.
   f. Allocate functions between the behavior and interconnection models.
   g. Include all important attributes in the object descriptions of each part, and budget attribute values to the attributes.
   h. Identify the work you would do to extend this description to an entire product line of knives. Identify the domain involved in that work.

2. What effects on the design would result from making the three parallel core steps occur serially?

4.8 References

Kronlof, K., 1993: *Method Integration: Concepts and Case Studies.* Chichester (U.K.): Wiley.

Oliver, D. W., 1995: Systems engineering & software engineering, contrasts and synergies. *Fifth Annual International Symposium National Council on Systems Engineering* (St. Louis, Mo.), vol. I, pp. 701–708.

Saaty, T. L., 1983: Priority setting in complex problems. *IEEE Transact. Eng. Mgmt.* **EM-30,** 140–155.

Selic, B., G. Gulekson, and P. T. Ward, 1994: *Real-Time Object-Oriented Modeling,* pp. 484–486. New York: Wiley.

5

Assess Available Information

5.1 What Core Step 1 Is

This chapter describes core step 1, assessing available information, how to receive and assess the information that is made available to a systems engineering team. If the team is trained in modeling, the information available from users, operators, heritage systems, clients, and marketing can be captured in models as described in the succeeding chapters. Both the process and the system descriptions that result are rigorous. In assessing the available information, systems engineering teams must

- Collect the existing information.
- Combine all collateral information, including change documents which may be received during the collection period.
- Classify problems, define issues, and trace requirements to origin.
- Resolve issues.
- Generate and review requirements database and operations concept.
- Correct any problems in the engineering database.

Along the way systems engineers must overcome a number of problems. Not the least of these is the manner in which the information arrives. The most common form for systems engineers to receive their information is in large complex text documents. Frequently the requirements will be mixed with other forms of information which must be separated. The separated requirements may be redundant, contradictory, incorrect, incomplete, unverifiable, and poorly written. The other primary source of information is heritage systems which typically were not designed with any rigorous methodology and have little readily usable information available without reverse-engineering the existing product.

This chapter describes a classification, a taxonomy, for natural-language text requirements to provide a consistent basis for discussing them. It describes relationships among them. It goes on to provide a detailed process for carrying out a complete assessment and classification of the text material. This is difficult work when the text is thousands of pages in length.

The systems engineering best practice defined in this book describes how the text can be augmented with executable models which will be rigorous and supported by computer tools when that modeling work is funded and encouraged by management. Management acceptance of time spent in the up-front modeling process is essential to overall success of the methodology. While great lip service is often given to these phases, the temptation is great to do a makeshift job in order to get to "the important stuff."

If the information is provided in the form of rigorous executable models, there will be a context model, both static and dynamic, for the system or components under consideration. These models will include the interconnections and interfaces associated with assembly of the components to make a whole, the excitations of the system or components, the conditions under which this occurs, and the responses to those excitations. These models are reviewed by applying the technical core process to them. This enables engineers to use their experience and creativity to find the unknown missing things, "unknown unknowns." If the executable models have been captured in automated tools, the tools can be used to check for consistency and correctness of the models. This procedure will find errors in complex details that are hard for engineers to spot otherwise. The expense of correcting an "unknown unknown" error is small in the earliest stages of development, and very large in late stages. Both automated checking of models, and review by experienced and creative engineers are essential to find errors early. This chapter is about the review and early correction of the available information.

5.2   A Requirements Taxonomy

We first develop a taxonomy which is used to categorize the requirements as they are encountered and developed.

At any point of time in a project the engineers deal with two kinds of information: the initial information at the beginning of the project and the developed information created during the project. Initial in-

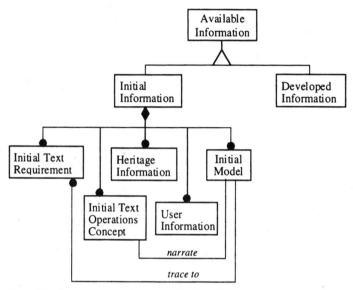

Figure 5.1 Associations between available information.

formation received at the beginning of a project is often largely in the form of text. It consists of text requirements, heritage information, user information, text operations concepts, and models. These associations are shown in Fig. 5.1.

The text requirements trace to the models. Exactly how they trace into the several kinds of modeling elements depends on what kind of requirements they are. Types of requirements will have to be developed. The text operations concept narrates the excitation response interactions among the subject system and the external systems with which it interacts. The text requirements are classified in three important ways:

1. By their origin
2. By the work to be done to fix them
3. By their use

When engineers identify and classify requirements, they can create the needed traceability links for the requirements and correct the identified problems discovered among them. Figure 5.2 is an information model showing this classification for text requirement. Note that these three classifications are independent.

A single requirement may be, for example, original, functional, and verifiable by test. Each requirement is classified by origin, work done, and use. These categories are used throughout the design process in

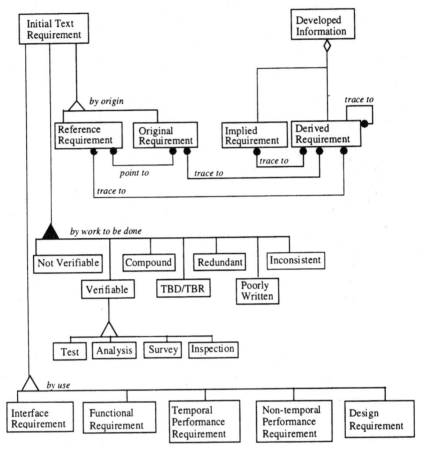

Figure 5.2 Classification of text requirements.

tracking the needs and validity of any of the requirements and in creating traceability links.

5.2.1 Classification by origin

Every requirement must start somewhere. This classification tracks where that somewhere is.

The majority of initial text requirements are classified as *original requirements*. These are, quite simply, those requirements which were expressed directly in the text documents given to the systems engineering team and often appearing in contracts. Original requirements are frequently expressed in sentences such as "The system shall obtain a speed of at least 100 kph [kilometers per hour]." Some of these requirements do not define the system, but rather point to reference requirements, another category.

The other category of original requirements is that of *reference requirements*. These are entire sets of other requirements such as any of the ISO standards. An original requirement might state that the rollover protection system (ROPS) must meet NEMA 123-456, which is a standard for ROPS established and maintained by NEMA.

The *original requirements* are closely related to another category: *derived requirements*. As the original requirements are studied and as modeling proceeds, additional requirements are found. These are the derived requirements, and they trace to the original requirements from which they were derived. Derived requirements may be derived from other *derived requirements*. They are part of the *developed information*.

Another category of requirements is *implied requirements*. These have no precursor in any documentation. They represent omissions in the imperfect initial information. When they are identified and created by engineers, they become part of the *developed information*. They occur less frequently than do other types of requirements.

5.2.2   Classification by the work needed to be done

When requirements are initially identified and examined, they often have one or more defects which must be corrected. The defects are identified and corrected by the engineers before proceeding to other steps in the core process.

The first determination that needs to be made is whether the requirement is *verifiable*. For a requirement to be verifiable, there must exist some measure that can be used to determine whether the system as designed or produced satisfies the requirement. There are both quantitative and qualitative measures which can be used.

Those requirements which are verifiable requirements are further broken down by the approach that will be used to verify them. The four subclasses are

- Test
- Analysis
- Survey
- Inspection

Test and analysis lead directly to quantitative results. Survey is used in the extremely important situation of establishing user preferences. This may be done through surveys with questions. It is done more effectively by obtaining responses from users who try out product prototypes. General Electric maintains a large facility at its Louisville appliance park, where appliance users come and utilize new versions. Their reactions are analyzed statistically. Inspection is used for validation when an examination of the product will show that a requirement has been met. For example, a requirement for the color of something can be verified by inspection.

Regardless of which means is to be used, once a requirement is determined to be verifiable, the verification procedure must be designed and entered into the acceptance test suite. System-level models which capture executable excitation and response of the system provide a direct link between the specification development and the acceptance test suite.

If a requirement is found to be *not verifiable,* then there is work to be done. It is likely that system analysis with the core technical process will be necessary to formalize what was meant by the requirement and to recast it in a verifiable form. An example of this situation is provided in the last part of this book, which is a coherent example of the modeling process.

Compound requirements state two conditions which must be met within one statement such as in "The wheels shall be round and made of rubber." Here two requirements exist. In this case it should be split into two separate, traceable requirements. These two new derived requirements will, of course, have to trace back to the original compound requirement in order to be able to demonstrate to the customer that all the expressed requirements were met.

Redundant requirements are a hard category to find. It is fortunate that they are relatively benign. They increase the tracking load and, if they are numerous enough, can make the system appear more complex than it really is. When redundant requirements are detected, they can be merged after careful consideration that they truly are redundant.

Inconsistent requirements are quite commonly found in system specifications for large projects. The specs are built by teams, each responsible for some end functionality, and these functionalities may have conflicting objectives which need to be sorted out during system design. It is important to detect conflicting requirements as soon as possible to avoid making incompatible design decisions for parts of the system. Every bit of delay increases the cost of correcting the requirement.

Often the original specification documents will include to-be-defined (TBD) and to-be-resolved (TBR) issues in places where the requirements are known to be incomplete. These requirements must be scheduled for resolution and tracked closely because their eventual definition can have profound impact on the system design.

Poorly written is the last subclass in the work to be done classification. Ambiguous and other hard-to-understand requirements fall into this grouping. They must be rewritten.

5.2.3 Classification by their use

Text requirements are classified *by use* so that they can be traced or budgeted properly to appropriate modeling entities, i.e., functions or components. This classification helps the project to monitor completeness and correctness of the modeling by resolving issues such as all performance budgets have been made to components. The kinds of requirements by *use* are

- Functional requirements which state what the system must do. They trace to the functions which will accomplish them. In the models these functions are encapsulated in objects and appear in the executable behaviors. They do not state how the system will be built, only on what it shall do.

- Temporal performance requirements which give values for the amount of time there is for the system to respond to stimulus. These time values are budgeted to the functions that carry out the response.

- Nontemporal performance requirements which give values for properties of the system such as cost, weight, size, power consumption, availability, and security. These quantities are budgeted to the components which make up the system. The components are objects and must have attributes that match these quantities. It is the components and sometimes the structure of the assembly of components that have properties such as cost, weight, moment of inertia, and mean time between failure.

- Interface requirements which specify input/output, limits of flow, and timing at the interfaces between components. The behavior of the components at the interface must be adjusted to meet the interface requirement. These requirements are increasingly important because equipment from many manufacturers and sited all over the world must interact and intercommunicate. Industry standards in interfaces are critical. At the time of writing this book, the lack of accepted interface standards for wideband coax (coaxial-cable) modems is, along with cost and software issues, a limiting factor in introducing two-way communication in the cable systems wired to 60 percent of U.S. homes (Perry, 1996). In large complex systems thousands to tens of thousands of interfaces exist and must be consistent for the system to work.

- In the real world, the specification documents which one receives frequently contain *design requirements,* which predetermine a design choice. For each of these it is important to raise an *Issue* (which traces to the design requirement) with the customer of whether this requirement is meant to apply, or whether it is a misstatement of a requirement in the form of design. The issue traces to a *resolution.* The *design requirement* becomes either an *adjudicated constraint* which will be followed, one of the other kinds of requirements, or it is eliminated.

The classification information in Figs. 5.1 and 5.2 can be combined. The information above describing design requirements tracing to issues tracing to resolution, and then to adjudicated constraints or other kinds of requirements can be added in. Since the engineering work also develops models based on any initial models received, a developed model object can also be added. This results in the complex information model of Fig. 5.3.

An association which emerges from the modeling shown in Fig. 5.3 is that the developed information consists of derived requirements, implied requirements, adjudicated constraints, and developed models. All the types of requirements and adjudicated constraints trace to elements in the developed model, which extends the initial model received with text.

Figure 5.3 is complex and is more readily understood from partitions such as those seen in Figs. 5.1 and 5.2. However, it summarizes five pages of written text and is more rigorous than the text.

In a form such as Fig. 5.3, a team of engineers can walk through the associations one by one to verify that they make sense. In this form the information is unambiguous, and executable and can be used as the basis for generating a database schema that will represent all of these information associations. When complex information models such as that shown in Fig. 5.3 are created, they can fail to properly capture reality and can need modification. They are, however, unambiguous and can be checked by engineers and with tools to find and remove such failures. Information models can be used to create a database schema for information storage.

5.3   A Behavior for Assessing Available Information

As we have seen, when a team developing a large, complex system receives thousands of pages of available information in the form of text requirements, there is a large amount of work to be done to assess the information:

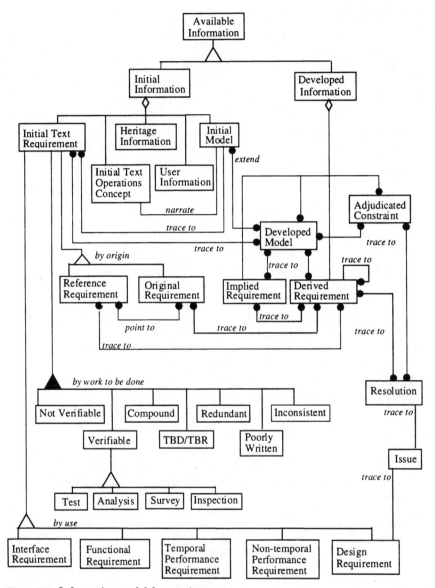

Figure 5.3 Information model for requirements.

- Identify and correct the problems in the requirements.
- Classify the kinds of requirements so that they can be properly budgeted and traced and engineering progress tracked.
- Create needed traceability links.

Fortunately, tools exist, some with hypertext automation, to speed this process. A database with information about tools is developed and maintained on the World Wide Web by the International Council on Systems Engineering (INCOSE 1996).

The process for assessing available information can be described as a behavior with a model.

5.3.1 Decomposition of the behavior of core step 1

Figure 5.4 provides an FFBD view which decomposes the behavior of core step 1, assess initial information. An FFBD is used here, without showing input/output, to simplify a complex diagram.

The FFBD of Fig. 5.4 contains two major parallel parts. The upper part, functions 1.1 to 1.24, describes what is done in correcting, classifying, and tracing text requirements. There are six major sequential groupings of tasks in this upper path:

1. Collect the existing information.
2. Combine all collateral information, including change documents which may be received during the collection period.
3. Classify problems, define issues, and trace to origin.
4. Resolve issues.
5. Generate and review requirements database and operations concept.
6. Correct any problems in the requirements database.

The first job to be done is to gather information. If this is the start of a program, then one gathers the heritage, user, text requirements, and operations concept information. If this is part way through the program, one gathers the prior context and component models.

The next job is to incorporate the user and heritage information with the text requirements and to identify any reference requirements. The requirements from the reference sources must be obtained and merged with the other requirements information.

If requirement changes are received, they are identified and traced to source documents to establish what is affected by the changes.

With the raw requirements in hand, the next job is to identify the requirements and to separate explanatory statements and boiler plate from the requirements. As identified requirements emerge, they are

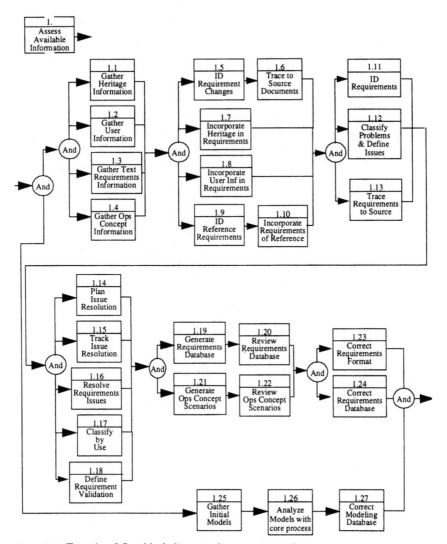

Figure 5.4 Functional flow block diagram decomposition of core step 1.

classified *by source* and *by work to be done*; and issues are developed. It is convenient at this time to ensure that all requirements trace to their source. In the later stages of the development the context and object models are reviewed and issues raised regarding the models.

The next job is to plan issue resolution, track that work, resolve the issues, classify requirements *by use* (now that issues are resolved), and define the means of validation.

As this work is done, a database of paper or an electronic database of information is developed. The job now is to generate a complete and consistent database and to review it. This is then followed by correcting any requirements format problems that were found in review and correcting the database information.

If one is dealing with models at this part of the program life cycle, then there will be available both context information and operations concept information in the form of initial models. The lower part of the FFBD of Fig. 5.4 describes the steps in assessing the initial models. First the models are collected. Next they are analyzed with the core technical process.

If these are executable models, they can fully define the system context. They will represent the excitations of the system and the system responses. These scenarios provide the stimuli that drive the components responses. It is important that they are complete and are correlated with the validation suite which is developed. Capturing them as behaviors in executable models is a potent way to specify what the system or component must do. The scenarios must be reviewed and the database for modeling scenarios corrected.

The sets of scenarios developed in this first core step are vital as inputs to the succeeding core engineering steps which model what the system does internally.

When the available information has been assessed, then core step 1 is complete for this iteration. The next step in the core process is ready to be undertaken. The next three steps are interdependent and are carried out concurrently.

5.4 Summary

In the development of large complex systems there is substantial effort and engineering cost expended in assessing the large requirements documents that are made available. These efforts and costs can be reduced substantially with modeling. When a modeling approach is applied, the information is substantially condensed. A page of modeling is equivalent to 5 to 10 pages of text. Further, the models can be checked for correctness by engineers and tools, and they can be transformed rigorously into the notations and views needed by particular engineering disciplines. When models are used fully, text descriptions are not lost. Instead, they are created as data dictionary items whenever a modeling element is created. This provides for traceability without having to create traceability for large volumes of text. The links exist within the models.

In practice it is not a matter of choice of the engineering organization whether to use text documents only, models only, or text documents with some models. In most real situations the manner in which requirements are handled is established by the acquisition process defined by the acquiring organization or by management. The engineering professionals need to respond efficiently and proactively to any of the situations.

5.5 Exercises

1. The available information is taken from a problem statement that was written for software engineering development and is intermediate between a requirements statement and an operations concept. The available information is for an ATM system:

   Design the software [*an ATM machine system*] to support a computerized banking network including both human cashiers and automated teller machines (ATMs) to be shared by a consortium of banks. Each bank provides its own computer to maintain its own accounts and processes transactions against them. Cashier stations are owned by the individual banks and communicate directly with their own bank's computers. Human cashiers enter account and transaction data. Automatic teller machines communicate with a central computer which clears transactions with the appropriate banks. An automatic teller machine accepts a cash card, interacts with the user, communicates with the central system to carry out the transaction, dispenses cash, and prints receipts. The system requires appropriate record keeping and security systems. The system must handle concurrent access to the same account correctly. The banks will provide their own software for their own computers; you are to design [*the ATM system*] the software for the ATMs and the network. The cost of the shared system will be apportioned to the banks according to the number of bank customers with a cash card.

   a. Break the paragraph into individual sentences and classify these sentences by the work to be done.
   b. Correct the identified problems for each sentence.
   c. Identify any derived requirements or implied requirements that result from *b*.
   d. Attach to each statement that results from *c* details as to how it shall be validated.
   e. Classify each statement according to its use.
   f. Adjudicate any design requirements as reasonable or needing transformation to one of the other types. Correct any which need transformation.

2. Give three examples of
   a. Original requirements
   b. Reference requirements
   c. Implied requirements
   d. Derived requirements
3. Provide a text description of the relationship of design require-ments to implied requirements (see Fig. 5.3).
4. Develop a narrative requirements statement for a design of a fold-ing table.
5. Apply the process of Fig. 5.4 to the answer for question 2.

5.6 References

INCOSE, 1996: International Council on Systems Engineering Web Site, http://usw.in-teract.net/INCOSE/workgrps/tools/tooltax.html.

Perry, T. S., 1996: The trials and travails of interactive TV. *IEEE Spectrum* (April), 22–28.

6

Define Effectiveness Measures

6.1   What Core Step 2 Is

Core step 2, define effectiveness measures, establishes the criteria, the effectiveness measures, by which alternative designs and architectures will be judged. It provides the guidance of what is most important to the developers of structure and behavior models. For criteria that are matters of preference, it establishes the stakeholder groups and surveys that identify and establish a set of effectiveness measures. For criteria that can be expressed as statements of engineering performance, it generates the equations that define them in engineering terms. It sets up the surveys that are required to prioritize all of the effectiveness measures.

The numerical evaluation of the effectiveness measures is not done in this step, it is a part of the later core step 5, trade-off, which is discussed in Chap. 9.

Effectiveness measures are a basic abstraction used by management to analyze business and formulate business strategy. They are examined in Chap. 15.

6.2   Importance of Effectiveness Measures

Effectiveness measures are the small subset of the requirements that are so important that the system will fail if they are not met and will be a huge success if they are met. They are the important things that the product will do. They incorporate the visionary goals of management and engineering, which may exceed what users and operators expect and presently can appreciate. They are the criteria used to make the trade-off decisions of what to build. They drive the system solution. The design of a system is an ill-posed problem that has no solution without a set of criteria to guide choices. The effectiveness measures correspond to the regularization functions used in optimal control or in calculus of variations. They are few in number, usually less than a dozen, even for large, complex systems.

The effectiveness measures are critically important because they incorporate what customers, owners, operators, and users want and will use in their decisions on whether to buy a particular product. They define the fit of the product to the marketplace. They are critical because all the stakeholders—users, customers, owners, operators, engineers, and management—must agree on them, or there will be future problems.

If these criteria are not both correct and agreed to, then the system development can be plagued with costly requirements changes. It may miss its market. The effectiveness measure results are extremely useful in reviews with management and with customers, users, and operators who do not want to know all the technical engineering details but do want to know about these critical system criteria.

Figure 6.1 shows an object structure model that captures the context for systems engineering, considered as an organization. Only the design engineering disciplines, suppliers, and manufacturing engi-

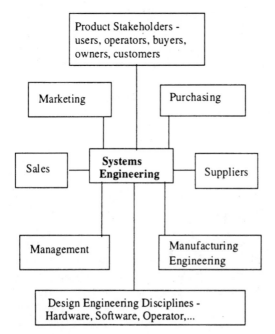

Figure 6.1 Context for systems engineering.

neering disciplines need and want to receive the engineering details. The details they need to receive is a version of the system detail transformed into the views and notations of the discipline. The product stakeholders and management need information about the system, especially effectiveness measures, in a form that is useful to them. The product stakeholders do not need all the technical data.

The use of effectiveness measures as decision criteria for trade-off gives the core technical process for engineering complex systems its distinctive behavior.

Trade-off in software engineering is known as *optimization* and *complexity*. The heart of trade-off in software engineering is complexity or space for speed. An $O(n)$ algorithm executing n operations may run in $O(n \cdot 2)$ time, while a less complex algorithm to perform exactly the same function may run in $O(n \log n)$ time. Similarly, software can be adjusted to store more intermediate calculations and run faster, or to use less storage space and run slower. Speed can be traded against the size of the data storage. These optimizations can and often are performed after code is initially running. This is the integration phase of software development.

Systems engineering employs effectiveness measures and trade-off in a distinct and formalized manner which is different from the practice in software engineering. This difference must be taken into consideration when attempting to apply software engineering methodologies to systems problems.

6.3   An Industrial Example

When effectiveness measures are first posed, they are often phrased in customer and user terms rather than in engineering equations and quantities. They must become measurable and transformed into engineering quantities, or they must be posed with alternatives.

An interesting illustration is the development of the Boeing 777 (Norris, 1995). At the conclusion of the negotiations with United Airlines, which placed the launch order for the 777, a handwritten note stated:

> In order to launch on-time a truly great airplane, we have the responsibility to work together to design, produce, and introduce an airplane that exceeds the expectations of flight crews, cabin crews, and maintenance and support teams and ultimately our passengers and shippers. From day one:
> - Best dispatch reliability in history
> - Greatest customer appeal in the industry
> - User-friendly and everything works.

The Boeing engineering team included engineers from the airlines from day 1. The bulleted measures above had to be transformed into two kinds of measurable goals:

- Measurable engineering goals
- Preference goals from surveys of customers

Reliability is a clear engineering goal and can be quantified. Engineering goals derived from "greatest customer appeal in industry" would likely include flight range, passenger comfort, and aircraft availability. They can be quantified by interacting with the customers and attaining agreement on the numerical values critical to success.

"User-friendly to flight crews, cabin crew, passengers, and so on" can also be quantified, but only by careful survey of the wants and preferences of these groups of people. This can be done with real attainable feature alternatives, access to representative groups, and valid statistical analysis of the results. The findings can then be translated into engineering alternatives and goals.

As the engineering solution emerges, the results can be explained in terms of what will be achieved in dispatch reliability, customer appeal, user-friendliness, and reliability of all parts of the aircraft. This is the information needed and understood by most of the stakeholders.

6.4 How Effectiveness Measures Drive the Solution

How the effectiveness measures drive the solution is shown with a simple example. The three functions shown in Fig. 6.2 provide the basis for the example.

Functions A, B, and C are completely independent and have separate and distinct inputs and outputs. They can be rearranged in any of the possible series-parallel combinations without affecting the out-

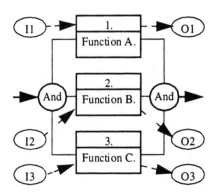

Figure 6.2 Behavior of three independently concurrent functions.

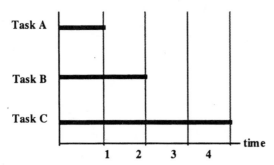

Figure 6.3 Timeline.

come: O1, O2, and O3. If they are done in a sequence, or two in a sequence with one parallel, the same outputs are produced. A simple practical example of three such functions is setting a dinner table, cooking the dinner, and talking with a guest.

For this trivial example we assume that there are estimates of how long it takes to perform each of these tasks, as shown in Fig. 6.3. Task A takes one time unit, task B takes two units, and task C takes four units.

We assume that we have only one kind of resource, object R, with a fixed cost per unit that can perform all three of these functions. We can use several of them in the solution.

6.4.1 Problem: system 1

- The effectiveness measure is *least cost for system 1.*
- What is the near-optimal solution?
- Answer—one object with the three functions serialized as shown in Fig. 6.4.

There are six equivalent behaviors to do this, as shown in Fig. 6.5.

6.4.2 Problem: system 2

The effectiveness measure is the *least time to complete for system 2.*

What is the near-optimal solution?

Answer—there are two solutions:

- System 2.1: three objects, each performing one function
- System 2.2: two objects, one performing functions A and B, one performing function C.

System 2.1 is shown in Fig. 6.6.

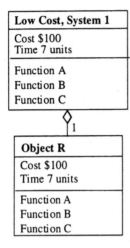

Figure 6.4   System 1 built from object R.

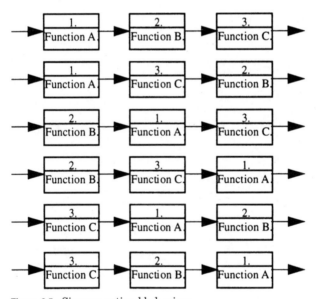

Figure 6.5   Six near-optimal behaviors.

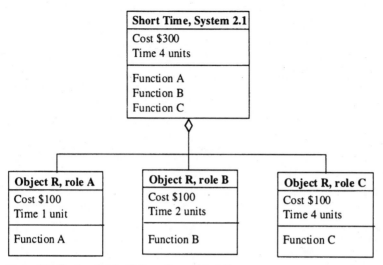

Figure 6.6   System 2.1 built from three object Rs.

The behavior of system 2.1 is the concurrent behavior shown in Fig. 6.2, which can use three resources or objects to perform it. Three instances of object R are used in three different roles. Note also that the behavior does not demand any interfaces among the three objects used. Interfaces might be necessary for other reasons, but not because of the behavior. The nontemporal attribute of cost adds going up the aggregation tree. Time does not add. The timeline is the result of the behavior and is obtained by executing the corporate behavior of system 2.1.

The alternative solution, system 2.2, is a solution to this problem and to a more restricted one, as described below.

6.4.3   Problem: system 3

The effectiveness measures are

- Least time to complete for system 3
- Lowest cost for system 3

What is the near-optimal solution?

Answer—there are two solutions:

- System 3: two objects R, one performing functions A and B serialized, the other performing function C. Because there are two ways to serialize functions A and B, there are two solutions.

Figure 6.7 shows object R used in two roles.

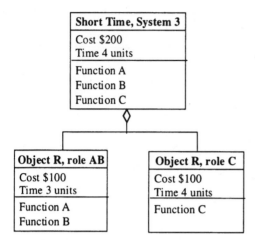

Figure 6.7   System 3 built from two object Rs.

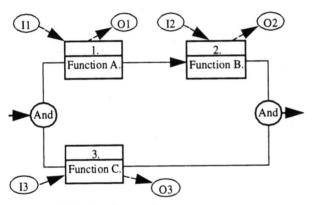

Figure 6.8   Behavior of system 3.

The overall completion time for system 3 is the same as that for system 2, as shown by executing the behavior of Fig. 6.8. It is less than that of system 1. The optimal structure found for system 3 is identical to the solution found for system 2.2.

The cost of system 3 is two-thirds that of system 2.1 and twice as great as that of system 1. The results of the example are summarized in Table 6.1.

The effectiveness measures drive the solution that is adopted. They guide and reduce the work of modeling behavior and structure by informing the engineers which alternatives to explore. The alternatives exist because behavior can be mapped to the parts in different ways, taking advantage of independent concurrency in the behavior of the

TABLE 6.1   System Alternatives and Effectiveness

System alternatives	Time	Cost, $	Effectiveness measures
System 1	7 units	100	Cost
System 2.1	4 units	300	Time only
System 3	4 units	200	Time and cost

system. Numerical evaluation of the effectiveness measures requires knowledge of both the behavior and the structure of alternative system designs. It requires knowledge of the attributes of the parts of the structure. It requires access to stakeholder groups who can express their preferences among alternatives.

Even in this trivial problem, effectiveness, behavior, and structure were all considered. The development of these three models is a set of concurrent dependent activities.

The effectiveness measures not only drive the solution to the problem but also guide the management of the team performing the work. They become a guiding principle for prioritizing the focus of the work, for allocating workforce to the tasks, and for assessing risk (Reugg et al., 1993).

6.5   Types of Effectiveness Measures

It is useful to classify effectiveness measures based on the kind of work that must be done to evaluate them.

Figure 6.9 depicts three kinds of effectiveness measures:

- Those that can be calculated with equations from the attributes of the parts of the system and the structure of the system: attributes such as weight, cost, power, or reliability

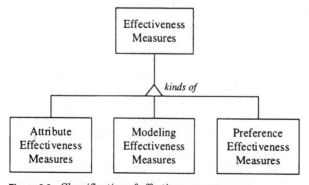

Figure 6.9 Classification of effectiveness measures.

- Those that can be calculated from modeling and analysis: modeling of behavior, simulation of probability of detection, etc.

- Those that can be obtained from survey of the preferences of owners, operators, and users using their choices among solution alternatives

6.6   Priorities among Effectiveness Measures

Complex systems are similar to the trivial example above in being driven by only a few effectiveness measures. However, complex systems involve thousands or more parts. The relationships between the effectiveness measures and the attributes of individual parts span several tiers of decomposition of the system and many linear and nonlinear relationships. Both the budgeting of attribute values to parts and the rollup of attribute values to effectiveness measures need the precision and efficiency of computer capture and execution with models.

A list of individual effectiveness measures as criteria does not completely establish the solution to choose. Compare systems 1 and 2.1 in Table 6.1. Is the gain of reduced time from 7 units to 4 units worth the added weight of two object Rs and added cost of $50.00? This can be decided in several ways:

- By examining a table such as Table 6.1 and choosing.

- When the trades are continuous functions rather than a coarse set of choices, it can be done by finding minima in the functions and then choosing among them.

- By prioritizing the effectiveness measures into a single cost function by assigning priorities or weights for each measure. The solution with the lowest value of cost function is then the system of choice.

Statistically valid systematic methods of assigning such priorities have been developed. The advantage of the single cost function is that it provides a single number on which to base the selection of the design to be used. The advantage of examining the set of individual effectiveness measures and how they vary with alternatives is that one can see where the sharp maxima and minima occur and where the broader maxima and minima occur. It is sometimes prudent to select a somewhat less optimal design if the tolerances on the attributes of the parts can be larger. This selection is a selection based on quality versus risk and should be quantified with a proper requirement or effectiveness measure.

The selection of the effectiveness measures from among all the possible performance requirements and the selection of the weighting factors both require setting priorities by assessing the opinions of informed individuals. The individuals participating need to represent all important product stakeholder groups. The nature of the statistical methods used make it equally easy for individuals of diverse backgrounds and education to participate.

Two methods recommended for setting priorities for complex systems are the *analytic hierarchy process* (AHP) (Saaty, 1983) and the *multiattribute utility theory* (MAUT) (Roy and Vincke, 1981).

In the AHP process individuals consider the relative importance of the effectiveness measures in pairs, two at a time, until they have exhausted all the pairs. A scale for assigning importance is provided by the method. These results are summarized in a matrix, and the principal eigenvector of the matrix provides the values for the priorities. If all the effectiveness measures can be computed analytically, then these priorities are used directly as weighting factors for the regularization function that will establish the near-optimal design.

Some of the effectiveness measures may be of the type that are matters of user preference. In this case the designs are considered in pairs for each of the effectiveness measures by the individuals participating. These results are combined with the weighting factors to yield a preference for each design. The method provides a check for consistency and significance of the results.

The AHP and MAUT methods provide a rational basis for the selection of a particular design candidate.

6.7   Information Model for Core Step 2

The nature and use of effectiveness measures has been discussed above and illustrated with a simple example. It is useful to provide more rigorous models of the work done in creating effectiveness measures and of the information used. Figure 6.10 captures associations among the information objects. The reasons for the associations in this model are that they are used in the work that is done. A discussion of the information model proceeds from a description of the work steps to be done. The work steps are shown in Fig. 6.11. These figures are discussed together because of their intimate association.

All the effectiveness measure identification is done in conjunction with the major stakeholders: owners, operators, users, management, marketing, customers, etc. The first set of four steps (Fig. 6.11) accept all currently available information and identify the stakeholders who will participate with the engineering team. Sometimes marketing represents groups of these people. There follow three concurrent paths.

In the top path the team defines the effectiveness measures that are related to the attributes of the parts and to structure, such as cost, weight, and reliability. Equations are associated with the attributes and have these attributes as their arguments. The associations

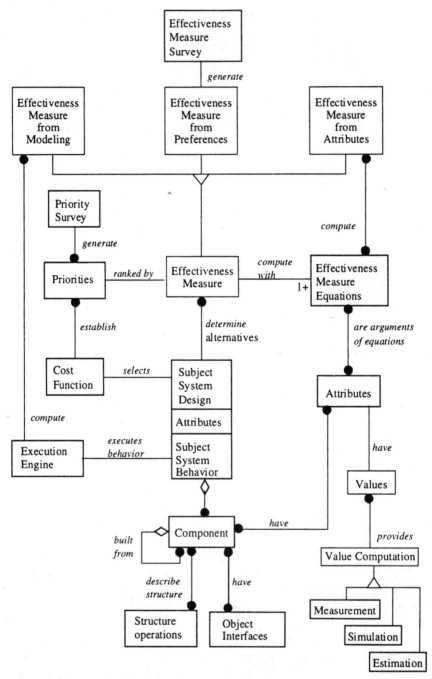

Figure 6.10   Information model for creating effectiveness measures.

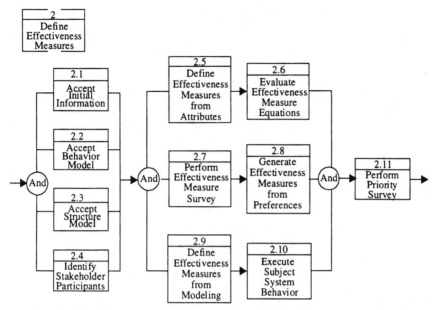

Figure 6.11 FFBD view of defining effectiveness measures, core step 2.

are shown on the right side of Fig. 6.11. The attributes must be captured in the structure model, core step 4.

In the middle path the team defines and performs the surveys that generate effectiveness measures related to preferences. An example would be a survey to establish the seat environment for passengers that would make an aircraft the most appealing in airline use. The associations are shown in the top center of Fig. 6.11.

In the scenario shown in Fig. 6.11, the team defines effectiveness measures on the basis of modeling associated with execution of behavior. This implies that there is work in progress to define behavior, core step 3. This path is particularly important when the overall success of the behavior is not known but behavior is understood and probabilities are known or estimated for the steps in the behavior. Examples are probability of success in detecting a flaw, detecting a military threat, in destroying a target, completing a communication, and so on. These problems often involve communication bandwidths and frequency and size of communications. They yield to simulation and Monte Carlo calculations for which behavior must be known. The left side of the figure shows the associations of an execution engine (a computer tool or person) with the subject system and the effectiveness measures.

The last step in Fig. 6.11 is to perform the priority survey that establishes priorities for a cost function. The center part of the figure shows that the effectiveness measures determine the alternative subject system designs to be considered. It shows that the effectiveness measures have priorities which are generated by the priority survey. The priorities establish the cost function that selects among the alternative designs.

The effectiveness measures have a determinative influence on the behavior and structure developments that establish alternative architectures. They provide the insight to the engineers to efficiently develop a modest number of likely alternatives from among the multitude of possible alternatives.

6.8 Summary

The work is done jointly with the stakeholders. It establishes the effectiveness measures and the equations and surveys to evaluate them. The attributes identified must be included in the structure model. The defined effectiveness measures guide the structure and behavior modeling in defining a modest number of important alternative solutions for the system. This core step provides the mechanism for getting effectiveness measure values from stakeholder preferences, structure, and behavior. It provides the mechanism for generating priorities for the effectiveness measures and a cost function that picks out the near-optimal solution.

The use of trade-off and effectiveness measure criteria which are derived from the product stakeholders is a distinguishing best practice in the engineering of complex systems. The complexity is handled by the use of powerful abstractions in computer modeling of behavior and structure. Defining product with high value, competitive performance, low cost, and good fit to the market is a result of trade-off with effectiveness measure criteria.

6.9 Exercises

1. Repeat the analysis of the problem described in Sec. 6.4. Use the same three concurrent functions (Fig. 6.2) and the same timeline (Fig. 6.3). Consider the same combinations of effectiveness measures.
   a. Find the alternative designs possible when two resources are available as shown in Fig. 6.12.
   b. Extend Table 6.1 to include the additional alternative designs.
2. Identify stakeholders for the following:
   a. Halogen table lamp
   b. Farm tractors
   c. Quality-assurance consulting

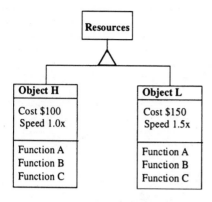

Figure 6.12 Two resources.

3. In general, in the United States, black olives are supplied in cans; Spanish (green) olives, in clear, glass jars. What effectiveness measures might account for this difference?

4. Design a set of effectiveness measures, using the process in Fig. 6.11 for

 a. An integrated-circuit fabrication plant

 b. An Internet browser

 c. A clock radio

 d. A procedure for financial auditing

5. For each of the effectiveness measures in question 2

 a. Classify the kind.

 b. Prioritize the measures and state the reason.

6.10 References

Norris, G., 1995: Boeing's seventh wonder. *IEEE Spectrum* (Oct.), 20–23.

Reugg, R. G., K. J. Field, and B. Boldblatt, 1993: Design for manufacturability/affordability—The F414 story. *Defense Manufacturing Conference* (San Francisco, 1993), vol. II, pp. 97–109.

Roy, B., and P. Vincke, 1981: Multicriterion analysis: Survey and directions. *Eur. J. Operat. Res.* **8,** 207.

Saaty, T. L., 1983: Priority setting in complex problems. *IEEE Transact. Eng. Mgmt.* **EM-30,** 140–155.

7

Create Behavior Model

7.1 What Core Step 3 Is

Core step 3, create behavior model, creates the behavior of whatever thing or object the engineer is considering. If the engineer is defining the context of the system or subsystem, it is necessary to define the behavior of each external object in the environment that excites the system. As the excitations are defined, the responses of the system or subsystem need to be defined. These excitations and responses are behaviors. They capture in rigorous and executable form the information which is expressed in text operations concepts or requirement statements. They first define the intrinsic behavior that the system or subsystem shall have. This is the behavior as allowed by nature, incorporating the sequences and alternatives demanded by reality and preserving the concurrencies allowed.

The intrinsic behavior is often transformed to a design behavior by serializing concurrencies or pipelining sequences for performance reasons.

The design behavior is the emergent behavior of the interacting assembled components that constitute the system. It results in the same set of responses to excitations as did the intrinsic behavior, but may be faster and less expensive when implemented.

Generally the creation of behavior models occurs concurrently with the definition of effectiveness measures and with the creation of structure models. The effectiveness measures guide and reduce the work of creating behavior and structure models by defining what is of greatest value. The structure models provide for efficient choice of the best pieces and parts to use, and they help the engineer keep the behaviors being created within reasonable reach of the feasible. In this competitive global marketplace it is essential to push the system close to its limits, but it is also vital to stay within feasibility and to do the engineering at low cost.

Behavior models play a particularly important role in the reengineering of systems which are poorly documented. In this case it is frequently important to reverse-engineer and synthesize an understandable higher-level behavior of the system from the existing lines of code or from the behaviors of a multitude of individual parts. The existing emergent behavior of the system must often be preserved in the new system with enhancements. Yet the available detailed documentation of behavior may only describe the behaviors of individual parts or of lines of code or may not match the actual system.

7.2   How to Create Behavior Models

Chapter 3 describes the basics of modeling behavior. This chapter draws on those results to define the detailed steps involved in creating a behavior model. The detailed steps are described in text, are made explicit with a model, and are illustrated with a simple example.

Figure 7.1 is a functional flow block diagram of an engineer's behavior in creating a behavior model for the object or thing under consideration.

The first three steps in the engineer's behavior, 3.1, 3.2, and 3.3, are concurrent and in general have no established order. The information already developed about effectiveness measures is accepted and inter-

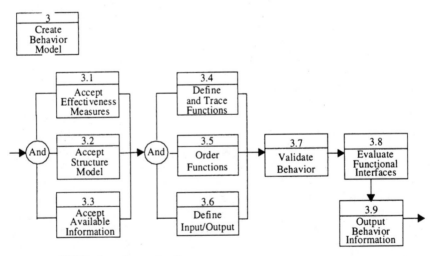

Figure 7.1   FFBD view of core step 3.

preted in step 3.1. For the modeling of a particular subcomponent, some of the effectiveness measures may be unimportant and others important, requiring interpretation. For example, in the development of a satellite, designing to minimum weight is an important effectiveness measure. Yet the physical weight of a custom high-speed integrated-circuit chip may be unimportant. However, the power consumption of the kinds of chips used may be very important to satellite weight because of the impact on power storage, solar energy arrays, and heat dissipation. Power consumption is likely associated with chip processing speed and hence the time for completion of a behavior.

The information developed in prior modeling of structure is accepted in step 3.2 and used in this modeling of behavior.

All the applicable available information is accepted and used in step 3.3. Often this includes text requirements and an operations concept which describe what the particular subcomponent must do. The available information may include behavior models developed earlier that are to be used or refined.

The second set of three concurrent steps in Fig. 7.1, steps 3, 3.4, 3.5, and 3.6, build the behavior needed at this stage of the engineering. Step 3.4 defines the functions that are needed and develops traceability links to text requirements which are applicable. The definition of the functions may suggest derived requirements associated with them which require traceability links to the functions and to parent requirements.

It is possible to do the engineering development using models and a data dictionary rather than with text requirements. Presently this approach is rare in practice. When the modeling approach is used, the functions will be a decomposition of a function in a previous behavior model. The text requirements exist as explanations in the accompanying data dictionary and are automatically linked to functions and parent requirements as they are developed.

Step 3.5 of Fig. 7.1 orders the functions. Steps 3.4 and 3.5 are not sequential. Defining the functions will involve thinking about their order, and ordering the functions will result in the discovery of new functions needed or in the modification of ones already selected. These two steps are concurrent. The result of completion of these two steps is the information needed for an FFBD view of the behavior. The information can be captured by constructing this view with a graphic tool or by creating part of a behavior model.

Step 3.6 of the figure defines the input/output items for each function. In I/O-intensive or data-intensive systems, the I/O information may be more important, relevant, and available to engineers than the ordering of functions. It may be very important to the definition of the functions. The I/O function view of behavior, a data-flow diagram, may be of greater interest than a functional flow block diagram. This step is concurrent with 3.4 and 3.5 and may cause modification of their results.

When all three definition steps have been completed, the result is an executable behavior. Step 3.7 is the execution of the behavior, manually by engineers or automatically with a tool. It validates the behavior. The execution will find problems such as starvation or deadly embrace. By associating time budgets with each function, the execution will generate an overall timeline for the behavior. If this style of modeling has been carried out consistently during the development of the tree of parts that constitute the system, the timeline for a subcomponent can be studied for its impact on an overall response thread of the system to an external excitation. In many developments there is no deterministic time of completion for the functions, but probabilities of completion can be estimated for them. In such a case it is often possible to execute the behavior as a Monte Carlo calculation to generate a probability for overall success. This is useful for detection-type of systems such as medical resonance imaging, flaw detection, radar, and sonar systems. It is useful for systems with statistically known excitations such as communication systems and management information systems.

Step 3.8 evaluates the functional interfaces. It is particularly useful in situations in which the magnitude of input/output is known and the rate of generation and consumption is known for functions. In these situations the flow at interfaces can be established once the behavior has been demonstrated to be error-free in step 3.7. Wait times due to lack of input are established. Accumulation of output is determined and can be correlated with the amount of storage capacity available or required.

The final step, 3.9, generates all the behavior information needed for the engineering information base in the form required. It is important to remember that engineering is an art of finding a near optimal solution with a minimum of effort. If some of the steps in Fig. 7.1 can be skipped in a particular problem without negative impact, then that is done.

If it is necessary to cycle from any later step to any earlier step, then that is done. There are too many possible backward loops to show them in the figure. The backward loops were all accounted for in the perform change control process step 2, as shown in Fig. 4.5. This step provides a complete process for the discovery of any issue and its resolution by any alteration of the progression of work, whether the issue involves the personal work of only one engineer, or involves the entire engineering team and revision of contract with a customer.

Details for perform change control are described in Sec. 16.5.

7.3 Example of Behavior Development: Bottling Wine

In order to discuss a system behavior, elements external to the system must first be developed. These external elements form the *context* for the system. As suggested before, the context can be stated in several ways:

- Executable requirements, captured in models
- Requirements expressed in text
- An operations concept described in narrative prose

In addition, effectiveness measures are developed in parallel and guide efficient development of behavior and structure models.

For the purposes of this example, bottling wine, we will assume the existence of context information without debating its technical merit or how it came to exist. Figure 7.2 shows the context using an information model. This is the structure information which is the input to step 3.2 of Fig. 7.1.

Very often a large, complex problem can be broken into weakly interacting parts by examining the context of the system. It is then useful to have separate teams develop the weakly interacting parts and carefully combine the results and make them coherent. To simplify this example, only the interactions between the winemaker and the

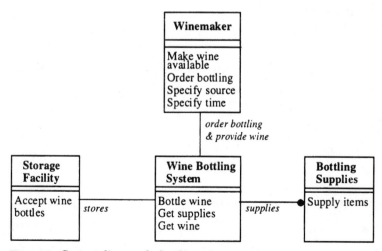

Figure 7.2 Context diagram for bottling wine.

wine bottling system will be considered in this chapter. The other interactions in the context are suggested as an exercise.

The context can be described with text as a set of requirements.

7.3.1 External system behavior

Name of the external system(s) causing an excitation of the system

- Winemaker

The excitation behavior

- The winemaker shall order bottling of a specific number of bottles of wine.
- The winemaker shall specify the barrels of wine to be used.
- The winemaker shall specify the time for completion of bottling.
- The winemaker shall make the barrels of wine available.

Inputs to the system

- Location and identity of the stored wine from winemaker
- Location of other necessary supplies from bottling supplies
- Time of completion from winemaker
- Number of bottles to be filled from winemaker
- Start bottling command from winemaker

Functional requirements of system

- The system shall fill bottles with wine.
- The system shall cork bottles of wine.
- The system shall label bottles of wine.

Outputs from the system

- Bottles of wine to storage
- Request for wine barrels to winemaker
- Request for supplies to bottling supplies

Name of the external system(s) receiving the outputs from the system

- Bottled wine storage
- Bottling supplies
- Winemaker

7.3.2 Temporal performance requirements

Time duration or probabilities associated with the excitation scenario

- The excitation system shall provide a stimulus at uncertain intervals with the highest demand of 100 bottles per day.

7.3.3 Nontemporal performance requirements

- Number of bottles to be produced.
- The system shall produce bottles of wine at a rate up to 100 bottles of wine per day.
- Material cost per bottle $1.00 or less.
- Labor cost per bottle $1.00 or less.
- Investment cost of $400.00 or less.
- Predetermined design: none.
- Reference requirements that refer to documents and models that apply to the system: none.

7.3.4 Operations concept for system context

The winemaker decides that it is time to bottle the wine in one of the barrels. She tells the wine bottling system of this decision and provides information about which wine is to be bottled, the number of bottles, and when it is to be completed. The system uses supplies from bottling supplies to bottle the wine and prepare the bottles for sale or consumption. The prepared bottles are placed in a wine rack ready to be taken to storage in the storage facility.

7.3.5 Behavior of the winemaker

The static context model of Fig. 7.2 provides only partial information about the excitations of the system. It shows only the functions carried out by the winemaker. The behavior of the winemaker for excitation of the wine bottling system is completely defined in Fig. 7.3.

The four functions listed in the object picture for winemaker in Fig. 7.2 are all captured in Fig. 7.3, with their ordering and input/outputs.

Note that as presented here, the text descriptions and the models are somewhat redundant. The combination is most efficient when the text is created in a data dictionary as an explanation for each element in the models.

7.3.6 Effectiveness measures

1. Bottle wine at minimum cost.
2. Complete the bottling as quickly as possible.
3. Ensure that there is no foreign matter in the bottles of wine.
4. Bottle only good wine.

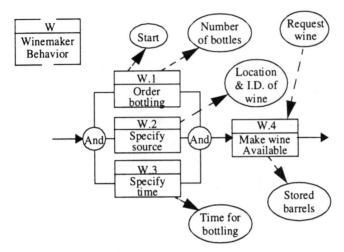

Figure 7.3 Behavior of the winemaker.

The effectiveness measures capture a small subset of requirements that are vital for success in the marketplace for competitive cost, schedule, and quality reasons.

7.3.7 Intrinsic behavior

Having been given the context diagram and other text requirements, or a text operations concept, we are now ready to begin developing a model of the behavior for our system. For most systems the engineers have preconceived design ideas which may, even unconsciously, affect their decisions in modeling the behavior. Especially at these early stages of development, care must be taken to avoid introducing artificial limitations. The behavior of the system will be developed in stages in the example in the way it might emerge in real work. What happens in real work is highly interactive with discoveries and return to earlier work. It is not neat.

Top-level behavior. Consider the problem of bottling wine, the work of bottling when the wine and other needed items are available but stored.

The first set of tasks includes getting the wine, the corks, etc., to the area, perhaps a kitchen, where the bottling will be done. This is *intrinsic behavior* in that it must be done by any bottling system whether it is transporting the items to the feeders in a bottling plant or carrying items from a home basement to a kitchen. Thus, we begin the design by breaking the behavior into two functions taking place serially:

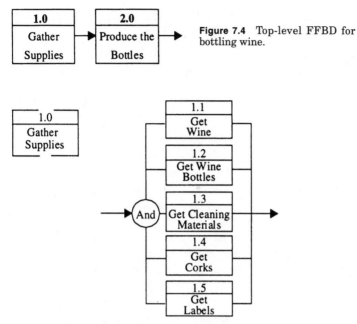

Figure 7.4   Top-level FFBD for bottling wine.

Figure 7.5   Gathering samples for bottling wine.

- Gather supplies.
- Produce the bottles.

These are shown in Fig. 7.4 using the FFBD notation.

Expanding gathering supplies.   There are several subtasks within *gather supplies*. In particular, we find the wine, get the bottles, get the corks, get the cleaning supplies, and get the labels. A critical question to ask is whether these tasks can be done in any order, or whether there is an imposed sequence. The answer in this case is that they can be done in any order. This is represented in Fig. 7.5 as a concurrency in that functional flow block diagram. The arrows, once again, represent sequence. The AND shows that the following steps may occur in parallel.

This is the concept of intrinsic behavior. Although this set of steps need not be performed in parallel, they can be done in parallel and so they are modeled that way.

Expanding the "Produce the bottles" task.   As with gathering supplies, there are several subtasks involved to produce the bottles. The bottles must be filled, corked, labeled, and cleaned. In addition to this basic

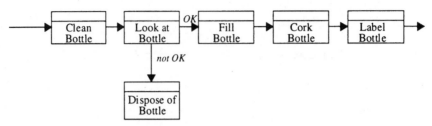

Figure 7.6 Fill the bottles for bottling wine.

set of functions, a few other functions are also necessary to have a robust behavior for bottling wine. Our effectiveness measures stated: "Ensure there is no foreign matter in the bottles of wine." We derive from this a requirement that the bottles be clean prior to being filled.

Thus we introduce several functions for cleaning the bottle and testing to determine whether it is sufficiently clean to use. Figure 7.6 shows the FFBD for this portion of the behavior. An additional semantic construct was needed to describe what happens to unclean bottles. The function *look at bottle* is a *branch point, or a selection point,* for the behavior with conditions for each of the alternative paths that follow. If the bottle is clean, the filling process follows; if the bottle is dirty, it is discarded.

If one reverses the steps of clean, fill, and cork the bottle, one has a corked, clean, *empty* bottle. These steps need to be done in this sequence. Nature and reality do not allow them to be reversed. This is the concept of intrinsic behavior. It captures what nature allows in its most general form.

Putting it all together. Figure 7.7 now shows the completed FFBD for the intrinsic behavior of bottling wine. The actual design behavior of the system depends on the available resource, the effectiveness measures that have been adopted for optimization purposes, and the number of bottles to be produced.

7.3.8 Emergent behavior

While Fig. 7.7 presented a final version of the intrinsic behavior, we have not yet finished with the behavior modeling. We now have to consider what the desired emergent behavior is. Factors which will alter the behavior that do not involve the structure of the final system should be considered. Considerations of this sort tend to limit the overall generality of the intrinsic behavior.

Deriving the appropriate emergent behavior from the intrinsic behavior is one of the key creative portions of systems engineering. *No*

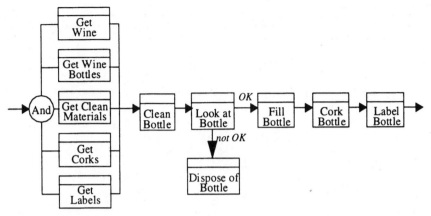

Figure 7.7 Completed FFBD for bottling wine.

amount of formal methods and approach can overcome bad decision making. Neither can they replace experience and creativity in engineering. We stress as best practice the use of executable models to help evaluate the decisions before a large commitment is made to producing the parts of the system. With that as general guidance, we push on to crafting the emergent behavior.

The effectiveness measures in the available information have not yet been used in the example. Much of the impact of the effectiveness measures will be on the mapping from behavior to structure. They also play an important role in developing the emergent behavior. Focus on the first two effectiveness measures

1. Bottle wine at minimum cost.

2. Complete the bottling as quickly as possible.

3. Ensure that there is no foreign matter in the bottles of wine.

4. Bottle only good wine.

and look at the intrinsic behavior as shown in Fig. 7.6. Minimum cost may not be quick. Some modifications can be made to the behavior at this point to balance these opposite pulls. In particular, we look at the decision making involved with inspecting the bottle. The intrinsic behavior takes into account only the need to have a clean bottle into which to put the wine. The bottle is thrown away if it is not clean after one washing. This may lead to the disposal of many bottles which might become clean if they were washed a second time. We can modify the behavior to reduce the cost of disposing of bottles with little impact on completion time. The proposed change is shown in Fig. 7.8.

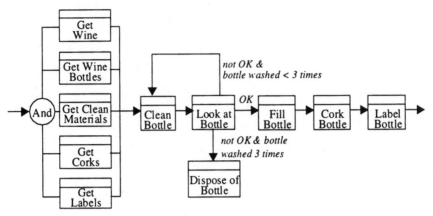

Figure 7.8   Modified FFBD for bottling wine.

In the justification for making this change we used some rather loose reasoning that one effectiveness measure would be improved and another would be minimally affected. Choices of this sort are the heart of systems design and greatly impact the merit of the total system design. In Fig. 7.8 the bottles are washed a maximum of three times, but two times or some other number of times might be optimal. It is in core step 5, perform trade-off analysis, that these trade-off decisions are fully defined and performed quantitatively. The trade-off analysis cannot be carried out until decisions have been made about how the system will be built, what objects will be used, the attributes of those objects, and what alternative structures are to be considered during core step 4, create structure model.

Although this behavior may now seem complete, it is still defective in one important aspect, which demonstrates the importance of engineering experience, creativity, and wisdom. It is related to effectiveness measure 4, "Bottle only good wine," which has not yet been taken into account. The defect in the behavior is that one tastes the wine before doing the tasks to ensure that one bottles only good wine. It is left as an exercise to add the necessary functions, branches, conditions, and iterations to incorporate "Taste the wine."

7.3.9   Completing the behavior: adding inputs and outputs

What has just been modeled is only one view of behavior: the functions and control. In order to have a semantically complete—and therefore executable—model, the inputs and outputs must be added. Figure 7.9 shows the function flow block diagram of Fig. 7.4 augmented with input/output for each top function.

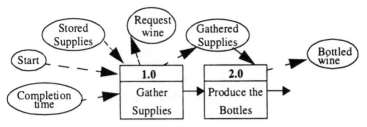

Figure 7.9 Top-level behavior for bottling wine.

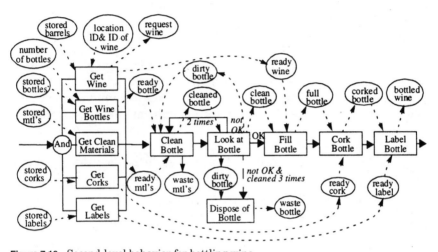

Figure 7.10 Second-level behavior for bottling wine.

The inputs and outputs for the next-level functional flow block diagram can also be added to produce the second-level behavior of Fig. 7.10, in which second-level input/output has been added and the I/O items stored supplies, which come from the external system stored supplies, and gathered supplies have been decomposed into their second-level parts.

This now provides enough information, expressed formally, to start at the beginning and simulate the system's operation. To do this, we employ the models for external systems in this systems context, in this case the behavior model for the winemaker and the behavior model for stored supplies. The external systems provide the necessary stimulus to our model to fully define its synchronization with the external world and to observe our system's internal behavior as responses. The models are explicit and leave no ambiguity as to what the system is to do.

7.3.10   Views of behavior

When the inputs/outputs, functions, and the ordering of functions by control operations are all included in the model, behavior is fully modeled and executable. There is, however, a drawback to this view. The full models of behavior contain a great deal of information and can be hard to read. To overcome this, two useful simpler views can be used:

- A view of function and its ordering by control (the functional flow block diagram we have been using, is such a view)
- A view of function and input/output such as a data-flow diagram

The various diagraming techniques for the elements of behavior have been developed over many years starting as early as the 1950s, when the FFBD was first introduced. Such diagrams convey information that is difficult to express in a textual language with the same level of completeness. With any successful diagraming techniques, semantic information must be readily apparent to engineers developing and reviewing system designs.

This function and input/output view of behavior has been captured in several different diagrams which use different syntax. To name only a few:

- Data-flow diagram
- N-squared chart
- IDEF0 diagram
- Requirement allocation sheets, in text

Figure 7.11 is a data-flow diagram produced by removing all the control symbols from the behavior.

This data-flow diagram (Fig. 7.11) with the control information removed can be rearranged to make the information it represents more readable. Figure 7.12 shows the rearranged version, which serves as an example of the importance of layout in any of these diagraming techniques. Although the semantic content is the same between the two versions of the data-flow diagram, the understandability of the content for humans is dramatically improved in the second diagram.

The view of behavior shown in Fig. 7.12 captures all the input/output relationships with functions. It does not carry all the information to describe whether functions participate in concurrency, simple sequencing, or alternative path branching. It does, however, contain enough information to give insight concerning the control information just as the function and control view provides some insights to the data-flow considerations.

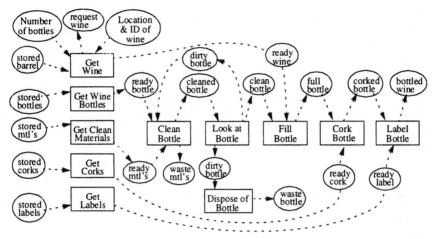

Figure 7.11 Data-flow diagram for bottling wine.

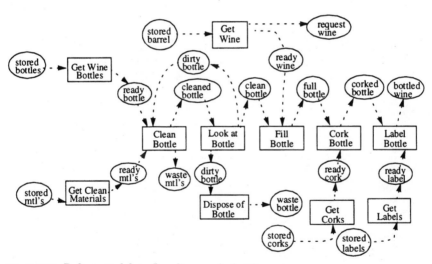

Figure 7.12 Reformatted data-flow diagram for bottling wine.

A closer look at the data-flow diagram for bottling wine reveals a limitation imposed by the functional flow block diagram. The limitation is that our FFBD requires all the gathering supplies activities to be completed prior to beginning any of the bottle preparation and filling tasks. One look at the data-flow diagram, especially the reformatted version, shows that this is clearly not necessary. Only two of the gathering supplies tasks, "Get wine bottles" and "Get cleaning materials," need to be completed before the first of the bottle preparation

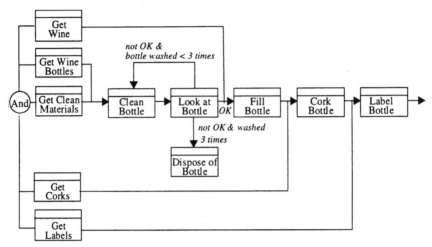

Figure 7.13 Revised FFBD.

tasks can begin. Figure 7.13 shows the impact of these changes on the original FFBD in Fig. 7.7. It is worthwhile, therefore, to consider what decisions we made that led to an unnecessary limitation.

A quick review shows that nearly the first decision made caused the problem. Figure 7.4 divided the behavior into two elements: *gather supplies* and *produce the bottles*. This first division created the unnecessary limitation, yet at the time it appeared to be a reasonable expression of intrinsic behavior. Which FFBD is more desirable to use, Fig. 7.8 or Fig. 7.13? That question cannot be answered until the behavior information is combined with structural information that defines how the work will be done. Other variants of behavior may be found to be important as structure alternatives are considered. This reinforces the need to perform core steps 2, 3, and 4 concurrently. It is a major strength of the modeling techniques that they detect and raise such issues early in the development and provide means for quickly resolving the issues quantitatively to find a near-optimal solution.

7.3.11 Behavior, structure, and effectiveness measures

For this part of the example, assume that the dominating effectiveness measure is to bottle the wine as quickly as possible. If only one person is to perform this task manually, then the work of gathering items (Fig. 7.5) must be serialized.

There are 5 factorial or 120 ways to do this. One person using any of these 120 serialized sequences is a design, a mapping of the behavior onto a particular set of objects. This transformation of the intrinsic behavior into a design behavior does not alter the response of the system. Such transformations occur in the development of large, complex systems.

If you were an engineer working on a single component downstream from the initial serialization of a concurrency, you might have no idea that the sequence on which you were working was once a concurrency. If additional resource becomes available for incorporation into the design, it may be valuable to recover the intrinsic behavior and possible concurrencies. It is important to record and keep the information of the intrinsic behavior, the design behavior, and the issues and reasons for the transformations in going to design.

Intrinsic sequences may also be transformed to optimize effectiveness measures. If three people are available to bottle wine, then the sequential tasks may be done concurrently, by setting up a pipeline process:

1. Clean

2. Look

3. Fill

4. Cork

5. Label

Exactly how the pipeline is done depends on the length of time required for each task, the number of people or amount of resource available, and the effectiveness measures applied. In this case a reasonable architecture with three people is to have two people clean bottles because they must be filled and rinsed repeatedly, and have one person fill, cork, and label bottles. In complex systems quantitative trade-off is performed to make such decisions.

Note that a best practice of systems engineering work is to follow the steps of the core systems engineering process. One creates effectiveness measures, one creates an intrinsic behavior, and one examines sets of objects to perform the behavior. Which set of objects to use and how the behavior is apportioned among them is a matter of trade-off against a set of criteria. The result is an accepted architecture which encapsulates the design behavior, which is a transformation of the intrinsic behavior that meets needs and is allowed by reality.

If the effectiveness measures were altered, then the entire solution could change even with the same resource availability of three people. Consider the following altered effectiveness measures:

1. Have the best party possible.

2. Always have ongoing work to avoid criticism.

3. Bottle no more than 3 bottles of wine to serve as the "annual memorial wine bottles."

4. Drink the rest.

A potential solution is to have tasting taking place in parallel with every other step, a modification of the intrinsic behavior. Allocate no more than one person to work on bottling at any time. The wine bottling example has to this point illustrated the relevance of

- Intrinsic behavior imposed by nature.

- Design behavior, transforms of the intrinsic behavior to optimize the design.

- Emergent behavior, the behavior exhibited by the integrated system. It should be the design behavior.

- Concurrency in considering behavior, structure, and effectiveness measures.

- The semantic structures (functions, input/output, control) needed for behavior.

7.4   Scenarios and Response Threads as Paths through Behavior

It is often desirable, at any tier of development, to partition the creation of the behavior modeling to simplify the problem and distribute it among teams. The excitation and the response behaviors of complex systems often encompass many alternate parallel paths. One of the powerful techniques for simplification and distribution is to consider one by one the paths through the excitation behavior of the external systems. Each of these excitation paths is called a *scenario*. For each scenario there are one or more response paths from the system, depending on the conditions at the time of the excitation. Each of these response paths is called a *response thread*. The analysis of systems by the use of excitation scenarios and response threads is a powerful way to do the modeling described here and to partition the work among teams. It is also important to realize that the scenarios and response threads must merge into coherent and error-free behaviors which contain branch points that define all the alternative paths. When scenarios and responses are defined independently by separate groups of people, they can easily be defined such that they are incompatible.

A second technique for partitioning the modeling of systems with complex behavior first develops the "normal" behavior of the system—the behavior when everything goes right. After this has been done, the engineer considers each step in the behavior and how the behavior should be altered for safety, for reliability, and for all possible things that might go wrong (Carson, 1995). Common examples are recovery and rollback of computer-based systems after a system crash, vending machines that handle coins and slugs, and automobiles with safety belts and air bags.

7.5   Behavior, Context, and Traceability: An Information Model

This chapter has described how to model behavior, how behavior is related to context, and how traceability is maintained between text requirements and model elements. A simple example has illustrated the concepts. Figure 7.14 is a complex information model that summarizes these many pages of text on a single page. A complex model such as this has the disadvantage of carrying such a large amount of detail that it requires careful study for comprehension. It has the advantage of enabling the reader to see all the information on one page and to focus carefully on the detail in limited regions of the model while seeing how that region relates to the whole. The figure combines parts of earlier figures. The basic structure of behavior is shown without shading. The classification of requirements by how they are used is shown with dark shading; associations among context elements are shown with intermediate shading.

7.5.1   Explanation of the context region

Examine the object element in the top right part of Fig. 7.14. Every object is built from many other objects. This is shown by the recursive aggregation. Every object may play several different roles in the modeling of a complex system. The role of the object depends upon how the engineers view the object on the basis of what they are developing for the system. For example, an automobile engine is the subject system to the engine design team. The engine is a component to the automobile design team; it is an external system to the transmission design team. It is an output from the engine manufacturing facility, an input to the automobile assembly plant, and an input and output to the just-in-time logistics system that delivers parts to the assembly plant. A single object has all of these roles for different engineering teams.

Every subject system is interconnected with one or more external systems which excite it and to which it responds. The interconnection is called an *interface* and is often sufficiently important that it is considered to be an object, subject and external, and is fully documented. Both kinds of systems have attributes, and have a behavior.

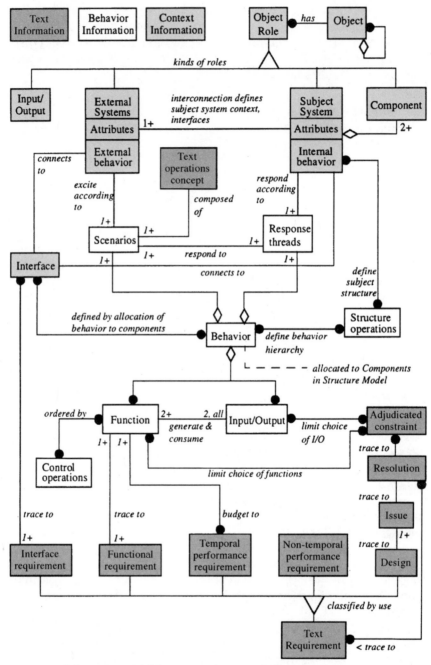

Figure 7.14 Information model for text requirements, behavior, and context.

7.5.2 Explanation of the behavior region

The behavior object is shown in the center of Fig. 7.14. As explained in earlier chapters, it is built from input/output and from function. The functions are ordered by control operations.

To simplify this already complex diagram, associations that define the control operations and that classify the input/output are not shown. Structure operations define the behavior hierarchy through a hierarchy of functions and of input/output. These are the same structure operations that are used to define the subject system structure. Each external system has or encapsulates an external behavior. That behavior can be decomposed into a set of many scenarios, each of which is an alternative path through the external behavior. Similarly, each subject system has or encapsulates an internal behavior. That behavior can be decomposed into a set of many response threads, each of which is an alternative path through the internal behavior of the subject system. For every scenario, there is one or more response threads. For each response thread, there is one or more scenarios that excite it.

7.5.3 Explanation of traceability and budgeting

Functional requirement traceability. The functional requirements trace directly to the functions which implement them.

Temporal performance requirement budgeting. The temporal performance requirements are time durations which must be met by entire response threads. When the temporal performance requirements are created, there is generally no knowledge of how many functions and what functions will implement the response. Consequently, the temporal performance requirements are usually a single time duration number or probability distribution that applies to an entire response thread. Because a number of functions will implement a response thread, the single number or probability distribution must be broken or budgeted into increments which are assigned to the individual functions.

How this budgeting is done depends on the details of the behavior, which functions are in parallel or in series. It can be done in advance of defining the structure, but it must be revisited and likely redone for each of the alternative design structures when they have been established and the functions mapped to the structures. It is most efficiently done when behavior creation and alternative structure creation proceed concurrently. A particular function might be assigned to a person, a machine, a slow computer, or a fast computer. The time to execute that function will depend on the choice made. Usually it is the overall response time of the response thread which is important and required rather than the time to complete any one function. It is very useful to create traceability links among scenarios, response threads, and temporal performance requirements when the latter are received in text form (White, 1994). This occurs naturally when the system is developed with models and the scenarios and response threads are executed to produce timelines based on the budgets assigned to the functions.

Nontemporal performance requirement traceability. These requirements trace to the attributes of objects in the structure model; they do not trace to elements in the behavior model.

Design and traceability. Often engineers receive design in the documents for requirements. This may happen because the system is constrained by other existing systems or by the realities of logistics, interoperability, or suppliers. Often, however, the imposed design is inappropriate and needs to be rewritten as a requirement. Because of this, these text statements are referred to as *design* rather than as *design requirements*. It is important to raise an issue with the source of the design statements, and develop a resolution to the issue. That resolution will throw the design statement away, will transform it into one of the other types of requirements, or will keep the design statement as an adjudicated constraint that dictates what will be used. It may dictate that a particular input/output, function, or object be used. The traceability links to objects appear in the information models for structure in Chap. 8.

Interface requirements. The interface requirements trace directly to the interfaces. They are critically important to ensure that components which are developed independently will integrate smoothly and to provide for interoperability.

7.6 Pitfalls in Developing Scenarios and Threads

When many engineers are developing the scenarios and response threads for the system and its context, it is very important that the scenarios and threads be aggregated into coherent behaviors or obtained by decomposing coherent behaviors. It is very easy to create sets of scenarios and response threads which cannot be combined coherently into a behavior and which will lead to integration problems when the system is built and assembled. There are techniques being used, such as *use case* development (Jacobson et al., 1992), which do not guarantee the compatibility of the scenarios and response threads. Neither do they support trade-off by keeping behavior and structure separate, but rather they inherently mix the two. They are efficient and useful in working through a single design alternative, but must be redeveloped if the structure is changed by adding or deleting objects, or by combining or subdividing objects. They are much more useful in software engineering where trade-off is less of a major issue than in systems engineering for which trade-off is a distinguishing best practice. When an executable behavior is allocated to a design, the use cases can be generated automatically by executing the behavior and tracking the individual paths.

7.7 Summary

How to create behavior models has been explained as a process and with a simple example. The important associations among the modeling elements have been described with information models and in text.

The examples have shown that the definition of effectiveness measures, the creation of behavior models, and the creation of structure models are closely related. Discoveries and new insights in any one of these activities has major implications for the others. They are concurrent activities. The effectiveness measures guide the engineers in efficiently creating the intrinsic behavior model that will meet marketplace needs.

Chapter 8 shows how the effectiveness measures guide the engineers in efficiently creating the structure models that record the selection of alternative components and structures which constitute design and architecture. It shows how the intrinsic behavior is transformed to a design behavior to match alternative designs.

7.8 Exercises

1. Create behavior models at the top level for the bottling supplies and storage facility objects in Fig. 7.2.
2. Link the two models above to the top-level models for winemaker (Fig. 7.3) and for wine bottling system (Fig. 7.13). Add any behavior elements needed. You will find it necessary to decide whether the wine bottling system makes requests which were not modeled in the book.
3. Create a parts list for the input/outputs of the wine bottling system (see Figs. 7.10 7.11). Consider in particular stored supplies and gathered supplies.
4. Consider all the changes found necessary to add to the top-level behavior of the wine bottling system. Propagate any changes needed into the second-level behavior of the wine bottling system (Fig. 7.13).
5. Introduce the necessary functions, branches, and conditions to add "Taste the wine" to Fig. 7.13.

6. Consider behavior relating to automobiles:
   a. Use the process in Fig. 7.1 to create a behavior model for the context level of an automobile.
   b. Create a behavior model for an engine.
   c. Compare the models developed in questions *a* and *b*. What changes are necessary to make the engine fit at a lower tier within the automobile?
7. Does the behavior shown in Fig. 7.13 adapt to an assembly line? Describe how it does or why it does not.

7.9 References

Carson, R. S., 1995: A set theory model for anomaly handling in system requirements analysis. *Fifth Annual International Symposium of the National Council on Systems Engineering,* vol. 1, pp. 515–522.

Jacobson, I., M. Christerson, P. Jonsson, and G. Overgaard, 1992: *Object-Oriented Software Engineering,* p. viii. Workingham (U.K.): Addison-Wesley.

White, S., 1994: Traceability for complex systems engineering. *Fourth Annual International Symposium of the National Council on Systems Engineering,* vol. 1, pp. 49–55.

8

Create Structure
Model

8.1   What Core Step 4 Is

Core step 4, create structure model, is the work done by engineers to create models of how things are built from parts, both physical and logical, and what parts to use. Professionals in different disciplines may prefer to call these models *design models, object models, information models,* or *architecture models.* The choice of terms is difficult because any single concept is often termed differently by the workers in different engineering disciplines, and the naming is important to the workers in each field.

With the advent and popularity of object-oriented software methodologies, the software engineering world is using concepts of abstraction of things (objects) and the encapsulation of behavior by objects, that have been practiced in mechanical, electrical, and other engineering professions for many years. It is critically important that the systems engineer be able to communicate rigorously with all the engineering disciplines by transforming the systems information into the views, representations, notations, and terms understood by each discipline. This chapter focuses on several aspects of structure modeling:

- A behavior model for the process of core step 4

- An example of selecting parts and creating a structure model

- An information model for core step 4

- How architecture and design are generated by the repeated core steps of systems engineering technical work

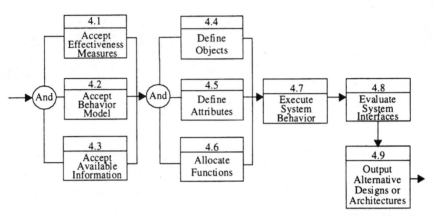

Figure 8.1   FFBD view of core step 4.

- How architecture is related to effectiveness measures and reusable components
- How design is simplified by architecture and reusable components

8.2   Creating Structure Models

Chapter 2 describes the basics of modeling structure. This chapter draws on those results to define the detailed steps involved in creating a structure model. The detailed steps are described in text, are made explicit with a model, and are illustrated with a simple example.

Figure 8.1 is a functional flow block diagram of an engineer's behavior in creating a structure model for the object or thing under consideration.

The first three steps in the engineer's behavior—4.1, 4.2, and 4.3—are concurrent and in general have no established order. The information already developed and being developed concurrently about effectiveness measures is accepted and interpreted in step 4.1. For the modeling of a particular subcomponent, some of the effectiveness measures may be unimportant and others important and requiring interpretation.

The information developed in prior and ongoing modeling of behavior is accepted in step 4.2 and used in this modeling of structure. The behavior information may describe the intrinsic behavior of an object as dictated by reality. It may be useful to transform this behavior as the structure modeling proceeds.

All the applicable available information is accepted and used in step 4.3. Often this includes text requirements and an operations concept which describe what the particular subcomponent must do. The available information may include adjudicated constraints that have been resolved with the originator of the requirements. The adjudicated constraints dictate or limit the choice of which objects to use.

The second set of three concurrent steps in Fig. 8.1 build the structures needed at this stage of the engineering.

Step 4.4 selects the objects that will be used from what is available in house, from supplier offerings, and from catalogs or libraries of parts. Usually there are several different sets of objects that might be used with different advantages for the different sets. To consider all the possibilities is very expensive in engineering resources. The alternatives are efficiently pruned to a moderate number by considering the effectiveness measures. When lowest possible cost is an effectiveness measure, for example, many expensive object choices can be rejected with little analysis. Several structure alternatives may need to be carried forward to trade-off analysis. The choices under consideration can be expressed directly in the modeling using *classification* to define the potential alternatives. This ability is very useful for later reuse of components and for very high levels of process automation with tools.

Step 4.5 defines the attributes of the objects. Steps 4.4 and 4.5 are not sequential. Defining the attributes will involve consideration of a number of objects and of the effectiveness measures. For example, in the development of a satellite, designing to minimum weight is an important effectiveness measure. Yet the physical weight of a custom high-speed integrated-circuit chip may be unimportant. However, the power consumption of the kinds of chips used may be very important to satellite weight because of the impact on power storage, solar energy arrays, and heat dissipation. The pertinent attributes are derived from the effectiveness measures and from the nontemporal performance requirements, many of which are expressed as equations with arguments. The attributes are the arguments of those equations. An attribute which does not affect effectiveness or performance is not needed. Every attribute that affects performance or effectiveness must be included for relevant objects.

Step 4.6 allocates functions (called *methods* in object-oriented software) to the objects. Often for physical objects the assignment of functions to objects is obvious and inflexible. A garbage disposal in the design of the kitchen is there to grind up garbage. However, some physical objects and especially people and computers are extremely flexible in what they can do. This does require that the people be trained and that the computers consist of both the hardware and software required for operation. Step 4.6 is concurrent with step 4.4, which identifies objects.

The behavior desired and the corresponding functions may be known before the objects are selected. The process of encapsulating functions in the objects often leads to discoveries that change the objects being used. Some of the most valuable of these discoveries occur during context analysis. They unexpectedly map behavior and objects out of the system and into the environment or move some object and its behavior from the environment into the system. They can result in major shifts in product performance and competitiveness. As the functions are assigned to the objects, interconnections among objects will be established.

When all three steps have been completed, the result is a set of alternative structures with an embedded and executable design behavior. The design behavior may be a transformation of the intrinsic behavior.

Step 4.7 is the execution of the structure of the designs, manually by engineers or automatically with a tool. It validates the design behavior. The execution will find problems such as deadlock or race conditions. It is at this point that time budgets can be assigned to each function with assurance that the time estimates are consistent with the properties of the object. The execution will generate an overall timeline for the designs. If this style of modeling has been carried out consistently during the development of the tree of parts that constitute the system, the timeline for a subcomponent can be studied for its impact on an overall response thread of the system to an external excitation. In many developments there is no deterministic time of completion for the functions, but probabilities of completion can be estimated for them. In such a case it is often possible to execute the behavior as a Monte Carlo calculation to generate a probability for overall success.

Step 4.8 uses the execution of behavior to evaluate the system interfaces both external and internal. This establishes the consistency of design with interface requirements. It is particularly useful in situations in which the magnitude of input/output is known and the rate of generation and consumption is known for functions. In these situations the flow at interfaces can be established once the design behavior has been demonstrated to be error-free in step 4.7. Wait times due to lack of input are established. Accumulation of output and storage of input are determined and can be correlated with the amount of storage capacity available or required.

The final step, 4.9, generates all the structure information needed for the engineering information base in the form required.

8.3   Example of Structure Development: Bottling Wine

Substantial information about the bottling wine system has been developed in Chaps. 6 and 7 and in the exercises. The effectiveness measures, requirements, context, and behavior have been described.

8.3.1   Requirements review

Effectiveness measures

1. Bottle wine at minimum cost.
2. Complete the bottling as quickly as possible.
3. Ensure that there is no foreign matter in the bottles of wine.
4. Bottle only good wine.

Nontemporal performance requirements

1. Number of bottles to be produced.
2. The system shall produce bottles of wine at a rate of up to 100 bottles of wine per day.
3. Material cost per bottle $1.00 or less.
4. Labor cost per bottle $1.00 or less.
5. Investment cost of $400.00 or less.

8.3.2   The first parts selection: define objects

The top-level selection among things to use for the wine bottling system is the choice between a manual system and a fully automated system as shown in Fig. 8.2.

Such a selection can be made only if the properties, attributes, of the objects are known (step 4.5) and can be compared with requirements. When the attributes are closely related to one or more of the requirements and when the differences make the choice clear (this case), then the choice can be made in core step 4. This efficiently prunes the total amount of engineering work to be done. Often, however, there are hundreds of parts involved and the relationships between requirements and attribute values are complex. In this case a full trade-off needs to be made (core step 5, described in Chap. 9).

It is nontemporal requirement 2 (above) that is compared to the properties of a manual versus automated system. The need is for only 100 bottles per day, which can be met with the manual system. The investment required for the manual system is substantially less, so it

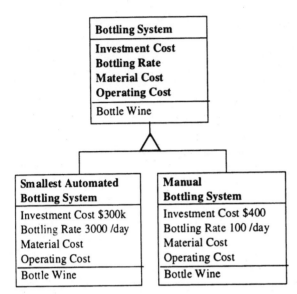

Figure 8.2 Top-level selection among objects.

is chosen. Information about the smallest automated system comes from suppliers of such systems. Other intermediate situations can exist, such as a requirement for bottling 1500 or 700 bottles per day, which require more detailed engineering analysis.

8.3.3 The first parts list or aggregation

It is necessary to determine all the parts that will make up the manual wine bottling system. Often many of these objects have been identified or considered during the ongoing development of behavior, and those results can add to the efficiency and completeness of this step. Figure 8.3 shows such a list.

Although better alternatives may be found, this list is adequate for this example. Investment cost is budgeted at $400. The parts listed in Fig. 8.3 are

One or more people (an appropriate number requires further analysis)

A dedicated kitchen which is assumed to be available at no additional cost

Bottle washing equipment

- One or more wash injector that forces hot water and low-suds detergent into bottle

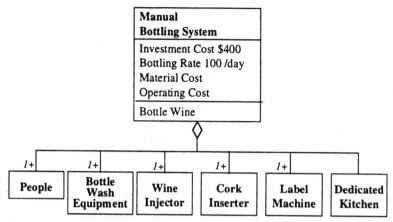

Figure 8.3   First parts list for manual wine bottling system.

- One or more powered brush to scrub the bottle
- One or more rinse injector to force rinse water into bottle
- One or more manual cork inserter to force cork into bottle
- One or more label moistener to wet the label, a damp sponge on a dish
- One or more labeling fixture to hold bottle and help position label
- One or more wine injector to pressurize the wine barrel and force wine into bottle

It is necessary to budget the investment cost to the parts in the figure as design targets, to find actual investment costs for them, and to sum the actual costs for comparison with the investment requirement. This calculation cannot be performed until the number of parts is found by trying different alternatives.

8.3.4 Allocate functions

To find the number of parts to use, we allocate the wine bottling functions to different numbers of people. The FFBD view of intrinsic behavior of the wine bottling system is repeated from Chap. 7 in Fig. 8.4 for use in this analysis.

Time estimates are needed for one person to do each of the tasks in the figure. These times can be summed to see if the desired bottling rate of 100 bottles per day can be met.

The best values for times or for attributes of objects are obtained by measurement of the activity or object. When this is not possible, sim-

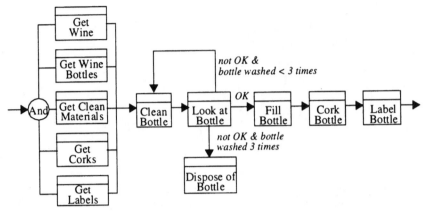

Figure 8.4 Modified FFBD for bottling wine.

ulation gives the next-best values. When that is not possible, estimates are made on the basis of related experience. Actual measurements should be made as early as possible in the development cycle to confirm budgets and estimates. Note that all the times given above would be different if automated equipment were to be used.

Time estimates for a manual bottling system

- Get wine barrel and prepare it: 30 min
- Get wine bottles: 30 min
- Get cleaning materials: 10 min
- Get corks: 5 min
- Get labels: 5 min
- Clean bottle: 3 min (filling with wash solution, brushing, and rinsing)
- Look at bottle: 0.25 min
- Fill bottle: 1 min
- Cork bottle: 0.5 min
- Label bottle: 0.5 min

Case 1: allocation to one person. If the functions shown in Fig. 8.4 are allocated to one person, then the five concurrent tasks that make up *gather materials* must be serialized; there are five factorial ways to do this, all of which take the same total time. The choice among these alternatives is not important to the system concerns, except for one important consideration.

Adding up the time estimates above for serialized tasks, gather supplies will take 1 h 20 min. What else does the person have to do in an 8-h day? Eat lunch, 30 min. Two work breaks of 10 min each. Clean up the kitchen at the end of the day of work. Note that these times were not included in the intrinsic behavior, and for a good reason. They are specific to people doing the work and are not required by an automated system. For this design solution they must be considered because they impact the work accomplished and the operating cost.

This is an example of discovery during the creation of structure that impacts creation of behavior. The time for cleanup at the end of the day is estimated at 30 min. Gathering supplies, lunch, two breaks, and cleanup take 2 h 40 min, leaving 5 h 20 min for bottling wine. Cleaning, filling, corking, and labeling one bottle takes 5.25 min. One person must perform this in series. One person can produce only 61 bottles per day. *This design is rejected as being not feasible.*

Case 2: Allocation to three people.   If the tasks for bottling wine are allocated to three people, there are a number of ways to make the assignment, one of which is shown in Fig. 8.5. The design also captures decisions as to how many pieces of equipment are made available.

Because we have the intrinsic behavior and time budgets or estimates for each step, we can manually execute the behavior for this assignment. This execution can be done automatically with an appropriate design capture tool. The top-level task *gather materials* is done by the three people in parallel.

- Person 1 takes 30 min to get wine
- Person 2 takes 30 min to get the bottles
- Person 3 takes 20 min to get the corks and labels
- The elapsed time for the task is 30 min

Cleanup at the end of the day is shared by all three, so that it takes 10 min. They take two 10-min breaks and a 30-min lunch at the same time. These activities take 90 min and leave 6 h 30 min for bottling wine. Cleaning and looking at the bottles is now done by two people at the same time so that the time per bottle is reduced from 3.25 to 1.63 min. Filling, corking, and labeling the bottles takes 2 min so that the total time per bottle is 3.63 min. The three people can bottle 107 bottles per day on this basis using only one set of equipment. This means that several pieces of bottle wash equipment must be shared by two people. Further modeling will show that this is readily done if they synchronize their activities. Such synchronized parallel resources

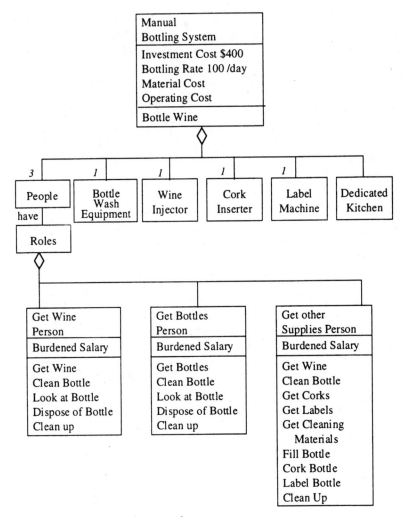

Figure 8.5 Allocation to three people.

are frequent solutions to system problems. An explicit model of this transformation of behavior is left as an exercise.

Case 3: the simplest allocation. A major problem in case 2 is that one of the persons must periodically wait for others to complete their tasks. This shows up directly in automatically generated timelines as wait periods. There are simpler and better feasible solutions than case 2. If only two people are applied and each person does all the functions on the same equipment, the throughput is better than the two previous cases. This solution is left as an exercise.

Case 4: allocation in the context of the problem. Very often the most important alternative allocations of functions to objects is done in the context of the problem. The critical question is whether any of the functions that were assigned to the wine bottling system could be done better by one of the external systems in the context. Sometimes imposed constraints prevent such allocation changes. In every case it is valuable to think creatively about the issue.

Cleaning the bottles takes appreciable time because they must be soaped, scrubbed, and rinsed. Some may not be clean after one cleaning. If clean bottles are obtained from bottling supplies, the cleaning step can be totally eliminated. The bottles need to be stored to stay clean with a provision to return to the supplier any that do not pass an inspection for cleanliness. In this case one person can produce about 160 bottles per day, two people 375 bottles, and three people 584 bottles. The cost of purchasing clean bottles and of keeping them clean in storage, as well as the storage itself, should be considered.

8.3.5 Interfaces among people

Where interfaces occur and what happens at the interfaces depends on how the functions are allocated among the objects.

In case 1, there are no interfaces among people. In cases 3 and 4, the people do not interact directly, but their activities must be synchronized because they share the same equipment for performing the bottling. When tasks are performed by people, they can be trained to synchronize their work using visual and voice cues. This is not the case for computers and machines, which require a resource with its own behavior to ensure synchronization. The synchronization can be based on broadcast timing as in the case of a coxswain calling the stroke for a crew team. It can be based on successive release of shared facilities as in this example. It can be based on quickly servicing demand as the demand occurs as in the case of several elevators serving the occupants of a building.

In case 2 there is a synchronization between two of the people and an interface between each of them and the third person who is filling, corking, and labeling bottles.

8.4 Information Model for Structure

The information model for structure is very similar to the information model for behavior illustrated in Chap. 7. The decomposition of behavior into input/output and function ordered by control operations has been deleted to simplify a complex diagram. Two structure items have been added: *attributes,* which are a part of every object description;

and *component interfaces,* which exist whenever objects are built from other objects. Both information models capture associations with context and with text requirements. In Fig. 8.6 the added structure items are more deeply shaded to facilitate finding them in the diagram.

The information item *component* has been moved to the middle right side of the figure. Component remains one of the roles which any object may take. A *subject system* is built from two or more components. Each component may, in turn, be assembled from two or more components. Behavior is allocated to the components and shown in the example in this chapter. The functional requirements are associated with the components because functions have been allocated to the components and the functions trace to the functional requirements. For any component, one can look up the functions it encapsulates. One can trace from these functions to the functional requirements they satisfy. One of the strong features of the modeling described here is that it enables one to reallocate functions among components and automatically maintain the traceability.

Temporal performance requirements budget to the functions encapsulated in the components. These budgets must be reexamined whenever the allocation to components is altered because different things have different capabilities in their speed of executing the same function. The components have attributes, and the nontemporal performance requirements such as cost, weight, reliability, power consumption, and memory size budget to the attributes in accord with an appropriate aggregation equation.

When *design* is found in the *text requirements,* an *issue* is raised with the originator of the design and a *resolution* is reached. One of the possible outcomes of that resolution is an *adjudicated constraint* which predetermines what components shall be used. Another outcome of the resolution is that the design was inappropriate and is reexpressed as a text requirement. In that case the resolution traces to text requirement.

8.5 Architecture and Design

The descriptions above show a repeated process for development of design or architecture, but do not indicate the conditions, circumstances, for developing architecture versus design. System designs produce a near-optimal solution for a particular system problem. Architectures produce a set of rules or constraints that limit design choices but lead to near-optimal designs for a whole family of system problems. Architectures define the invariant properties across a family of products: the aspects of design which will be the same for all members of the family. If one is building a grade school or a home for

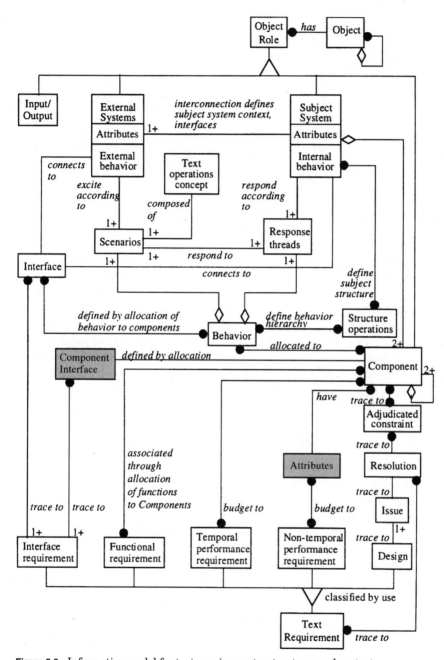

Figure 8.6 Information model for text requirements, structure, and context.

the elderly, specific and detailed designs (blueprints) are required for each building. Because both types of buildings need to provide safety and fast access to the outdoors in an emergency such as a fire, they may both be built to an architecture that dictates one floor construction with access to the outdoors from every classroom or patient room. Architectures provide constraints to structure and behavior that are near-optimal for a whole class of problems. Architectures deal with the relationships among classes of things and classes of behavior. Mainframe computers and client-server computer systems are two architectures for computer systems.

The same core technical systems engineering technical process is applied to model the many stages of complex system design or system architecture (see Table 8.1). What changes in developing architecture rather than design is not the process but what the process is applied to (Oliver, 1995).

Application of the core process in this fashion produces the requirements and designs for the parts tree for the system. The core process generates the parts tree, the interconnection information, behaviors (functional requirements), performance requirements, the response information needed for test and validation, and a build plan for each node of the parts tree. The things, components, and objects in the parts tree would be described as object instances by a software engineer. They are particular things selected because their property (attribute) values and their behaviors result in a near-optimal design solution as established by trade-off.

It is important to realize that the design space is very large, and that finding a near-optimal solution is complex. The algorithmic complexity of the problem has been shown to be *NP-complete* (Chapman and Rosenblit, 1995). This means that there is no known efficient algorithm for finding an optimal solution. As the problem size increases, the number of steps needed and the time required to solve the problem algorithmically may increase exponentially.

TABLE 8.1   Application of Core Process for Design

Applied to	Generates
Business using product (concept analysis)	Business design and value of product segments
Product (system analysis and design)	Product design and subsystem requirements
Subsystems (subsystem analysis and design)	Subsystem design, sub-subsystem requirements

Engineers solve such complex problems by restricting the components or objects to be considered to a limited set which are either available from suppliers or can be designed and built at acceptable cost and risk. They further simplify the problem by restricting the manner in which the components or objects behave and are interconnected. The description of these behavioral and structural restrictions is what we call an *architecture*. Architectures describe the kinds of components or objects to be used and how the kinds of components or objects are interconnected.

Note the words "kind of" in the last sentence. An architecture may typically call for interconnection by bus structures or by point-to-point wiring. There are many instances of busses and of point-to-point wiring. The word "bus" as used here is a class name. It is a generalization of more specific bus classes such as PCI bus or VME bus. Architectures can usefully be described with classes and class relationships. Designs become particularizations of the architecture.

Table 8.1 describes design, but does not illuminate how architectures are developed. Both architectures and reusable components or object classes are the result of domain analysis (Oliver, 1995). What differs between design development and architecture development is what the core process is applied to (see Table 8.2).

Domain analysis is the process of analyzing the application of a product to a collection of businesses. It establishes the value of the product and its major segments to the businesses. It results in a modification of the businesses, a new architecture for them with the product in place. It establishes that all the product is valuable to the businesses or that particular segments of the product are of benefit to them all. If only particular segments of the product are of value across the businesses, it will be important to make the major product subsystems match the valuable product segments. One can then produce and deliver to each business the product segments of value to that business at minimum production cost. The structure of a good ar-

TABLE 8.2   Application of Core Process for Architecture

Applied to	Generates
Collection of businesses using product or product segments (domain analysis)	Business designs and common product or product segments of high value across businesses or time
Common products or segments (architecture analysis and design)	Common product architecture and reusable products or segments/components

chitecture is driven from an analysis of value to a collection of businesses or buyers.

Examples of this are both common and plentiful. If one wants to buy a car (class) and has selected a particular brand and model (subclass of car), one can still select a six-cylinder engine (subclass of engine) from the available kinds of engine (class) depending on the performance or the economy that is desired by a user. A good architecture for automobiles gives the buyers choice in automobile performance and operating cost because that choice has value to the buyer for the buyer's use or business. Although this use of "class" and "instance" may appear to be a trivial renaming of common ideas, it is not trivial but rather an important distinction between the concepts of class and instance, and aggregation and classification, which are blurred or absent in much engineering work. By using these concepts and abstractions rigorously, both the system models and the descriptions of the systems engineering process can be made rigorous. If rigorous, they can be automated and executed by computer, and then information can be transmitted by systems engineers to the other engineering disciplines without error and ambiguity.

8.6   Architecture, Applications, Effectiveness Measures, and Reuse

When architectures are evolved from market experience or developed from effective domain analysis, they endure for an appreciable time. Over time the architectures will change. Many businesses have remained locked to a formerly effective architecture and have suffered severe business contraction by not moving to appropriate new architectures in their product as rapidly as competition. In the computer world mainframes, multitasking operating systems, minicomputers, and client/server systems serve as examples. It is useful to list major factors that drive architecture and its change:

1. The general behavior required by a domain of application

2. The effectiveness measures

3. The kinds of objects available for the application domain; the available classes for architecture.

Pyle et al. (1993) have developed a useful taxonomy for real-time systems that classifies applications according to the general behaviors that are required. Five primary features with binary values define 32 primary classes of applications.

The effectiveness measures drive the architecture solution. If availability is a high-priority effectiveness measure, and if the hardware components have individual failure rates too high to meet the availability, then a redundant architecture with software to detect failure and provide recovery will be necessary. This effectiveness measure will have to be prioritized against other parameters such as cost and weight.

The effectiveness measures also change over time. In early phases of the introduction of medical x-ray computerized tomography (CT) imaging equipment, the product architecture was driven by performance (image quality and dose to patient), throughput, and field service. Hospitals with such a machine were at state of the art. As CT machines became standard equipment in hospitals, architectures meeting acceptable performance and low cost became important. In latter phases of the market where sales were saturating, field service and availability dominated and automated remote machine diagnostics impacted the architecture.

Over time there were major changes in the available components from which to synthesize systems. In the case of x-ray CT systems these changes overlapped the changes in effectiveness measures. Computer hardware shifted from minicomputers to microcomputers. New bus options became available and software could be distributed.

Application of the systems engineering technical process provides for modeling of all of these factors and trade-off among the options.

8.6.1 Design simplification with architecture

Design work is made efficient by using the architectural models and a limited set of component choices to prune the design solution space, shorten the design process, and produce similar and consistent designs over several product developments and releases. For a feasible design, all the requirements must be met in addition to the effectiveness measures. For a near-optimal design the specific objects chosen to include in the design must result in near-optimal values for the effectiveness measures.

The critically important factors for developing the design are

1. The architecture to be used.

2. The specific emergent behavior required by the specific application.

3. The effectiveness measures for the specific application at a particular time in the market evolution.

4. The kinds of objects available for the specific application; the available classes for design. They are limited by the state of technology and change over time with technical advancement.

8.7   Summary

The process for creating structure models has been described as a behavior and illustrated with an example. It proceeds concurrently with the definition of effectiveness measures and the creation of behavior models. Alternative mappings of the desired emergent behavior onto alternative sets of components generate alternative designs and architectures.

The number of possible designs and architectures, the solution space, is very large. The general problem is NP-complete. For efficient engineering, it is important to prune down the number of choices to be considered without loosing the best alternatives. Effectiveness measures help guide this pruning during the work. The application of established architectures prunes the work.

Architectures are developed with the same technical systems engineering process that applies to design. In developing architecture the process is applied to a domain—to a collection of businesses and the product and product segments that have value across the businesses. The same process is used to create designs, but it is applied to a specific application—a specific business and the product that has value to that business.

The three concurrent core steps—define effectiveness measures, create behavior model, and create structure model—together result in design or architecture alternatives. Quantitative trade-off is used to select among these alternatives. Trade-off is the subject of the next chapter.

8.8   Exercise

1. Work through case 3 from Sec. 8.3.4. Is it as productive as the use of three people as assigned in case 2?
2. Consider the rewashing of bottles that are not clean after the first pass. Create appropriate attributes for the object bottle. How many attributes are needed? Assume a set of numbers for the attributes, and estimate the impact on productivity of rewashing bottles. Estimate the cost of rewashing versus the savings in bottles.
3. Create a design behavior for case 2. Allocate to three people. Include the synchronization of the two people cleaning and inspecting bottles. Draw a timeline for each of the persons.
4. Modify Figs. 7.2 and 8.3 to define case 4, which allocates cleaning the bottles to the external systems (the context).
5. Develop a structure model for a system for baking cookies. Use a recipe from a cookbook as the behavior model.
    a. Decide what the boundaries (context) of the system will be.
    b. Develop objects for the system.

   c. Allocate the behavior to the objects.

   d. Develop attributes for the objects.

6. Consider a caveperson throwing rocks to kill an animal and a missile defense system. Develop a structure description to represent both of these systems.

7. Describe the relationship of functional requirements to behavior (see Fig. 8.6).

8. Give three examples of product lines that have experienced stable architectures for 10 or more years.

9. Give three examples of businesses that failed because they did not adapt their architectures.

8.9   References

Chapman, W. L., and J. Rosenblit, 1995: Complexity of the system design problem. *International Symposium and Workshop on Systems Engineering of Computer Based Systems* (Tucson, Ariz., 1995), pp. 51–57 (IEEE#95TH8053).

Oliver, D. W., 1995: Systems engineering & software engineering, contrasts and synergies, *Fifth Annual International Symposium National Council on Systems Engineering* (St. Louis, Mo.), vol. I, pp. 701–708.

Pyle, I., P. Hruschka, M. Lissandre, and K. Jackson, 1993: *Real Time Systems,* Chichester (U.K.): Wiley.

9

Perform Trade-off Analysis

9.1 What Core Step 5 Is

Core step 5, perform trade-off analysis, is the work done by engineers to choose among the alternative designs or architectures that emerge from the three preceding modeling steps. It is the effort that establishes that a design meets both the functional and performance requirements and is feasible. It is the work that selects from among the several possible feasible designs or architectures the one most nearly optimal for the marketplace.

The output from trade-off is the selected design or architecture that will be implemented. Architecture and design exist at every tier of the system parts tree. A useful, high-value product can impact and alter the architecture and design of the business that incorporates it. An architecture and design also exist for the system, its subsystems, subsubsystems, etc. The architectures and designs for different parts may be radically different. The choices among designs and architectures for each part of the system are based on the impact of that part on the system performance and effectiveness, not on part performance and effectiveness. Values for the important attributes of the parts must be known to calculate impact of the part on the system. This chapter focuses on several aspects of trade-off:

- A behavior model for the process of core step 5
- Complete identification and specification of attributes of objects
- Performance calculated from the attributes of objects or obtained from survey

- Physical measurement, simulation, and estimation to get attribute values
- Calculation of performance of each alternative
- Calculation of effectiveness for each alternative
- The trade-off decision
- An information model for trade-off
- A discussion of tools and automation of the process

9.2   Trade-off

The FFBD that refines step 5, perform trade-off analysis, is shown in Fig. 9.1. The inputs to this step from earlier steps have been described. They provide a complete executable description of the design or architecture alternatives. They define all the performance requirements and effectiveness measures, the defining equations, and the attributes needed to evaluate the equations. What is missing are the values of the attributes. Both the values of the attributes and the variances in the values are needed. Information is accepted in steps 5.1 through 5.3. In step 5.4, one or more of the alternatives is selected and then evaluated in steps 5.5 through 5.11.

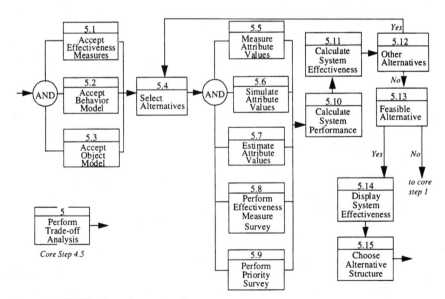

Figure 9.1   FFBD view of core step 5.

9.2.1 Values of attributes

The values of the attributes are obtained by measurement, physical simulation, and estimation. As a project evolves, the level of detail increases, and hardware and software are produced, it is possible to improve accuracy by replacing estimates with simulation, and simulation with measurement.

Measurement. The best values of attributes for calculation of system performance and effectiveness are obtained by measurement of the attributes on components produced under production conditions with production tooling. Modern systems have been built on aggressive schedules with 80 percent of the hardware built in this manner and tested as components prior to first assembly and test (Reugg et al., 1993). Measurements on prototypes or brass boards are somewhat less reliable because of the influence of actual production conditions.

Simulation. When parts are not available for measurement or when the measurement process is expensive or time-consuming, attribute values can be calculated by simulation. The results are valid only if the simulation technique has been verified to be accurate by comparison of simulation results with actual measurements. In some cases the simulations are not sufficiently accurate for absolute values of attributes, but can be used effectively to interpolate between more expensive measurements.

The simulations used in step 5.6 for these purposes are based on the equations of physics, chemistry, biology, materials science, communications engineering, computer science, etc. They very often use numerical techniques to account for complex boundary conditions. They simulate the physical and logical reality of the components. They are not the executions of behavior models discussed earlier.

Estimation. When neither measurement nor simulation is possible, one resorts to estimation. The need for estimation declines as work progresses. The very best available engineering experience needs to be used for estimation. People are generally consistent in their estimates. However, some people habitually estimate high, some on target, and some low. It is important to track the sources of the estimates and compare them to historical data. Multiple estimates for the same attribute are developed with survey techniques.

The values for attributes improve as the development proceeds. Preproduction prototypes are often hand-assembled by very knowledgeable craftspersons. Parts may have been hand tooled and adapted to fit the evolving design without all the information incorporated in the system design models. For software, alpha test quality often does not include all the rigorous features of production software. Portions may be stubbed out, and vital areas such as error recovery may be incomplete. Any of these conditions can affect the results of measurements on components and the system. It is necessary, therefore, to compare current results with prior values used in trade-off analysis. If large discrepancies occur, they must be tracked down and explained. If the discrepancies persist, the prior trade-offs need to be reexamined.

9.2.2 Survey

Some of the alternative components that are defined during the development of designs and architectures need to be selected on the basis of user, operator, or owner preferences. The important criteria are appearance, feel, sound, ease of use, etc. This work is carried out in step 5.8, perform effectiveness measurement survey. It is carried out for those components which are important to prioritized effectiveness measures and which are selected on the basis of preference.

The development of complex systems often spans a number of years. There may be an appreciable passage of time between the early prioritizing of effectiveness measures in core step 2 and the definition of the major design and architecture alternatives for trade-off. It is often desirable to repeat the prioritizing of effectiveness measures in step 5.9 with a selected survey group which has been shown the alternative designs and architectures. Because these efforts determine acceptance in the marketplace, it is important to get them correct. It is also important to change them only occasionally to prevent excessive change in requirements during the development.

The techniques described in Chap. 6, like the analytical hierarchy process, are used to perform the surveys of preference and priority to get quantitative and useful results.

9.2.3 Calculate system performance

The earlier core steps—(2) define effectiveness measures, (3) create behavior model, and (4) create object model—have defined the performance equations and the attributes which are their arguments. As attribute values are obtained, the performance is calculable for any of the candidate designs at any level of parts hierarchy. Feasibility of a candidate design is shown when its calculated performance meets or exceeds the system-level requirement. The calculation of system performance, step 5.9, from the parts tree and the attributes of the components can be automated when the design is captured in executable models.

9.2.4   Iterate

If no design meets the specified system performance, then one iterates. Alternatively, one relaxes some of the requirements, or the project is abandoned as being infeasible.

9.2.5   Calculate system effectiveness

System effectiveness measures are calculated in the same manner as is performance. These measures are calculated only for those candidate designs that are feasible, which meet performance requirements. Automated calculation using the parts tree, structure information where required, defined attributes, and defined equations provides a major savings in time and cost.

9.2.6   Other alternatives

If any design and architecture alternatives have not been evaluated, the process returns to step 5.4.

9.2.7   Display system effectiveness

Often there are 3 to about 10 effectiveness measures which depend on a number of attributes of hundreds or thousands of parts in complex and nonlinear ways. There is the choice of examining the impact of the design alternatives on the set of effectiveness measures, or of combining the effectiveness measures into a single cost function with weighting factors. The advantage of the single cost function is that it provides a single number on which to base the selection of the design to be used. The advantage of examining the set of individual effectiveness measures and how they vary with alternatives is that one can see where the sharp maxima and minima occur and where the broader maxima and minima occur. It is sometimes prudent to select a somewhat less optimal design if maxima vary slowly with attributes so that the tolerances required on the attributes can be large.

There are a number of convenient ways to display the effectiveness measure results. If the alternatives are discrete, use component A or B or C, then a table, a bar graph or a spreadsheet can capture much of the information, (Ghassemi et al., 1994). If the alternatives are continuous, like a weight or a physical dimension, then multidimensional graphs can be plotted using visualization tools. A variety of techniques are available to look at multivariate data. Three-dimensional geometry, color, shape, motion, and spatial positioning can all be used to represent different aspects of the data.

Several quality methodologies such as *house of quality* and *quality function deployment* (Clausing, 1994) define views which capture this type of information.

9.2.8 Choose alternative structure

The choice of a design solution based on effectiveness often requires consensus among management, customers, and other stakeholders.

9.3 Information Model

Four objects, which are shaded in Fig. 9.2 were added to the earlier model (Fig. 6.10) to account for performance as well as effectiveness. These objects include nontemporal performance requirements and the nontemporal performance equations from which they are calculated. They include temporal performance requirements and the timelines that are compared to them.

Simulation, measurement, and estimation provide values for the attributes of the components. Nontemporal performance equations use the attribute values as arguments of equations that calculate the performance of the system. The calculations rely on the parts tree and, in some cases such as reliability or moment of inertia, on system structure. The calculated values are compared with the required values of performance at system level to establish feasibility of the system.

The temporal performance requirements are response times that must be met by the system. When the behavior and structure are captured in executable models, they can be executed by an execution engine to produce overall system timelines. The timelines are the response threads through the system based on the individual response times or response-time probabilities for the components. The execution engine can be a computer tool or a team working manually. The manual work is time-consuming and difficult to maintain error-free.

The many different physical simulations which must be performed to obtain attribute values for trade-off require many different sophisticated modeling tools, such as those for stress, heat transfer, fluid flow, crack propagation, chemical reaction, communications fidelity, and logic evaluation and design. Their inputs are related to the information stored in the system modeling tools, and they provide attribute values needed by the system modeling tools. In addition, there are text generation and text requirement management tools. The present situation is described below.

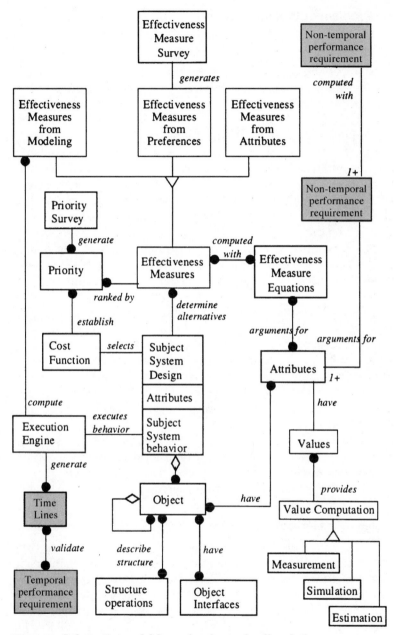

Figure 9.2 Information model for performing trade-off analysis.

9.4 The Problem of Tool Integration

Multiple tools exist for managing the initial information, for the behavior and structure modeling, for rollup of attribute values to performance and effectiveness, and to perform the surveys. Powerful visualization tools exist to capture multidimensional tradeoff results and to display them to management, users, and customers. There are tools for risk analysis and scheduling and for configuration management of all the information. There are many tools for physical simulation of components. Most of these tools have been developed independently and do not communicate with one another. The integration of the tools into an environment is presently left to the engineering organization buying the tools. Integrating a large number of tools with tailored binary interfaces results in costly maintenance as the tools are independently revised by their vendors.

The problem is difficult because the same named piece of information is not used with the same meaning in different tools, the data structures are defined differently, the systems for managing data are different, and many tools provide no access to their stored data. It is a matter of engineering to reconcile the data structures and data management systems. More difficult is the lack of any accepted guide to the information required to do systems engineering and specific unique meanings for each piece of information. It is a vision of this book that metaprocess descriptions of systems engineering described in executable models can provide rigorously defined information and become a basis for tool evolution into integrated environments. The metaprocess definitions must come from systems engineering professionals.

Similar steps have been taken in mechanical engineering and in digital engineering to make possible the integration of design tools and manufacturing tools. Feasibility of the tool integration has been demonstrated in these other fields after certain prerequisites have been met.

9.4.1 Prerequisites for tool integration

There are a number of fruitful approaches and architectures, like CORBA, DCE, and PCTE, to implement tool integration (Epperson, 1994). None of these approaches can succeed unless the work to be done is well defined so that functionality is consistent across the tools. None of these approaches can succeed unless the information items are treated with consistent meaning in all the tools. Prerequisites for automation of systems engineering with an integrated toolset are

1. A well-defined engineering process captured in executable models.

2. A set of information models for each step in the process.

3. A rigorous implementation standard for exchange of data. Several exist (Epperson, 1994).

Without this information, tool vendors automate particular methodologies which are incompatible with one another, make different semantic assumptions about entities given the same name, and have no available standard for creating interfaces among tools. With the information presented above, the following is possible:

1. Comparison of the different systems engineering methodologies in use.

2. Automation of the metaprocess so that the views and notations needed for different systems engineering methodologies can be generated and projected from an abstract model stored in the tool. Multiple views are consistent by generation from the data in an abstract model.

3. Generation of detailed requirements and specification in executable form in the views and notations of the downstream engineering disciplines.

4. Maintenance and enhancement of large systems by modifying requirements in models and regenerating the downstream details. This is much less costly than changing downstream detail directly, and it maintains system documentation throughout the maintenance and enhancement cycle. It eliminates future reverse engineering.

5. Integrated toolsets that span the systems engineering work.

6. Ability to search the architecture solution space or the design solution space semiautomatically by specifying search rules and evaluating effectiveness reports. This is the efficient way to develop new-product releases based on product already in the market. It has been applied in other fields.

9.4.2   A comparison with mechanical engineering evolution

Mechanical engineering and some of the other engineering disciplines predate systems engineering and as a result have evolved further. They have gone through stages of development, documentation, and automation that systems engineering is just entering. It is instructive to look at analogies with these older disciplines as a means of understanding the stages through which systems engineering is likely to pass

Rigorous capture of details.   Mechanical engineering must capture the details and the tolerances of three-dimensional geometry; it must describe parts accurately. The English language alone is inadequate. For all but the simplest cases, systems engineering must capture the needs of users and describe the behavior and structure of a system that will meet those needs. Natural language alone is inadequate to handle the detail. Mechanical engineers accomplish this through the application of a drafting process that allows engineers to define objects in three dimensions using three orthogonal views. Any other rotated view can be derived from the three by mathematical and graphic techniques. The foundations were described in 1801 in *La Geometrie Descriptive,* by Gaspaard Monge. Systems engineering has not yet agreed on a rigorous definition of process, the information captured at each step, and a language for expressing systems work.

Automation. Mechanical engineering was initially automated in the 1960s and 1970s with the advent of minicomputers. Companies like Applicon, Gerber, and Computer Vision provided tools to capture geometry. But these tools could not communicate with one another or with the many tools in manufacturing which must capture the design geometry and modify or transform it. The manufacturing tools create machine tool cutting paths, geometry for fixtures, allowances for part shrinkage during sintering, and so on.

The need for an integrated set of tools led to the formation of professional organizations dedicated to defining the semantics and information required for geometry definition and transformation. These efforts were stalled for many years until the definitions began to be written in computer-executable form. The language chosen for this was Express; other languages could have been chosen. With the rigor of executability, it has been possible to create the STEP/PEDES standards and for vendors to develop tools which can be integrated into an environment. Major aircraft have now been designed by Boeing with automated geometry transfer (Norris, 1995).

Systems engineering needs to provide detailed information to other engineering disciplines in their own languages and notations which are and will remain inconsistent with one another and consistent with their own traditions. It must provide information to the product stakeholders—operators, users, managers, marketing, customers, etc.—in forms that they can understand. It is essential that there be rigor in the systems information and automated transformation to the tools of the other disciplines and product stakeholders. This will require rigorous process and information models for systems engineering to be followed by the development of integrated environments.

Semiautomated search of the system design space. Both systems engineering and mechanical engineering share the need to find near-optimal solutions to complex problems. Mechanical engineering often deals with complex part boundaries and must perform complex analyses that involve stress, temperature distribution, materials properties, and part fatigue. The solution of such problems has traditionally required the iterative solution of the analysis using separate sophisticated finite element tools for each of the disciplines—thermal, stress, etc. In recent years it has been possible to integrate such toolsets into an environment. Associated with the environment is a set of search tools combining analytical, rule-based, and heuristic optimization techniques (Ashley, 1992). An engineer prescribes the initial part shape and boundary conditions, then prescribes rules for conducting a design space search and for modifying the part boundary based on search results, and then monitors the alternative part shapes and effectiveness factors such as cost, weight, and reliability as produced by the analysis of the environment. The engineer does a maximum of thinking and exploration and a minimum of manual labor.

Typical time values for manual and automated system solution searches are listed in Table 9.1.

The capture of system designs in executable models in an integrated toolset is a necessary prerequisite for any automated search capability. The use of COTS products, reusable components, and new components with defined properties and behavior means that semiautomated generation of system design alternatives and their effectiveness is possible. The payoff in reduced cost of development and in time to market is large. Today this remains a research problem, a vision, which can be approached only by first achieving rigorous capture of details for the engineering process and for products, and by creating integrated tool environments.

TABLE 9.1   Comparison of Manual and Automated Searches for System Solutions

Project and number of parameters varied	Manual time	Automated time
Aircraft engine preliminary design, 100 parameters	10 weeks	1 week
Molecular structure design, 150 parameters	1 week	0.5 day
Cooling fan design, 18 parameters varied	8 weeks	0.5 day
DC motor design, 70 parameters	2 weeks	0.25 day
Power supply design, 35 parameters	3 weeks	10 h
Nuclear fuel lattice design, solution space $\sim 10^{10}$	1 week	2 days
Aerodynamic and mechanical design of turbine blades, 700 parameters and 36 different engineering codes (tools)	12–24 months	2–4 weeks

TABLE 9.2   Two Architectures

Architecture 1			Architecture 2		
Weight	Speed	Size	Weight	Speed	Size
102	654	3	90	511	5
14	876	3	26	934	1
44	521	2	56	634	1
8	783	1	20	945	1
65	981	5	53	546	4
80	501	3	68	782	3
21	619	4	33	682	3
11	789	3	24	833	2
38	838	1	50	934	4

9.5 Exercises

1. Develop a structure diagram for measurement. Include information describing how the measurement is taken.

2. Describe the relationship between effectiveness measure equations to cost functions (see Fig. 9.2).

3. Consider two tools used in design: the first a text editor and the second, a diagraming tool. What problems are used when the tools are used together?

4. Give an example of three or more tools which were designed to work together. What features enable them to work together?

5. Select a display technique which highlights the differences between architectures 1 and 2 in Table 9.2.

6. Would the display used in question 5 work if there were hundreds of values for each architecture?

9.6 References

Ashley, S., 1992: Engenious explores the design space. *Mech. Eng.* **114**(Feb.), 49.

Clausing, D. P., 1994: *Total Quality Development.* ASME Press.

Epperson, R. E., 1994: Integration strategies and technologies for computer-assisted systems engineering environments. *Fourth Annual International Symposium, National Council on Systems Engineering* (San Jose, Calif., Aug.), vol. I, pp. 913–920.

Ghassemi, K., E. Conway, and J. Hines, 1994: System modeling through parametric spreadsheet analysis. *Fourth Annual International Symposium National Council on Systems Engineering* (San Jose, Calif., Aug.), vol. I, pp. 433–439.

Norris, G. 1995: Boeing's seventh wonder. *IEEE Spectrum* (Oct.) 20–23.

Reugg, R. G., K. J. Field, and B. Boldblatt, 1993: Design for manufacturability/affordability—the F414 story. *Defense Manufacturing Conference* (San Francisco, 1993), vol. II, pp. 97–109.

10

Create Build-and-Test Plan

10.1 What Core Step 6 Is

Core step 6, create build-and-test plan, is the creation of a plan for how the subject system shall be built. It takes into account realities of time to market and needed competitive features, available resource for implementation, technical risk, time risk, schedule risk, procurement times, subcontracting, the involvement of partners, test, and validation. The plan is based on the engineering information that describes the chosen design or architecture emerging from core step 5, perform trade-off analysis. A detailed description of systems engineering planning with useful examples and lists has been published (Blanchard and Fabrycky, 1990).

The development of the plan includes both management and technical issues. It must schedule the work such that results are obtained when needed and resource is applied when needed; these are management issues. The results scheduled are outputs of the technical work which require technical knowledge both for their identification and for realistic estimates of effort for their development, technical issues. Both management and engineering need to contribute to core step 6. It is a step in the core technical process because it is paced by and requires the outputs from the preceding core steps. Development of the next tier of the system needs to proceed with the management and technical information from the build-and-test plan from the tier above.

The build-and-test plan is developed for the subject of interest at each tier of development. The engineering team may be working at the context tier where the subject of interest is the business using the product. They may be working at the system tier, where the subject of interest is the product. They may be working at the subsystem tier, where the subjects of interest are the major segments of the product. A build-and-test plan is created at each tier.

At each tier there are time-to-market issues and risk issues. At each tier there may be a discovery of a needed capability not within the scope or competence of the organization or of an unanticipated business opportunity that requires the cooperation of another business. At each tier there may be a discovery of items which need to be procured or developed by a subcontractor. As the program moves through the development phases, the build-and-test plan is refined to encompass the increasing amounts of detail needed for the increasing number of subsystems and components.

There are test issues at each tier which are fully resolved up front by the modeling of the core technical process. The models produced by the core technical steps produce the excitation scenarios and product response threads that are needed for validation and test. At the context tier the modeling specifies the test excitations and product responses that will validate that the product works in the business. At the system tier the modeling specifies the excitations and responses that must be met by the product segments. When modeling is applied to the development, both validation and test begin at the beginning of the effort and are integral with the system development. This relationship makes it straightforward to include design-for-test into the development and to create a regression test suite for use at each tier of development. The build-and-test plan shows the schedule for builds and for testing. It shows the interconnection between the engineering that creates behavior and structure models, and the actual incorporation of the behavior information into a test suite.

The schedule for builds may be based on several different considerations. The plan may schedule building the smallest components, and then combining them into larger and larger assemblies until the system is complete and validated. For very large systems with long development times, the schedule may call for partial builds of many components and subsystems so that portions of the system may be assembled, validated early for particular response threads, and even applied in the field by selected users to try out critically important system features. These choices are driven by business realities. They may result in incremental release of functionality to the marketplace, a multigenerational product plan.

Early builds of particular components can be executed for early assessment, or to reduce risks. This is a form of prototyping controlled by a defined process and path.

10.2   Creating a Plan

The creation of a plan involves the specification of a set of tasks, the ordering of the tasks, the inputs and outputs for each task, a selection among existing resources to do the work, assignment of tasks to resources, and time and performance conditions to be met (especially cost). This is the problem of creating a system. The problem of creating a plan is the same as for any other system: product development, process development, or business reengineering (Wymore, 1993). It has the same complexity, NP-complete, as other system developments (Chapman and Rosenblit, 1995). Automated computation of the optimal plan is limited by this complexity. Heuristics and human guidance must often be used to develop a sound plan.

Simple plans for small projects often involve only modest resource constraints, few or no alternative paths, and a need for completion within a specified reasonable time. Such plans can be developed readily with software that displays the critical path through the plan, slack times for the resources, and resource utilization.

The plans for large, complex systems involve multiple constraints, time limits that are difficult to meet, severe resource limits, and a complex set of alternative paths needed for mitigation of identified risks. Such plans require considerable iteration and effort to find an acceptable solution. They can be developed with the available planning tools mentioned above with some difficulty and iteration or with the core technical process and systems engineering tools. Systems engineering tools have not traditionally provided support for scheduling. They are likely to lack automated response to queries such as "what is the critical path."

The development of such complex plans is facilitated when they are produced iteratively as described here. High-level schedules and decisions are made as early as possible. These are refined and adjusted as more technical detail about the system is developed. This practical approach is often heuristic, using tools and algorithmic techniques as an aid.

10.2.1   Network scheduling approaches

Network approaches to planning consider the project plan to be an ordered set of independent tasks which may be represented as a network. The ordering operations include the precedence of tasks, concurrency of tasks when several follow a preceding task, and iteration. Any set of successive tasks through the plan is considered to be a path (corresponding to a response thread). Time estimates for the tasks are associated with each task. The time for all paths is computed, and the path with the longest time is noted. It is the critical path. The critical path limits when the project will be completed. A reverse computation is then performed for all other paths, and the slack time is found for each task. Resource utilization can then be shown.

These approaches and the supporting tools may or may not include provision for representing alternative branching in the network in addition to and distinct from concurrency. Such alternatives are vital when risk and its remediation are considered. For risk remediation, an alternative set of tasks is defined that begin a new direction for work if a high-risk part of the development does not show sufficient progress within a prescribed time or resource expenditure.

Program evaluation and review technique (PERT).   PERT is one of the algorithmic techniques which treats the plan like a network. It incorporates uncertainty in the time estimates into the analysis. This is done by assigning optimistic, likely, and pessimistic times in the estimates for completion of each task. Mean and standard deviation are estimated for completion of the project and for each task. Slack times are computed. Algorithmic solutions and tools to support them exist for PERT.

Critical path method (CPM).   CPM deals with issues of finite resource and modification of resource assignments. The tasks on the critical path become candidates for increase of resource. In fields such as the construction industry, this may be accomplished with premium payment for finishing tasks early. CPM supports the allocation of resource to control completion time. Algorithmic solutions and tools to support them exist for CPM.

10.2.2   Resource allocation

In engineering and in research it is sometimes the case that the time limiting tasks in the critical path require special talent that is limited in availability. It may or may not be possible to increase resource for particular tasks. Sometimes the cost increase of special talent must be balanced against the increased technical risk if the resource is not added. A critical talent may have to be shared across more than one program. Task precedence may be coupled to available talent and cost. The assumption of task independence that underlies many of the algorithmic approaches may not be valid in practical situations

Time may be only one of several optimization criteria; development cost, inclusion of a particular partner, or risk may be as or more important. There then exist several effectiveness measures for optimization of the plan. This is the general system problem of resource alloca-

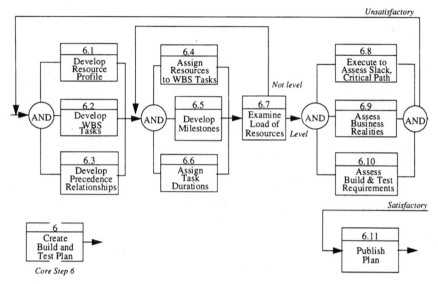

Figure 10.1 FFBD view of core step 6.

tion for which heuristic methods are used. The core technical steps provide such a process.

10.3   Behavior Model for Core Step 6

Figure 10.1 describes the steps taken to create a plan in terminology like that used in scheduling and planning. The objects to be used in planning are the resources, primarily people. An initial concurrent step, 6.1, is to develop a resource profile of the kinds of talent needed and the available resource in useful classes. This is a structure model. Another concurrent step, 6.2, is to develop the tasks to be performed. The third concurrent task, 6.3, is to develop precedence relationships among the tasks. This may also involve definition of alternative paths as well as precedence needed for purposes such as risk remediation. The result of tasks 6.2 and 6.3 is equivalent to the FFBD view of the behavior modeled by the plan.

The next three concurrent steps complete the behavior, map it to objects, and assign time performance attributes. Step 6.4 assigns the *resources* to *tasks*. This is identical to mapping functions to objects. Step 6.5 adds *milestones* to the plan. The milestones are outputs from the tasks. Their inclusion, with the tasks and precedence relationships, constitutes an executable behavior. In step 6.6 the task durations are added. This allows the behavior to be executed and generate timelines and slack times.

Frequently the next step taken is to examine the workloads assigned to the people to see if the loads are balanced. Some people may have excessive work to do, and others may be too lightly loaded. Step 6.7 examines the loading of resources. If the workloads are not level, the planning loops back to reassignment of resources, adjustment of milestones, and reassignment of task durations. This loop continues until the resources and tasks are commensurate. When the loads on people are balanced, the plan can be evaluated for other purposes.

In step 6.8 the plan is executed as a behavior. Slack times are established and the critical path through the plan is established. If the slack times are small, the plan is satisfactory so far as time is concerned. If the slack times are large, the plan is unsatisfactory and resources and tasks must be readjusted. Concurrently step 6.9 assesses the business realities which include risk, time to market, funding rate, competition, and validation of progress. The plan must mitigate identified risks with alternative paths and resource. It must get product to market in the available window, and meet competitive product features in that timeframe. The rate of expenditure must match funding rates. The schedule must include deliverables to validate progress as the work proceeds. Task 6.10 assesses the plan for incremental builds of product for early validation and for periodic release of product to customers. This is an iterative sequential approach to development of a series of plans and performing trade-off based on the criteria of steps 6.8, 6.9, and 6.10. The loop back to the beginning of Fig. 10.1 generates additional plans until one that is nearly optimal is found.

10.4   Information Model for Core Step 6

Figure 10.2 describes the information needed in this step. The subject system is built from a set of components which are assembled, tested, and validated to show that the desired emergent behavior has been attained. Validation must be done at the level of full integration because the properties of the system depend on the interactions of the components in both linear and nonlinear ways.

The sequential build-and-test plan orders the building and testing of the components. The order of building depends on and accounts for a variety of business realities. These realities may be time to market, funding rate, risk, competition, or need for early validation of progress. Any or all of these realities may be important. They constitute the optimization criteria or effectiveness measures for the creation of the plan.

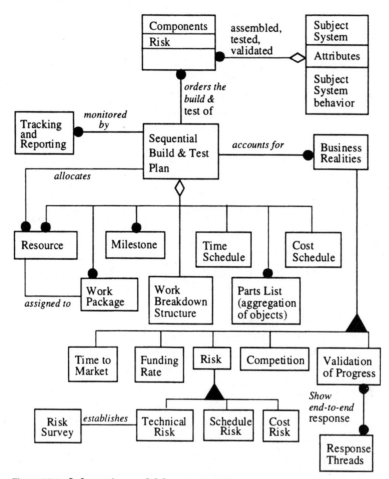

Figure 10.2 Information model for core step 6.

The risk may be cost risk, schedule risk, or technical risk or any combination of the three. The risk is associated with the individual components, whether they will be available and work properly within scheduled cost and time. The risk is recorded in models as an attribute of the components, but the risks need to be assessed for their importance to the success or failure of the system as a whole. They cannot be simply summed for the system, but must be assigned weights depending on their importance. There is no technique for measuring risk directly, such as weight or height. Rather, risk values and weights may be estimated by experienced engineers and managers assigned the responsibility, or they may be estimated by survey of an informed group of people using statistically valid techniques (Saaty, 1983). The importance of risk in planning depends on the important aspects of the application, captured in the effectiveness measures, particularly for technical risk. If the effectiveness measures include performance properties such as availability, safety, or security, then the risks associated with these properties of the system will be critically important.

Much of the planning work is based on estimates of the total size or cost of the development. Techniques and software exist for creating a historical basis of estimate and for estimating project cost and resource needs, PRICE models from Lockheed-Martin and COCOMO models (Boehm, 1981; Thusen and Fabrycky, 1989).

Validation of progress is accomplished by establishing that the response of things is correct. The system or component is specified, designed, or implemented properly if the responses to excitation are the needed responses. This is a matter of evaluating complete response threads through the system or of the portion of the threads for a particular component.

Tracking and reporting compares the plan against the time, cost, resource, and milestones for the completion of things, against validated progress based on response characteristics. Do the things do what was intended? The work breakdown structure defines the tasks to be performed, and these tasks are assigned to resources (people) as work packages. It is important that the work breakdown structure and the work packages correspond to the actual parts tree emerging from the project, rather than a contractual parts tree which has changed substantially during the project.

10.5   A Checklist for Planning Work

Although the planning work involves systems engineering management heavily, it is important that it be driven by both the technical realities and the business/management realities. These realities may be in sharp conflict at times and must be resolved. A checklist representative of planning is included here at the end of the chapter because of the importance of technical input to planning. It is vital to take into account all the engineering results by modifying plans whenever trade-off analysis results in an accepted design or architecture for the system or a component.

The checklist follows:

Plan based on the design or architecture information emerging from core step 5

- Understand
  - The Systems Engineering Process

- Specification to suppliers
- Specification to other engineering disciplines
- A process for handling discoveries and/or change
- The project tasks: top–down for deliverables and resources, bottom–up for feasibility

Define the work breakdown structure (WBS) plan tasks

- Identify tasks
- Create subtasks
- Determine subtask flow

- Capture subtask interdependence

  - Create PERT-type diagram, CPM diagram, or behavior model
  - Create decision basis, issue, and issue resolution rationale notes (Blanchard and Fabrycky, 1990)

- Determine subtask resource profile

  - Identify work environment needs
    - Workspace
    - Tools
    - Training
  - Estimate workforce needs of tasks
    - Person-hours
    - Labor category
    - Experience

- Assign resources to tasks

  - Define responsibilities associated with tasks
  - Document

- Assign subtask start and stop times on the basis of

  - Interdependency
  - Schedule negotiated with informed engineers and management
  - Resource availability

- Develop and insert milestones into plan

  - Insert a hierarchy of milestones
    - Major project-deliverable milestones
    - Top-level review milestones
    - Fine-grain progress and quality review milestones at engineering level to find unknown unknowns early

- Level resources and iterate until satisfactory
- Analyze plan according to criteria below
  - Elimination of negative variance
  - Reduction of slack time
  - Optimization for *cost-effectiveness*
  - Optimization of *time to delivery using critical path*
  - Optimization to account for all effectiveness measures, iterative and heuristic
  - Adjust plan to funding rate
  - Inclusion of tasks to mitigate risk
  - Inclusion of tasks for test and validation tied to excitation and response models
  - Partition of project output for successive release as needed for plan convergence or market needs
  - Definition of tasks and precedences for early validation based on partial builds
- Iterate to make plan converge
  - Introduce combinations/concurrence/resource changes as needed to meet plan criteria:
- Tailor company process and specification standards
  - Collect relevant process and specification documentation
    - Company standards (purpose is for reuse of best practice, not enforcing extra work)
    - Contractual standards (negotiate to keep work lean)
    - Applicable government standards [safety, environment, ISO (International Standards Organization) etc.]
  - Review for internal consistency and removal of all unnecessary work
  - Remove inconsistencies and any unnecessary work
  - Record issues and rationale for decisions
  - Document or store results
- Generate task plan and review for approval with appropriate authority and the contributing engineers
  - Cite plan objectives
  - Identify plan products
  - Fuse any preceding plan results

10.6   Exercises

1. List the elements of a build-and-test plan.
2. Describe the relationship of a build-and-test plan for an entire system to the plan for one of its components.
3. Develop a context diagram for the system which creates build-and-test plans.
4. Develop a structure diagram for the system which creates build-and-test plans. Map the behavior of Fig. 10.1 to this structure.
5. Create an overall systems engineering plan for getting a new model of pocket knife conceived, designed, and to market. Include a time schedule that is based on a work breakdown structure. Show milestones for parts, parts assembly, the full knife, progress reviews to validate progress, and cost to milestone.
   a. Identify what is to be reviewed.
   b. Assign resources to work packages that will result in the work being performed.
   c. Show time-to-market and funding-rate-limits met by the plan.
   d. Assume low-cost competition from overseas, and assess risks.
6. Identify three tools which are commercially available to aid in the development of plans. Do these tools cover the functions needed in planning? Do they integrate with system development tasks?
7. Identify 10 risks that every plan faces.

10.7   References

Blanchard, B. F., and W. Fabrycky, 1990: *Systems Engineering and Analysis,* 2d ed. Englewood Cliffs, N.J.: Prentice-Hall.

Boehm, B. W., 1981: *Software Engineering Economics.* Englewood Cliffs, N.J.: Prentice-Hall.

Chapman, W. L., and J. Rosenblit, 1995: Complexity of the system design problem. *International Symposium and Workshop on Systems Engineering of Computer Based Systems* (Tucson, Ariz.), pp. 51–57 (IEEE#95TH8053).

Saaty, T. L., 1983: Priority setting in complex problems. *IEEE Transact. Eng. Mgmt.* **EM-30,** 140–155.

Thusen, G. J., and W. J. Fabrycky, 1989: *Engineering Economy.* Englewood Cliffs, N.J.: Prentice-Hall.

Wymore, A. W., 1993: *Model-Based Systems Engineering.* Boca Raton, Fla.: CRC Press.

11

Concept Analysis

11.1 What Concept Analysis Is

Concept analysis is the study of the business which will use the subject system. The study establishes what features the subject system should have by analyzing the value of different features to the business, to its owners and to users of the system. This is shown in Fig. 11.1.

The tiers of analysis, domain analysis through component analysis, apply the same core technical process to different objects in the developmental parts tree that extends from components to domains or collections of businesses. The flow of the analyses may be bottom to top (synthesis), or top to bottom (decomposition), or a combination of the two.

At any tier, the analysis can terminate for part of the system and a specification may be produced for business partners or suppliers. In the domain and concept tiers businesses may be discovered which are necessary for product success, but are considered to be outside the business arena of the company developing the product. At the lower tiers, entire subsystems or particular components may be specified for external development or as a purchased subsystem or component from a supplier.

The subject system studied in concept analysis and the other tiers of analysis may be anything: a product, a process, a business, a plan, etc. They all have in common: a set of criteria for what is most important, a behavior, a set of parts to build them, and design/architecture alternatives in how the behavior is allocated among the alternative parts which are selected for the structure. The similarities among product, process, business, and plan may not be apparent because of different choices of common words used to describe the modeling items which are common to them all. Table 11.1 associates a few of the commonly used words with modeling items.

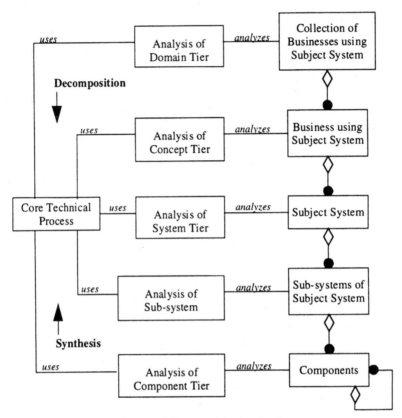

Figure 11.1 Tiers of analysis and decomposition/synthesis.

11.2 Applying the Core Technical Process to Concept Analysis

This chapter focuses on how to apply the core technical process to concept analysis. It does this with a simple example problem which uses a product as the subject system, but could have used a process, a business, or a plan. The example problem chosen is an automated teller machine (ATM). Solutions to representative parts of the ATM problem are described in this book to keep the discussion reasonably compact.

The ATM product was selected to be small and easily understood by people through their daily experiences, and to encompass interesting aspects of modeling. It has been used as an example in publications and other books. The approach used in this book is unique in going from concept through component specification with executable models as a systems problem. The approach is unique in using a single re-

TABLE 11.1   Modeling Items

Modeling items	Product	Process	Business	Plan
Parts that do things (objects)	People, components, or subsystems	People or equipment	People, departments, divisions, facilities	Resources
What is done (behavior)	Feature, response	Process step, production rate	Job, activity, task, responsiveness	Task, schedule
Criteria for choice (effectiveness measures)	Cost, needs, quality	Cost, productivity, quality	Cost, efficiency, quality. service	Cost schedule, time schedule, resource utilization
Interconnection of parts and total system performance (design/architecture)	Design	The process	Model	The plan

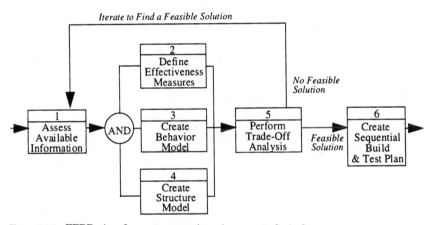

Figure 11.2   FFBD view for systems engineering core technical process.

peated technical core process, shown for reference in Fig. 11.2, applied first to bank context and then to the bank.

The approach eliminates unneeded modeling as much as possible to be efficient, and the example illustrates this balance of thorough modeling against rapidly eliminating alternatives to maintain engineering productivity. Where decisions can be made early and clearly regarding component choices for optimizing performance, this is done.

Where computation is required to decide among alternatives, the more formal tradeoff step, core step 6, is applied. In the example the decisions of both kinds are noted.

11.3   Core Steps Applied to the Context of the Bank with the ATM System

Concept analysis is applied to the business using the ATM system, rather than to the ATM system itself, as shown in Fig. 11.1. That business is a bank. Each of the seven steps as applied to the bank will be illustrated for concept analysis. The goal is to establish the concept for the ATM system based on value to the bank when it uses the ATMs in place of its present tellers and their manual entry of transactions.

11.3.1   Assess available information

The available information is taken from a problem statement that was written for software engineering development. Since we are considering the total ATM system, we expect that a range of system-related problems that need to be corrected in the available information will be found. The available information is taken from a problem statement in (Rumbaugh et al., 1991, p. 151). Substitutions to replace the word *software* with system names are inserted, italicized, and in brackets.

Initial information for an ATM system

> Design the software [*an automated teller machine system*] to support a computerized banking network including both human cashiers and automated teller machines (ATMs) to be shared by a consortium of banks. Each bank provides its own computer to maintain its own accounts and processes transactions against them. Cashier stations are owned by the individual banks and communicate directly with their own bank's computers. Human cashiers enter account and transaction data. Automatic teller machines communicate with a central computer which clears transactions with the appropriate banks. An automatic teller machine accepts a cash card, interacts with the user, communicates with the central system to carry out the transaction, dispenses cash, and prints receipts. The system requires appropriate record keeping and security systems. The system must handle concurrent access to the same account correctly. The banks will provide their own software for their own computers; you are to design [*the ATM system*] the software for the ATM's and the network. The cost of the shared system will be apportioned to the banks according to the number of bank customers with a cash card.

The usual situation is initial information that is partially complete, inconsistent in level of detail, partly requirements, partly design, and partly operations concept. Much of the information may be not be directly verifiable; some of it may even be false or misleading. Modifications to the initial information are produced in this first core step. Each of the modifications must be documented and tracked. They must be agreed to by all of the interested stakeholders. The art of systems engineering starts at this step. No methodology can tell an engineer what questions need to be asked about the system. For this education and experience are the guides. The best systems engineers learn how to ask the correct questions while avoiding unnecessary complexity, which can arise from rote dedication to a methodology.

The subsequent modeling process discovers additional problems and suggests their correction. The sentences in the initial information are open-numbered (1, 2, etc.) below. Modified statements are shown as lettered (a, b, etc.) sentences, and comments about them are separated by parenthetic numerals [(1), (2), etc.].

1. Design the software [an automated teller machine system] to support a computerized banking network including both human cashiers and automated teller machines (ATMs) to be shared by a consortium of banks.
   a. The ATM system shall replace interactions between bank tellers and bank customers with interactions between the ATM system and customers.
      (1) It is not yet known which existing transactions shall be replaced.
      (2) It is not yet known how much of the network belongs in the ATM system or if this may vary with different bank customers for the ATM system.
2. Each bank provides its own computer to maintain its own accounts and processes transactions against them.
   a. This statement contains design information about banks which may not represent the banking world. This will need to be substantiated or modified to match the real-world situation. In considering the context and boundaries of the system, we can choose to make this a requirement or consider the possibility that the computers are part of the system or perhaps that there is a third party that owns and operates the computers.
   b. Banks might use an external service such as First Data Corporation to track their transactions and provide both internal information to the bank and monthly reports to bank customers.

3. Cashier stations are owned by the individual banks and communicate directly with their own bank's computers.
   a. Cashier stations are owned by the individual banks.
   b. Cashier stations communicate directly with their own bank's computers.
      (1) Sentence 3 has been broken into two independent statements.
      (2) The two statements describe the structure of banks; again this needs to be verified. In the absence of verification, the two statements will be accepted as generally true of banks not yet using ATM systems.
4. Human cashiers enter account and transaction data.
   a. Human cashiers enter account and transaction data.
      (1) The statement describes the structure of banks.
      (2) The statement is accepted as generally true of banks not yet using ATM systems.
5. Automatic teller machines communicate with a central computer which clears transactions with the appropriate banks.
   a. The ATM system shall communicate the transactions it captures to the banks.
   b. The ATM system shall execute only those transactions for which validation is received from the banks.
      (1) Automated teller machines may mean only the hardware and software that interfaces with bank customers.
      (2) Automated teller machines may be only a subsystem or component of the ATM system.
      (3) The interface with banks is not yet clear.
      (4) For a viable product line, it may be necessary to configure ATM subsystems for particular banks, tailored to what the bank already owns or leases.
      (5) "Clears transactions" is ambiguous. It can mean validating a submitted transaction so that the ATM system can complete the transaction, or it can mean communicating the transaction to the bank without a validation procedure in place. Modified statement b assumes that it means validation, and the procedure for validation is not identified. The procedure could vary among different banks using the ATM system.
6. An automatic teller machine accepts a cash card, interacts with the user, communicates with the central system to carry out the transaction, dispenses cash, and prints receipts.
   a. The ATM system shall accept transactions after reading a cash card and receiving a valid PIN number from a system user.

    b. The ATM system shall dispense cash only for those cash transactions for which validation is received from the banks.

    c. The ATM system shall print receipts for the transactions executed.

       (1) The phrase "interacts with the user" is redundant with 1 above.

       (2) The phrase "communicates with the central system to carry out the transaction" is redundant with statement 5 above.

7. The system requires appropriate record keeping and security systems.

    a. The ATM system shall maintain correct records.

    b. The ATM system shall generate correct reports.

    c. The ATM system shall keep information secure.

    d. The ATM system shall keep money secure.

8. The system must handle concurrent access to the same account correctly.

    a. Simultaneous or overlapping requests to the ATM system for transactions on the same account shall be adjudicated at the point in the network where simultaneity or overlap is detected.

       (1) "Simultaneous" is ambiguous here. It can mean either that two requests are made at exactly the same time, or that the duration of two user sessions on the same account overlap.

       (2) Simultaneous or overlapping requests on the same account can be entered into ATM machines on different networks on different continents. Only a central facility serving that bank account can know that they are simultaneous and follow an appropriate procedure.

9. The banks will provide their own software for their own computers; you are to design (*the ATM system*) the software for the ATMs and the network.

    a. Design the ATM system.

    b. Begin the design work with concept analysis.

       (1) These are instructions.

10. The cost of the shared system will be apportioned to the banks according to the number of bank customers with a cash card.

    a. The ATM system shall operate at maximum benefit/total cost to the banks it serves.

       (1) Sentence 10 deals primarily with how the banks using the ATM system are to be billed, which may best be tailored for different bank customers of the ATM system vendor.

(2) Total cost/benefit to the bank will be a selection factor for banks choosing an ATM system vendor.

Requirements extracted from the initial information. The subentries in the preceding list are collected here and numbered. They do not constitute a complete set of requirements. Many are not verifiable. They apply at different tiers of hierarchy. Some of the subentries are not requirements. Some are statements about the banks as they exist or are instructions about the problem.

Requirements for the ATM system

11.1   The ATM system shall replace interactions between bank tellers and bank customers with interactions between the ATM system and customers.

11.2   The ATM system shall communicate the transactions it captures to the banks.

11.3   The ATM system shall accept transactions after reading a cash card and receiving a valid PIN number from a system user.

11.4   The ATM system shall execute only those transactions for which validation is received from the bank.

11.5   The ATM system shall dispense cash only for those cash transactions for which validation is received from the bank.

11.6   The ATM system shall print receipts for the transactions executed.

11.7   The ATM system shall maintain correct records.

11.8   The ATM system shall generate correct reports.

11.9   The ATM system shall keep information secure.

11.10 The ATM system shall keep money secure.

11.11 The ATM system shall operate at maximum benefit/total cost to the banks it serves.

Statements about the structure of banks

B1. Cashier stations are owned by the individual banks.

B2. Cashier stations communicate directly with their own bank's computers.

B3. Human cashiers enter account and transaction data.

B4. Simultaneous or overlapping requests to the ATM system for transactions on the same account shall be adjudicated at the point in the network where simultaneity or overlap is detected.

Instructions about the problem

I1. Design the ATM system.

I2. Begin the design work with concept analysis.

11.3.2   The three concurrent core steps: 2, 3, and 4

The next three core steps—define effectiveness measures, create behavior model, and create structure model—are concurrent. Because text in a book is read sequentially, the full concurrency cannot be shown in the written form of this example. It is often useful to consider the effectiveness measures very early because they provide guidance in thinking about the models. In the development of large systems, the problem will likely be apportioned among teams such that work is proceeding in parallel.

Defining effectiveness measures.   This work, like the assessment of the initial information, relies on the experience and creative thinking of the developers. The issue here is to determine what statements about the ATM system will make it succeed or fail when brought to banks in competition with other ATM systems. A first selection is made from the results of analyzing the initial information. The selection is made by applying either of the following criteria: (1) "If this were true the bank would buy our system! or (2) "If this were not true the bank would reject our system!"

11.7   The ATM system shall maintain correct records.

11.8   The ATM system shall generate correct reports.

11.9   The ATM system shall keep information secure.

11.10   The ATM system shall keep money secure.

11.11   The ATM system shall operate at maximum benefit/total cost to the banks it serves.

Statements 11.7 through 11.10 are chosen on the basis of question 2. Statement 11.11 is based on question 1. Bankers will choose the system that gives them the maximum benefit/cost. The problem now faced by the designer is whether this is a complete set of effectiveness measures. It is helpful at this point to think about the structure of the context of a bank.

Context structure for the bank.   At this point a simple context for bank is needed. The functions to be performed and the important attributes can be added later. Figure 11.3 shows an initial structure for the context of bank.

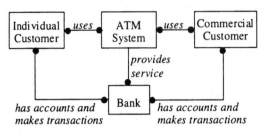

Figure 11.3   Initial structure of bank context.

The effectiveness measures have not taken into account the customers. Both individual and commercial customers have accounts with the bank and make transactions there with tellers. When the ATM system is installed, they may alternatively use the ATM system. It must be so attractive to them that they will use it in preference to the tellers. Otherwise the system will fail in the marketplace.

■ Customers shall prefer to use the ATM system over the bank tellers.

Effectiveness measures for the bank. An initial set of six effectiveness measures (EMs) can now be collected for the ATM system. If others are found during modeling, they will have to be added.

EM1. The ATM system shall maintain correct records.

EM2. The ATM system shall generate correct reports.

EM3. The ATM system shall keep information secure.

EM4. The ATM system shall keep money secure.

EM5. The ATM system shall operate at maximum benefit/total cost to the banks it serves.

EM6. Customers shall prefer to use the ATM system over the bank tellers.

Inspection of them shows that the first four deal with what the ATM must do. With further analysis, they can help with the analysis of the ATM system. Effectiveness measures EM5 and EM6 deal with value to the bank and value to the customer. They are of direct importance to the concept analysis.

To proceed further, it is necessary to define the customer, the behavior of the customer, and the structure of the bank. Only the individual customer will be considered to keep the example short.

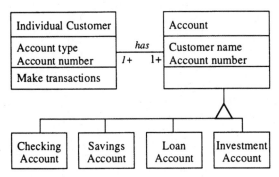

Figure 11.4 Structure for individual customer.

Creating behavior and structure models

Define the structure for individual customers. Figure 11.4 shows the association between the customer, a person, and the accounts, part of the bank, which the customer has opened. If there are other kinds of accounts, they can be added. This is enough information to help define the behavior of the individual customer.

Context behavior: the individual customer. When the behavior of the customer is captured, the major excitations for the system are obtained. They will be used not only in context analysis, but in defining components and in testing and validating the system and its components. Figure 11.5 shows many alternative paths in the behavior of the customer. Alternative paths are annotated with estimated probabilities of their usage. The customer may go to either the bank or an ATM. Once there the customer may perform a variety of transactions. The FFBD captures what the customer does and it raises two questions:

1. Why would the customer prefer the ATM system?
2. Which of the transactions are the heaviest load on the bank tellers and can be automated by the ATM system?

Preference for the ATM system. Customers are likely to prefer the ATM if it is in a safe place, has shorter lines than the bank, is closer to home and to work, and is easy to use. "Safe place" is a matter of finding locations, and will depend on conditions in particular communities. "Easy to use" is a human-machine interface design issue that will be considered as components are designed. It is important, but premature in concept analysis. "Shorter lines" and "closer to home" depend on the number of machines put in place. If one puts in place many more ATM machines than existing tellers, then the lines will be

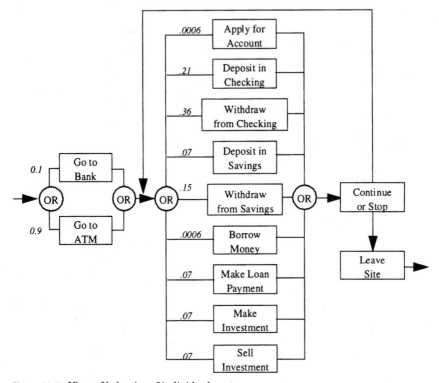

Figure 11.5 View of behavior of individual customer.

shorter. If one puts in place many more machines than branch bank offices, then the machines will be closer to customers than branch offices with tellers. If the ATMs are to be a third of the distance to a branch bank on average, then there must be about $3 \times 3 = 9$ ATM machines for each branch office. The effectiveness measures and behaviors are beginning to provide refined information about the structure of the bank and the ATM system.

Which transactions to automate. Applying for an account can be automated with some difficulty but results in loss of a manager directly assessing the applicants, and loss of an opportunity to sell additional services. Deposits and withdrawals from savings and checking are simple to automate. Repaying loans is often done in person or by mail. Making and selling investments is often conducted by phone or personal computer. The frequency of occurrence of these transactions with tellers can be obtained accurately and quantitatively from bank records. Transactions on checking and savings accounts are most frequent, with cash withdrawals from checking the highest. These frequencies of occurrence, after normalization, are the probabilities for choosing a branch of the large OR in Fig. 11.5, where representative values of probability are shown on each branch. If loans and investments are conducted dominantly by mail or phone, then automating savings and checking transactions can move 90 percent of the transaction from tellers to ATMs—provided the ATMs are attractive to use. Probabilities of going to the ATM or to branch banks are most reliable when measured by observing bank customers' choices with an installed system. In advance of an installed system, they are best obtained by survey of the bank customers.

Since there is no important trade-off for the context, we proceed to model the bank.

11.4   Core Steps Applied to the Bank with the ATM System

We accept the models already produced as available information, core step 4.1.

11.4.1   Structure of the bank with the ATM system: core step 4.5

Figure 11.6 models the important details we need to understand the benefit to a national bank. Unneeded details have been left out of the figure.

Only the gross structure and the tellers are shown. The numbers shown are estimates for a large bank. Numbers for a particular bank or national averages could be used. The national bank is supported by about 10 regional banks. Each of these is supported by about 20 local banks, and for each local bank there are about 10 branch banks. The dominant number of tellers work in the approximately 2000 branch banks. It is in the cost in these branches that the ATM system will have its major impact, although it will benefit all the banks. It is the branch banks that are located in the community to provide nearby service to bank customers whose deposits are loaned by the bank to generate income.

A classification for branch bank and bank attributes is given in Fig. 11.7.

The attributes of the subclasses are inherited from the bank. The values shown in Fig. 11.7 for branch bank are estimated average values for a typical branch bank. These values would be different for a particular branch bank (an instance) in a particular bank. That more precise data is available from the bank.

A more detailed teller model is given in Fig. 11.8.

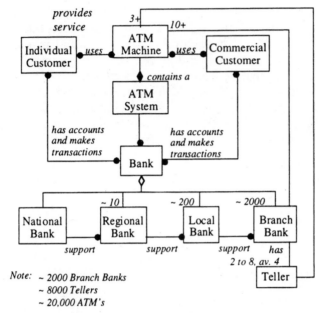

Figure 11.6   Structure of the bank.

The important attribute for teller for this analysis is the burdened salary.

11.4.2   Effectiveness measure for bank with the ATM system: core step 2

The two effectiveness measures identified as of greatest importance in this concept analysis are

EM6.   Customers shall prefer to use the ATM system over the bank tellers.

EM5.   The ATM system shall operate at maximum benefit/total cost to the banks it serves.

Effectiveness measure EM6 was used to generate some structural numbers about the number of ATM machines per branch office and per teller. That information and the structure and behavior modeling that has been done let us write equations for the benefit for the ATM system:

Total benefit = teller cost reduction + branch office cost reduction

At least three of four tellers can be replaced with about 20,000 ATM machines:

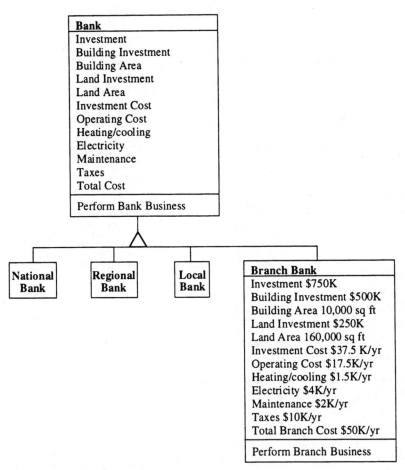

Figure 11.7   Classes of bank.

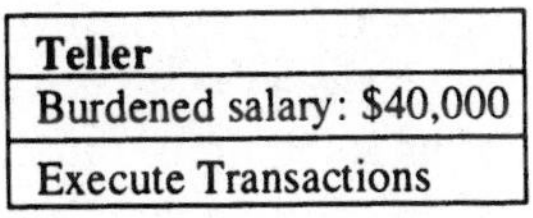

Teller

| Burdened salary: $40,000 |
| Execute Transactions |

Figure 11.8   The teller.

Teller cost reduction = no of branch banks × 3
× burdened salary of teller

Teller cost reduction = 2000 × 3× $40,000 = $240,000,000

At least 75 percent of branch offices can be moved into leased space of 500 ft² in popular locations such as supermarkets for about $25,000

/yr. These numbers can be refined in particular communities and with particular businesses:

$$\text{Branch office cost reduction} = 0.75 \times \text{no. of branch offices} \\ \times (\text{total branch cost} \\ - \$25,000)$$

$$\text{Branch office cost reduction} = \$37.500,000$$

$$\text{Total benefit} = \$280,000,000/\text{yr or } \$14,000/\text{yr} \\ \text{per installed ATM machine}$$

For a bank with an annual earnings of about 2 percent of deposits, this saving represents an equivalent increase in deposits of about $14 billion. The benefit is very large. To warrant the investment, the cost of the ATM system needs to be recovered in about two years. The selling price of the system should be less than about $560 million or $28,000 per ATM machine on the system. If the system can be created with a combined build, install, operate cost of about $14,000 per ATM machine, then there is an excellent business here.

11.4.3   Behavior of the bank with the ATM system: core step 3

In this example the behavior of the bank is not changed quantitatively. Rather, some of the activity in the bank is moved from tellers to the ATM system.

Figure 11.9 shows the excitations to which the ATM system must respond. The behavior model for the system is equivalent to a set of written functional requirements.

We already know that some of the excitations are unlikely. Since we have not fully evaluated their benefit, we represent all the excitations and responses. The ATM system stays on at all times, ready to respond to a user. Consequently, its behavior will look like an infinite loop. When the customer stops and so notifies the ATM system, the system goes back to its initial function of presenting to the customer the start instructions.

Figure 11.10 shows the responses and loops.

The eight functions in Fig. 11.10 are only top-level names. Each of them must be decomposed and refined into complete descriptions of exactly how the system responds to every input from the user and from the banks. This detail is left until the system and the components are designed. At this point in the development it is important to establish the responses required and the benefit of each response. To get at the benefits, it is necessary to have values for all the attributes

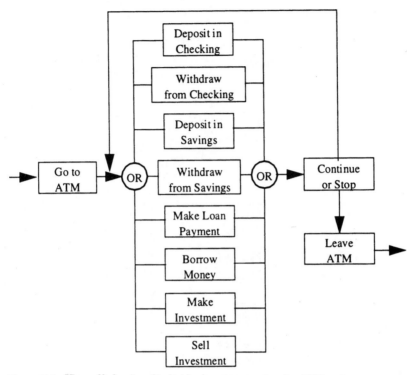

Figure 11.9 View of behavior of individual customer using the ATM system.

used in the effectiveness measures and requirements. In this problem they have been estimated during the model development. The job of getting accurate values is part of trade-off analysis.

11.4.4 Trade-off analysis of the bank with the ATM system: core step 5

The preceding analysis has shown large potential payoff to the bank. It has captured bank behavior and structure, ATM system behavior, the criteria for trade-off, and the equations. It has provided an upper limit for the cost of producing, installing, and maintaining the system.

The benefit/cost needs to be maximized, EM 5 to

- Provide the bank the largest benefit/cost ratio
- Be competitive with other suppliers
- Have a satisfactory profit margin for the business of supplying ATM systems

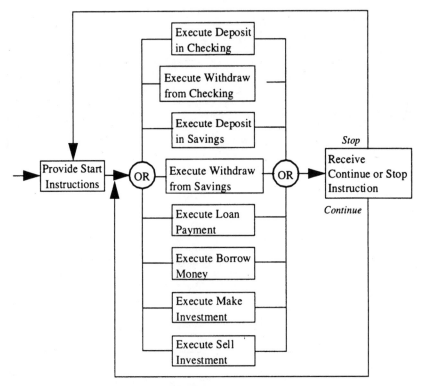

Figure 11.10 View of behavior of the ATM system.

Figure 11.5 identifies nine different features that may be embodied in an ATM machine. The list is representative of useful features but is not exhaustive. These nine features can be combined in 503 different ways. It is this explosion in the numbers of possibilities that makes algorithmic solution of system problems impractical. Creative engineering, heuristics, is used to prune the large solution space. The probabilities in the figure show which features have the largest benefit individually. Which transactions the bank should automate follows from the benefits shown in Table 11.2. Features 1, 2, 3, 4, and 6 should be automated initially. The decision is made without considering all 503 options.

Some of the features require similar kinds of support. Withdrawing money from any kind of account requires a money dispenser, a money supply, and periodic resupply of money. Deposits to any kind of account require a safe repository for the deposit, and a daily pickup of the deposited material. This information suggests how to package the features in different kinds of ATM machines that interface with the public. It is the analysis of the system tier which follows concept

TABLE 11.2   Feature Benefits to Bank

Feature	Benefit per installed ATM machine, $
1. Deposit in checking	1680
2. Withdraw from checking	2880
3. Deposit in savings	560
4. Withdraw from savings	1200
5. Borrow money	4.80
6. Make loan payment	560
7. Make investment (1)	560
8. Sell investment (1)	560

analysis that establishes the cost of these alternatives and the structure of the ATM system.

Figure 11.11 classifies the types of machine that are likely to emerge from concept analysis based on the modeling completed so far.

Attributes and functions are inherited and not listed a second time in the subclasses. The money machine and deposit machine are two obvious candidate products. Their relative merits depend on their relative costs. The transaction machine is an advanced workstation for banking that may become viable someday, but is a poor candidate for an early release of product. Analysis of the system tier can uncover other important types with very different costs.

Note that the computation machinery for trade-off was established in the earlier modeling steps. In the trade-off analysis it is necessary to get adequate values for the attributes. In this example, that means going to banks to get their measured and recorded data. That data is superior to engineering estimates such as those shown above. The data will vary from bank to bank and region to region. It may be important to get the data from several banks if the trade-off criteria do not provide wide margins for selecting product features.

Within the scope of systems engineering there are a multitude of computation and simulation methods that are used to find attribute values when measured values are unavailable. They simulate the performance and properties of physical and logical variables such as cost, weight, reliability, power consumption, algorithmic complexity, control loop error, and crack propagation. It is a responsibility of the systems engineering management process to ensure that the specialized engineering talent for this work is available and applied when needed.

11.4.5   Create the sequential build-and-test plan: core step 6

The modeling through trade-off has established the bank context, the behavior of the user, relevant bank structure, how the product changes

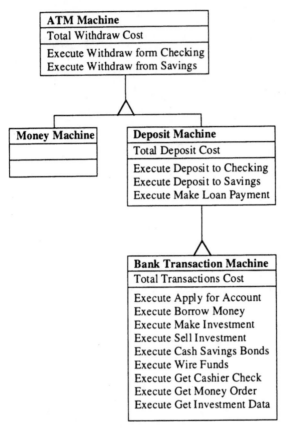

Figure 11.11   Types of ATM machines

the bank, behavior and requirements for the ATM system, and value to the bank. The next step is to decide how to implement this opportunity. The modeling has identified potential business relationships that are needed. In this example the bank may want to downsize and relocate branch offices into places such as supermarkets. A vendor of ATM systems with existing business relationships with national supermarkets can combine business reengineering consulting with the supplying of ATM systems. This is a matter of deciding what business the vendor of the ATM system product will pursue. It is the issue of how the vendor business will be implemented and what work must be done to make that happen. The business implementation plans will differ depending on the choices made. If the choices made do not completely span the system solution, then the products need to interface with the products of other companies, or partnerships need to be created. One possible business choice follows:

1. Supply hardware and software for the capture and transmission of transactions to a communication network
2. Lease communication facilities.
   a. Requires implementation of business relation with communication companies
3. Build custom interfaces to the MIS (management information system) of the bank
   a. Requires involvement with banks to define functionality and tailorable interfaces
4. Interface with a separate business that performs backend transaction processing and reporting
   a. Requires relationship with a company such as First Data Corp.
5. Service ATM systems, repair, and resell ATM equipment
   a. Ensures a capability to maintain an available system
   b. Provides a separate revenue source
   c. Provides a path to continuing business in a saturated market for ATMs
6. Consult to banks on installation of ATM systems and downsizing branch banks
   a. Ensures internal bank procedures for security of information and funds
   b. Requires relationships with supermarket chains
   c. Maintains a presence with banks to get sales

The plan, constructed for the ATM system at concept level, schedules implementation, test, and validation tasks for the following:

Creating relationships with banks, communication companies, transaction processing companies, and supermarket chains

Performing analysis of the system tier on the ATM system with focus on subsystems for

- Hardware and software for capture and transmission of transactions
- Hardware and software for diagnostics, field service, field installation, systems management, and validation of performance
- Hardware and software for interfaces with communications, banks, and transaction processing
- Management of the whole ATM system business

Recruiting, training, housing, and equipping personnel

The plan is not just about engineering, but about implementation of the ATM system business and validation of the work as it proceeds. At this level of understanding the plan will lack detail for implementation. Much of that detail is developed in the next tier of development, analysis of the system tier, described in Chap. 12.

11.5 Summary

Performing the systems engineering at any tier is an art of finding a near-optimal solution while expending as little engineering resource as possible. The modeling needs to uncover the subtle low-cost, high-performance solutions. The modeling needs to help the engineer quickly reject most of the multitude of nonoptimal solutions in the search for the low-cost, high-performance solution that is near-optimal.

11.6 Exercises

1. Write a set of requirements statements equivalent to those of Fig. 11.10.
    a. Trace these requirements to any of the eleven, 11.1 to 11.11, from Sec. 11.3.1 that were identified by analyzing the initial information and are "parents" for the ones you have written.
    b. Create any needed implied requirements. These are requirements which did not exist anywhere in the initial information and are not derived from any of them. They have no parents.
2. Create temporal requirements for the responses of the system shown in Fig. 11.10.
3. Assign time values to the functions in Fig. 11.10 where that is sensible.
4. Give examples of a system and its parts at each tier of design from domain down to component.
5. Give examples of questions which are asked and answered at each level of design for a power-generation business.
6. Briefly analyze the newspaper business at the concept level. Develop structure and FFBD diagrams. List all assumed available information.

11.7 References

Rumbaugh, J., M. Blaha, W. J. Premerlani, F. Eddy, and W. Lorensen, 1991: *Object-Oriented Modeling and Design*. Englewood Cliffs, N.J.: Prentice-Hall.

12

System Analysis

12.1 What System Analysis Is

System analysis is the study of the subject system which will be used by a business or businesses. The subject system may be a product, a process, a business to be reengineered, or a plan. System analysis is preceded by *concept analysis,* which establishes the value of features of the subject system to the business, to its owners, and to users of the system. On the basis of the value of the features, concept analysis establishes the top-level behavior of the subject system. That behavior captured in a model is equivalent to text requirements for the system. The results of concept analysis are the initial information for system analysis.

System analysis applies the steps of the core technical process to fully define the context of the subject system and then to decompose the system into its subsystems. The context of each subsystem is fully defined in its structure and in the excitations to the subsystem. The behavior of the subsystem in response to the excitations is defined. That behavior captured in a model is equivalent to text requirements for the subsystem.

This chapter describes system analysis by continuing the example of the ATM system. A complete development of all the requirements and models for all the subsystems is too large for inclusion in a book and is repetitive as an example. A representative subsystem is analyzed in this chapter. It will be selected to represent interesting aspects of modeling systems and to be familiar to many readers.

12.2   Core Steps Applied to the Context of the ATM System

Substantial information about the ATM system is developed in concept analysis and passed on to system analysis. Often the context description is not complete, as in this example. The core technical steps are applied to fully establish the context of the ATM system and to create the plan details for decomposing the system into subsystems.

12.2.1   Assess available information: core step 1

When a system is developed with concept analysis by one organization and system analysis by a different organization under contract, it is essential to thoroughly assess all the available information. When this proceeds by legal contract, the requirements for the system are usually received as a large set of text statements rather than in executable models with accompanying text.

When a large system is developed by a single organization, for example, an automobile by an automaker, the information produced by concept analysis can be passed on to system analysis in executable models with accompanying text. For large systems, the information will pass from one group to another group of people. Thorough assessment of the models received as initial information is essential.

In this small example, the models from Chap. 11 are accepted as satisfactory initial information. The work proceeds to the next three concurrent steps.

12.2.2   The three concurrent core steps: 2, 3, and 4

These three steps are concurrent. The step to begin with depends on the problem under study. If effectiveness measures and structure are well documented and behavior is less complete, one may begin with analysis of behavior. In actual engineering situations the engineer will move focus among the three steps as needed. For this example we repeat the effectiveness measures developed in Chap. 11 and go on to analysis of the structure of the ATM system context, which is not yet well defined. When the structure of the context is more complete, we can select the portions that we have space to explore in this example.

12.2.3   Effectiveness measure for bank with the system: core step 2

The initial set of six effectiveness measures (EMs), for the ATM system are repeated here. If others are found during modeling, they will have to be added.

EM1. The ATM system shall maintain correct records.

EM2. The ATM system shall generate correct reports.

EM3. The ATM system shall keep information secure.

EM4. The ATM system shall keep money secure.

EM5. The ATM system shall operate at maximum benefit/total cost to the banks it serves.

EM6. Customers shall prefer to use the ATM system over the bank tellers.

12.2.4 Structure of the context of the ATM system: core step 5

An initial context for the ATM system was shown in Fig. 11.3 and was adequate for analysis of value to the bank and to customers. It is missing a number of objects which will be essential for system analysis. Effectiveness measures EM3 and EM4 describe security. In the context there must be a *thief* who will steal money, a *spoofer* who will alter information or commit fraud, and organizations which will apprehend thieves and spoofers. Figure 12.1 shows the associations among these objects.

Business choices were made during concept analysis as to what the product would be and what parts of the ATM system would be leased or obtained through partnerships. Communication facilities are to be leased. Transaction processing and report generation is to be performed by the MIS departments of banks or by transaction processing companies like First Data Corp. Branch banks may be downsized into locations such as supermarkets. The ATM vendor provides consulting to banks on bank procedures and downsizing. If such business choices are not made during concept analysis, these objects must still be carried through the system analysis. In that case they may be viewed as either external systems in the context or subsystems of the ATM system with a deferred business issue identified and traced to them.

According to Fig. 12.1, the ATM customer has accounts with the bank and makes transactions. The customer uses the ATM system which the bank has bought. The ATM machine used may be local to the customer's bank or located anywhere in the world.

The ATM system uses leased communications to transmit and receive information. The activity begins at an ATM machine anywhere in the world. The combination of communication local and long-distance networks used is not known, the networks handle the addresses properly. Validation of the transaction is dealt with by queries to an appropriate site or sites in the bank where the bank database resides.

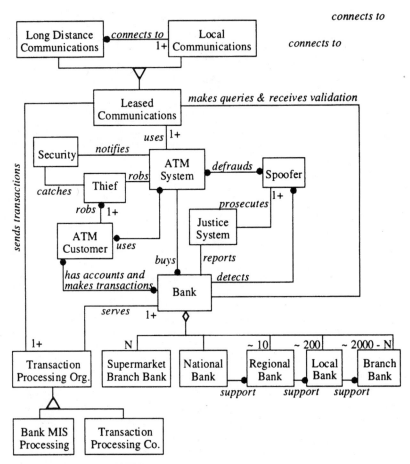

Figure 12.1   Context of ATM system.

The leased communication network also connects to the transaction processing organizations which process transactions and prepare reports for banks and ATM customers. Of these organizations, two types must be considered: those that are bank MIS processing organizations and those that are transaction processing companies. Interfaces to both types will be necessary. Several subsystems of the ATM system will likely be involved with the communication networks. It is premature to describe the ATM system decomposition and those associations. They are deferred until context definition is complete and the system analysis turns to the structure of the ATM system itself.

Spoofer is the established name for someone who breaks into computer systems and defrauds the ATM system. This is detected by the bank, which reports it to the justice system, which prosecutes the spoofer. Note that this portion of the context is compact. Its analysis leads to distributed computer security issues which are complex and which have a profound impact on the computer, communications, and software details of the ATM system. Security is accomplished by design of the computer-communication system (Schiller, 1994; Khanna, 1993) and by use of encryption (Beth, 1995; Simmons, 1992). The computer communication system design must also take into account issues of availability (Birman and van Renesse, 1996). These issues are best left to the expert detail designers. Only requirements for security and availability are specified by the system analysis.

A thief robs one or more customers or robs an ATM machine. The ATM system notifies security, and security catches the thief. This is a critically important part of the context to deal with if the system is to be acceptable to bank customers and to banks. It is expressed in effectiveness measure EM4.

The thief portion of the ATM system context is readily understood without specialized knowledge, and it leads to interesting modeling results. Accordingly, the remainder of this chapter analyzes this part of the context diagram. It is often very useful to partition large projects among teams on the basis of loosely coupled portions of the context diagram, and then combine the results. In this example the partitioning is used to reduce the size of the example.

12.2.5 Effectiveness measure for the ATM
system context: core step 2

The relevant effectiveness measure is EM4: the ATM system shall keep money secure. Although true and important, it cannot be verified and is unsatisfactory until further analysis creates derived requirements which are verifiable. The analysis continues by developing the behavior of the thief and the ATM customer.

12.2.6 Behavior of the thief in the context
of the ATM cystem: core step 3

There are two kinds of thief, as shown in Fig. 12.2: muggers and cabinet crackers. Each has a characteristic behavior.

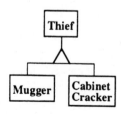

Figure 12.2 Kinds of thief.

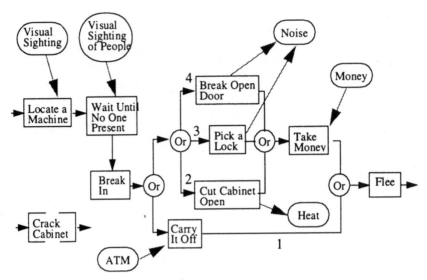

Figure 12.3 Behavior of cabinet cracker.

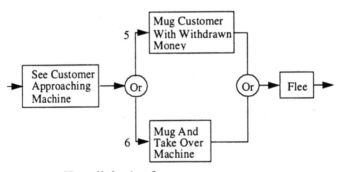

Figure 12.4 View of behavior of mugger.

A plausible behavior for the cabinet cracker is shown in Fig. 12.3. We have labeled the four paths, or scenarios, through this behavior.

A plausible behavior for the mugger is shown in Fig. 12.4. There are two labeled paths through this behavior.

There is a another object in the thief portion of the context diagram, the ATM customer, whose behavior causes excitations of the ATM system. Figure 12.5 is a plausible description.

This analysis of context has been partitioned to the thief part of the context. The effectiveness measure, the structure, and the associated behaviors have been described. At this point no trade-off between the ATM system and external objects in the context has been found. The analysis passes over core steps 5 and 6 to examine the responses and

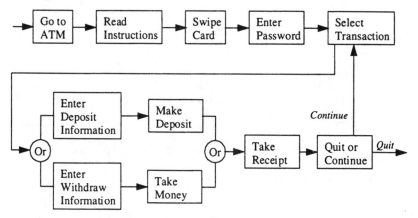

Figure 12.5   View of behavior of ATM customer.

the structure of the ATM system. This will lead to the definition of some of the subsystems of the ATM system.

12.3   Core Steps Applied to the ATM System

We accept the models created up to this point and pass on to the three concurrent core steps. The first one we apply is *create the structure model,* to create a first try at the structure of the ATM system.

12.3.1   Structure of the ATM system: core step 5

This step begins with a first try at listing the subsystems of the ATM system in Fig. 12.6. The objects included will very likely be modified as a complete analysis of the ATM system proceeds.

First guesses are shown for the functions needed in ATM system management, installation and field service, and transaction concentrator and router. The transaction concentrator and router collects transactions and queries over leased local lines from local ATM machines. It routes them to the appropriate network to get them to local and distant banks and to the transaction-processing organizations. It routes transaction validation back to the ATM machines. These guesses must be examined by carefully developing the related behaviors and trying allocations onto the objects. At this point the listing gives an idea of what the tentative subsystems may do.

This example is concentrating on the thief portion of the ATM system context. The subsystem involved is the ATM machine. For this example, then, we concentrate on the responses of the ATM machine and its needed attributes as a result of the excitations defined earlier. This is a small part of the total problem.

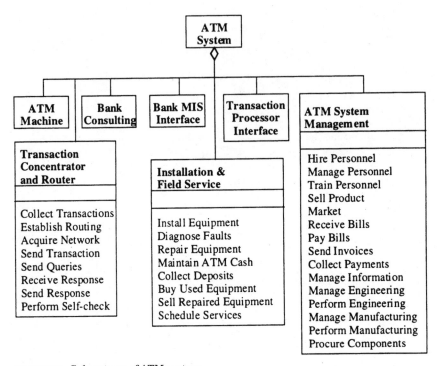

Figure 12.6 Subsystems of ATM system.

12.3.2 Behavior of the ATM system: core step 3

One possible view of the behavior of the ATM system is shown in Fig. 12.7.

It is the behavior of the ATM machine subsystem that is being studied because we have limited the scope of the example. This subsystem is interesting because the analysis involves responses and attributes to satisfy the ATM customer, and another set of responses and attributes to thwart the thief.

Responses and attributes to thwart the thief. There are four scenarios for the cabinet cracker (Fig. 12.3) and two scenarios for the mugger (Fig. 12.4). We will consider them one by one.

Scenario 1. The cabinet cracker carries off the ATM machine. This can be thwarted by making the machine heavy, by bolting it to the floor, and by assuring a location so that lifting equipment such as a tow truck or forklift cannot get close enough to it for loading of merchandise. The lifting force can be specified after consultation with security experts. An initial estimated budget of 4000 lb is made here as sufficient to prevent people from removing the ATM machine.

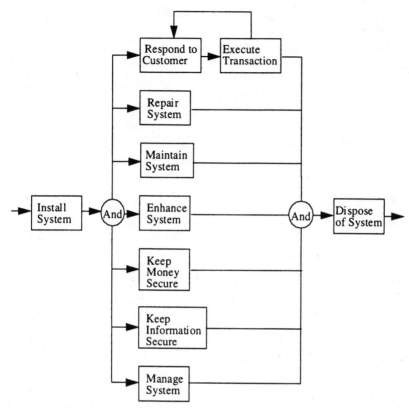

Figure 12.7 View of system behavior.

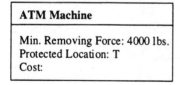

Figure 12.8 ATM machine.

The attribute values are the arguments of equations associated with performance requirements and are captured in Fig. 12.8.

1. *Requirement:* The ATM machine shall be secured such that a 4000-lb force is required to remove it.
   a. *Requirement type:* nontemporal performance
   b. *Attribute:* minimum removing force
   c. *Associated equation:* removing force = minimum removing force, 4000 lb

      d. Traceability: the requirement traces to effectiveness measure EM4

      e. Validation: validated by measurement

2. *Requirement:* The ATM machine shall be located such that lifting equipment cannot get close enough to it to load merchandise.

      a. Requirement type: functional

      b. Attribute: protected location = true or false

      c. Associated equation: protected location = true

      d. Traceability: the requirement traces to effectiveness measure EM4

      e. Validation: validated by inspection

Unfortunately, these derived requirements will increase cost.

    Scenario 2. The cabinet cracker cuts open the ATM machine with a torch. This can be thwarted with a heat sensor and an alarm to the security force. If, on the average, it takes the security force 15 min to respond, then the ATM cabinet must withstand cutting with a torch for 15 min.

3. *Requirement:* the ATM machine shall sense heat.

      a. Requirement type: functional

      b. Traceability: the requirement traces to effectiveness measure EM4

      c. Validation: validated by measurement

4. *Requirement:* The ATM machine shall send an alarm when the cabinet temperature exceeds 300°F locally.

      a. Requirement type: nontemporal performance

      b. Attribute: alarm temperature 300°F

      c. Traceability: the requirement traces to effectiveness measure EM4

      d. Validation: validated by measurement

5. *Requirement:* The ATM cabinet shall withstand cutting with an oxyacetylene torch for 15 min or longer.

      a. Requirement type: temporal performance

      b. Attribute: minimum cabinet cutting duration 15 min

      c. Traceability: the requirement traces to effectiveness measure EM4

      d. Traceability: the time budget traces to function *cut cabinet open*

      e. Validation: validated by measurement

    Scenario 3. The cabinet cracker picks the lock. This action can be thwarted by sensing the vibrations of picking the lock with a sensor and an alarm to the security force.

6. *Requirement:* the ATM cabinet shall withstand picking the lock by a trained locksmith for 15 min or longer.

     a. *Requirement type:* temporal performance
     b. *Attribute:* minimum lock pick duration 15 min
     c. *Traceability:* the requirement traces to effectiveness measure EM4
     d. *Traceability:* the time budget traces to function *pick a lock*
     e. *Validation:* validated by measurement

The cabinet cracker breaks open the door with clamps, drills, punches, or saws.

7. *Requirement:* The ATM cabinet shall withstand breaking the door by a trained locksmith for 15 min or longer.
     a. *Requirement type:* temporal performance
     b. *Attribute:* minimum door break duration 15 min
     c. *Traceability:* the requirement traces to effectiveness measure EM4
     d. *Traceability:* the time budget traces to function *break open*
     e. *Validation:* validated by measurement

Scenarios 3 and 4

8. *Requirement:* The ATM machine shall sense vibration.
     a. *Requirement type:* functional
     b. *Traceability:* the requirement traces to effectiveness measure EM4
     c. *Validation:* validated by inspection
9. *Requirement:* The ATM machine shall send an alarm when the detected vibration level exceeds TBD.
     a. *Requirement type:* nontemporal performance
     b. *Attribute:* alarm vibration level TBD
     c. *Traceability:* the requirement traces to effectiveness measure EM4
     d. *Validation:* validated by measurement

Scenarios 1 to 4. For all the scenarios it is necessary to notify security. The alarm needs to occur whether thieves attempt to cut the signal or to replace it with a generated signal.

10. *Requirement:* The ATM machine shall send a tamperproof alarm to security to notify that a theft is in progress when heat or vibration is detected.
     a. *Requirement type:* functional
     b. *Traceability:* the requirement traces to effectiveness measure EM4
     c. *Validation:* validated by measurement

The attributes and the functions developed are collected in the graphic description in Fig. 12.9.

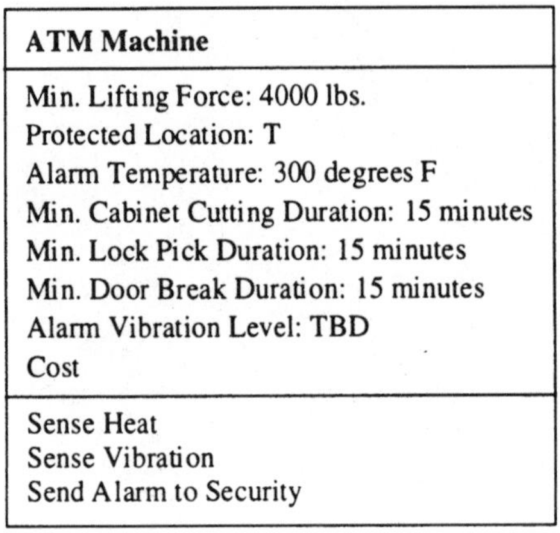

ATM Machine
Min. Lifting Force: 4000 lbs. Protected Location: T Alarm Temperature: 300 degrees F Min. Cabinet Cutting Duration: 15 minutes Min. Lock Pick Duration: 15 minutes Min. Door Break Duration: 15 minutes Alarm Vibration Level: TBD Cost
Sense Heat Sense Vibration Send Alarm to Security

Figure 12.9   ATM machine revised.

Although this specification for the ATM machine can be implemented, everything added for security is contributing to cost. It is certainly a candidate for trade-off against lower-cost solutions or against accepting higher risk of theft.

Scenarios 5 and 6.   These are the scenarios for the mugger. For these scenarios the important effectiveness measures are EM4 used above and EM6: customers shall prefer to use the ATM system over the bank tellers. Customers will not use ATM machines unless they feel safe from muggers. In these scenarios the mugger sees an ATM customer using a machine and either takes the cash withdrawn from that customer, or takes over the machine and withdraws money. In either case the ATM customer is threatened with violence and may be injured. Cameras and emergency buttons can be built into the machines. However, these devices will only ensure that help arrives more quickly to take the patron to a hospital. There is nothing that can be built into the ATM machine itself to prevent mugging.

12.3.3   Structure implications of the theft scenarios: core step 4

The machines can be placed in safe locations which are known to be free of mugging incidents. This suggests thinking about all the possible kinds of secure locations. Figure 12.10 shows the result of such creative thinking. Modeling only captures the results of the thinking.

In the context of ATM systems there are locations which can be used to house the ATM machines and provide them with electrical power and connection to communications. Some locations are secure, and some insecure. For any given location, this can be established by sur-

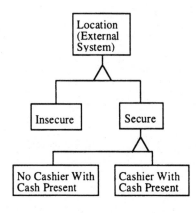

Figure 12.10 Classification of secure locations.

vey of people who are familiar with the locations. Among the secure locations there are two very interesting kinds:

1. Locations that have a cashier and cash present
2. Locations that do not have cash and a cashier present

If cash and a cashier are already present, then it is not necessary for the ATM machine to dispense money. Instead, it can dispense a receipt for which the cashier gives the ATM customer the money. In some cities and areas there may be no locations with these characteristics. In some cities and other areas, retail stores, drug stores, and convenience stores can serve this function.

This alternative is a different kind of allocation of behavior than has been described before in this example. It is an allocation of the function "dispense money" away from the ATM system and into the external objects in the context. In Fig. 11.11 it was assumed that all the ATM machines would dispense money withdrawn from either checking or savings accounts. This allocation into the context totally relieves the ATM system of the responsibility for the physical security of the money and risk to the customer. It also drastically reduces the cost of the ATM machine, which now does not need a money dispenser, protection from theft, or a repository for deposits. Deposits can be left with the cashier.

Many potential retail locations of this type are located close to the ATM customers, and these retailers benefit from customers with money in their stores at their cash registers. For this solution to the system problem, there are a few additional considerations. It is necessary to print a random number on the receipt and to display that number at the register so that fraudulent receipts cannot be presented. It is necessary to arrange for the transaction to be canceled if the

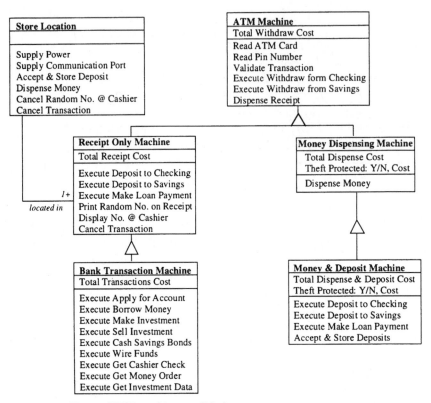

Figure 12.11   Types of ATM machine, modified.

retail store is temporarily short of funds and cannot honor the receipt. These restrictions can be readily incorporated into the requirements and represented in the models. These considerations cause a redefinition of the types of ATM machines, shown in Fig. 12.11.

The parent class, ATM machine, shows all the functions common to the ATM machines and the cost of these capabilities.

The *money-and-deposit machine* dispenses money and stores deposits. It may or may not be protected against theft, depending on location. When these machines are located inside bank lobbies, they do not require the protection of machines located outside or in unsafe buildings.

The *receipt-only machine* provides all the functions of the money-and-deposit machine because of the cooperative arrangement with the store location. An element left unclear is whether the transport of deposits from store to bank will be done by the ATM installation and field service subsystem or by the store when store receipts are taken to the bank. That issue is flagged but not analyzed until installation and field service and associated behaviors are analyzed.

The *money dispensing machine* does not have a repository for deposits. It may or may not be protected from theft, depending on location.

The *bank transaction machine* is a customer workstation for bank transactions of all kinds. When a business like this is starting, the bank transaction machine is a future release. Such releases often need a trial in a bank to prove their effectiveness. The cost-effectiveness is not clear from the analysis of benefit to the bank. Widespread introduction may await introduction and acceptance of electronic banking.

Clearly, this is a product line of ATM machines. The alternatives provide a basis for consulting with banks not only on their internal procedures but also on tailoring the distribution of ATM machines and types to the communities and customer populations they serve. Ability to locate low-cost receipt-only machines in cooperating stores can be an asset for the ATM system vendor with appropriate business relationships with store chains.

All of these results are the result of analyzing responses to the thief. The responses of the ATM machine to the ATM customer are described next.

12.3.4 Response of ATM machine to ATM customer

The behavior of the ATM machine is a response to the behavior of the ATM customer (Fig. 12.5). Within that response are some issues that transcend the ATM machine subsystem and the theft scenarios. The ATM machine is involved in the validation of the transactions to ensure that the card and password are valid and that accounts have funds adequate for withdrawal. The actual validation can take place in the ATM machine or in a remote location. These alternatives affect the amount of time the customer must wait for validation, the amount of use of communications, and the security of the information. Validation involves the spoofer and the network portions of the context diagram. The validation issues need to be examined from all these perspectives. For brevity, this example will consider the problem only from the standpoint of the ATM customer and the ATM machine, which are parts of the theft portion of the context under study for the example.

Figure 12.12 shows a plausible response to the ATM customer.

When the ATM machine is turned on, it first initializes. It then displays start instructions for the customer. When the card is swiped by the customer, the ATM machine reads the card. If the reading produces good data, the behavior continues. If the data is bad, the ATM machine displays a message to reswipe the card. When good data is

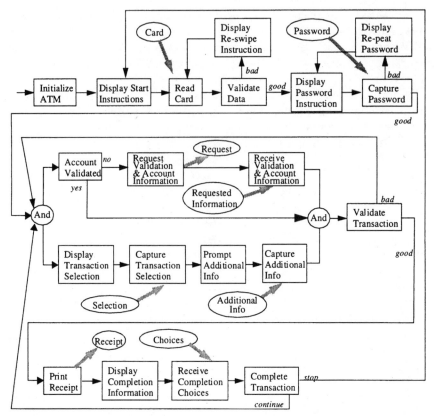

Figure 12.12   Behavior of ATM machine.

obtained, the ATM machine prompts the user for password information. A password is entered by the customer and captured. The password can be quickly checked locally with a checksum if the card number and password have been properly established. If the password is bad, the ATM machine displays a repeat password message. If it is good, the behavior continues with two concurrent branches.

On the upper branch the ATM machine requests information over the network for password verification, card verification, and account balances. There will be a time lag after which the requested information is received by the ATM machine. During this time lag activity proceeds along the lower branch. The transaction selection is displayed to the customer. The customer selects a transaction type. The selection of transaction amount is displayed, and the customer inputs the amount chosen. The overlapping of the two branches minimizes waiting time for the customer. Requesting and receiving the information needed concerning the card, password, and account balances in a single burst minimizes both time delay and communication use. However, for security reasons it may be undesirable to transmit account information back to the ATM machine.

When both branches are complete, there is enough information to validate the transaction. If the transaction is approved, the process continues. If not, it cycles back to the front of the two branches to attempt to match a transaction against the accounts.

If the transaction was allowed, a receipt for the transaction is printed. If the machine is of the receipt-only type, the receipt is taken to the cashier, who matches the printed random number against the displayed number at the register. The cashier pays the withdrawn amount and enters the completion choices of completed and stop. The ATM machine signals a completed transaction to the system. A cashier who is out of cash and cannot honor the receipt enters "not completed" and "stop." The transaction is aborted and not recorded by the system.

If the ATM machine is of the other types, ATM customers enter their completion choices and may stop or continue with additional transactions. When finished, the "stop" command is entered and the ATM machine displays the start instructions.

The plausible behavior just described has considered only a few of the anomalous conditions that can occur. Each step in the behavior needs to be examined for desired behavior of the ATM machine under all possible conditions (Carson, 1995). For example, what happens at any step if the customer walks away from the machine? Does it time out and return to displaying start instructions? What happens at any point if the ATM customer wants to quit or back up to a previous step?

Each step requires further detailed design of the displays to be presented and the data to be processed. These details are developed as the ATM machine is broken into its components. There are three kinds of ATM machines to consider: receipt-only, money dispensing, and money-and-deposit machines. It would be useful to develop them so that they share and reuse a maximum number of parts.

12.3.5 Structure of the ATM machine and related objects: core step 5

The development of behaviors has introduced a number of additional objects which are not a part of the ATM machine, but are associated with it. Figure 12.13 shows these associations. Models like this figure treat all the objects on an equal footing in showing the relationships among them. They are particularly useful in organizing information about the system because information about each of these objects may be important to record. They are often referred to as *information models*.

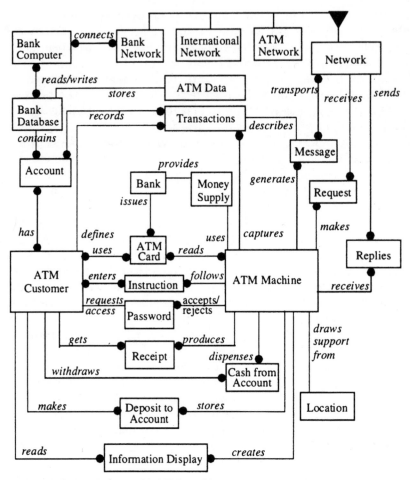

Figure 12.13 Associations with ATM machine.

This representation asserts that the ATM customer has accounts, defines transactions, uses an ATM card issued by the bank, enters instructions, requests access with a password, gets receipts, withdraws cash from an account, makes deposits to an account, and reads information displays. It asserts that the ATM system uses the money supply provided by the bank, reads the ATM card, follows the instructions, accepts or rejects the password, produces receipts, dispenses cash from an account, stores deposits to an account, creates information displays, draws support from a location, receives replies, makes requests, captures transactions, and generates messages describing the transactions.

The figure asserts that a network transports messages, receives requests, and sends replies. Because we do not know the structure of the network, it asserts that there are three inclusive classes of networks: ATM network, international network, and bank network. The bank network connects to an appropriate bank computer, which reads and writes to a bank database which contains accounts in which are recorded the account transactions. The bank database also stores ATM data, including the information needed for validating card numbers and passwords. The physical locations and structure of the computers, networks, and data storage media are in general not known. Their identities and routing addresses are known or are found by reading appropriate files.

Models such as this are very useful in defining all the objects with which the ATM machine interfaces. When database engineers are organizing the information that describes all the objects in the system, the information models provide a basis for organization of the data. When created with an executable notation, database schema can be generated from the information models. This is one of the intimate relationships between the detailed description of the system needed for specification and database development.

This example has examined only one of the several subsystems of the ATM system. Some of these other subsystems, especially installation and field service, will interface with the ATM machines and have a major impact on their operating cost. That information comes from study of the other subsystems and can be included in the models when it is available.

12.4 Exercises

1. Create a behavior for the ATM machine in response to the scenarios for the thief.
2. Create a behavior for the response of security to an alarm from the ATM machine.
3. Link the composite behavior of a thief with the behaviors of the ATM machine and security. Create a timeline for the interaction of the three objects.
4. Define a behavior for installation and field service that will
   a. Install the machines
   b. Supply money to ATM machines
   c. Retrieve deposits from ATM machines
   d. Respond to out-of-service calls
   e. Proactively test ATM machines using remote diagnostics
   f. Service broken or malfunctioning ATM machines

   g. Repair and sell ATM machines
   h. Estimate the cost per machine for these services
   i. Schedule installation and field service

5. Estimate the cost to provide each service.
6. Make a rough estimate of the cost of manufacturing each of the three types of ATM machine. Add the cost of the services required for each type of machine.
7. For a local bank with 20 branches, decide what numbers of the different types of ATM machine you would distribute in the community. What assumptions do you have to make?
8. Think of a set of rules or an algorithm for locating ATM machines.
9. Develop a system-level analysis of an electronic cash register.
10. What is the output of system-level analysis? What questions does it answer?

12.5 References

Beth, T., 1995: Confidential communication on the Internet. *Sci. Am.* (Dec.) pp. 88–91.

Birman, K. P., and R. van Renesse, 1996: Software for reliable networks. *Sci. Am.* (May), pp. 64–69.

Carson, R. S., 1995: A set theory model for anomaly handling in system requirements analysis. *Fifth Annual International Symposium of the National Council on Systems Engineering,* vol. 1, pp. 515–522.

Khanna, R., 1993: *Distributed Computing, Implementation and Management Strategies.* Englewood Cliffs, N.J.: Prentice-Hall.

Schiller, J. I., 1994: Secure distributed computing. *Sci. Am.* (Nov.), 72–76.

Simmons, G. J., 1992: *Contemporary Cryptology: State of the Art and Future Directions.* New York: IEEE Press.

Chapter

13

Subsystem Analysis

13.1 What Subsystem Analysis Is

Subsystem analysis is the study of the subsystems of the subject system which will be used by a business or businesses. The subsystem may have its own effectiveness measures, design constraints, and architecture which differ from those of the system. Subsystem analysis is preceded by analysis of the system tier from which it receives the context for each subsystem. The structure model of the context describes all the objects with interfaces to the subsystem. The behavior models for the context describe the behaviors of all the objects with interfaces to the subsystem. A behavior model for the subsystem describes how it responds to the excitations it receives from the objects in its context.

Subsystem analysis applies the core technical steps to review and validate the context information received from analysis of the system tier. This review is needed to find and correct errors and missing information in the models received. It is necessary for large systems because it will decompose into six or more subsystems with an engineering team assigned to each subsystem. These teams need to review and apply their collective experience to refine the models developed by the analysis of the system tier team. Since the subsystems interact, the teams need to review with one another the interactions among their subsystems.

When the context models have been corrected and accepted, each team applies the core technical steps to its subsystem. Each subsystem is decomposed into its components by allocating the behavior of the subsystem onto trial sets of components. This process defines the context of the component statically and dynamically. The behavior of each component is refined as a response to all the excitations it receives.

This chapter describes subsystem analysis by continuing the example of the ATM system. A complete development of all the requirements and models for all the subsystems is too large for inclusion in a book and is repetitive as an example. Analysis of the ATM machine will be continued in this chapter. The analysis will be carried to the specification of the components.

13.2   Core Steps Applied to the Context of the ATM Machine

Substantial information about the ATM machine was developed in analysis of the system tier in Chaps. 11 and 12 and is accepted for use here. However, only one part of the system context was explored during analysis of the system tier so that the only subsystem definitions and models that emerged were for the ATM machine. Models for the response of the ATM machine to the thief were left as an exercise for the reader, as was the behavior of security. The impact of analysis of the installation and field service subsystem was left as an exercise. Models are presented here for response to the thief, behavior of security, and impact of analysis of field service on the ATM machine. This is done without performing analysis or trade-off to optimize the content of the models.

Overall view of system behavior.   Figure 13.1 defines top-level behavior.

Response to thief.   Figure 13.2 is a view of the ATM machine behavior in response to the thief scenarios. Details of the tamperproof alarm signaling are contained in the function *send alarm* and require detailed design.

Impact of installation and field service.   Results are assumed here for the analysis of installation and field service without going through analysis of the system tier and trade-off. They may or may not be near-optimal. The distribution of machines locally is assumed to be

- Three money-and-deposit machines with alarms in the drive through outside the local bank, and one outside each of two branch banks; five total

- One money-and-deposit machine without alarm and protection inside the local bank, the 2 branch banks, and the 8 supermarket banks; 11 total

- One hundred receipt-only machines in 100 convenience store locations serving the local area; 100 total

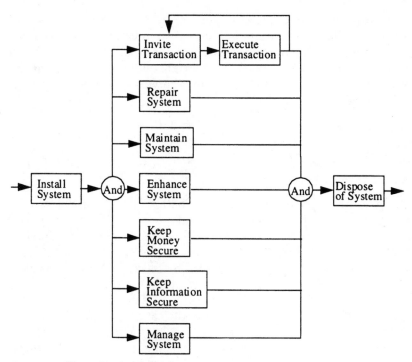

Figure 13.1   View of system behavior.

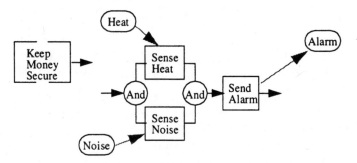

Figure 13.2   View of response of ATM machine to thief.

With this distribution the collection of deposits, supply of money, and supply of tape for the printers is handled by regular bank personnel and convenience store personnel. Installation and field service is organized regionally with responsibility for about 2000 machines for the 10 local banks in the region. Mean time between failures (MTBF) is required to be

- Receipt-only machines: MTBF = 5 yr/failure; 400 failures/yr regionally

- Money-and-deposit machines: MTBF = 1.0 yr/failure; 150 failures/yr regionally

The cash dispenser is expected to be both expensive and less reliable than many of the other components, so MTBF is less for the money-and-deposit machine than for the receipt-only machine. The failures are evaluated with remote execution of diagnostics. Failures of the receipt-only machine are serviced by having regular bank personnel replace the entire unit and by initializing and validating its performance remotely over the network. For each region, two service persons handle the failures. Such procedures limit field service personnel to about 20 persons for the system. Only when the impact of a service structure such as this has been considered can the operating cost of the different machines be ascertained. As the machine reliability goes up, the cost of servicing goes down, but cost of manufacture goes up. A full trade-off of theses alternatives is required in analysis of the system tier. The solution above is applied in this chapter. It provides operating cost information for the ATM machines and sets goals for their MTBF and reliability. For a thorough discussion of MTBF, reliability, and availability, and for specifying all reliability concerns, a good text on that subject should be consulted (Blanchard and Fabrycky, 1990, Chap. 13).

13.3   Core Steps Applied to the ATM Machine

13.3.1   Effectiveness measure for the ATM machine: core step 2

The initial set of six effectiveness measures (EMs) for the ATM system are repeated here. If others are found during modeling, they will have to be added.

EM1.   The ATM system shall maintain correct records.

EM2.   The ATM system shall generate correct reports. EM1 and EM2 require that the ATM machine shall

Interpret instructions correctly

Read cards correctly

Request information correctly

Interpret replies correctly

Validate passwords correctly

Validate transactions correctly

Reject bad data

Continue properly after receiving bad data

EM3. The ATM system shall keep information secure. The analysis of the system tier to apply EM3 to the ATM machine has not been carried out in the example. There is insufficient information to apply EM3.

EM4. The ATM system shall keep money secure. EM4 applies directly to the ATM machine.

EM5. The ATM system shall operate at maximum benefit/total cost to the banks it serves. Some guesses about installation and field service have been made to provide rough guidance in operating cost and ATM machine MTBF.

EM6. Customers shall prefer to use the ATM system over the bank tellers.

Because of system considerations, machines have been located for customer convenience. Locations have been selected to allay anxiety over personal safety. MTBF has been made sufficiently long that a customer should experience no machines out of order in more than a year of using nearby machines.

Ease of use and understanding must be designed into the ATM machine. This design work is an engineering discipline, generally called *design for manability and human factors analysis.* Good discussions of the discipline are available (Blanchard and Fabrycky, 1990, Chap. 15; Woodson, 1981). The ultimate issue is not the design, but the evaluation of the design by users. This can be done with a prototype and a users survey with the prototype. When the specifications are captured in executable models, the prototype can be rapidly generated by automatically transforming the specifications into code and adding the details, like screen layouts, which were deferred to the designers. A set of criteria, like those listed below, are needed to evaluate user reaction to the prototype. On the basis of a valid survey, 80 percent of participants on their first use shall:

- Find the information displays self-explanatory
- Follow the sequence of user actions successfully
- Make their choices without error
- Complete their transactions
- Express satisfaction in using the ATM machine

This is a specific example of early build and validate.

13.3.2   Structure of the ATM machines: core step 5

It is not a single ATM machine under study, but a family of them. The decomposition of the machines into their components is needed. In addition, there will be associations among the family members that show how parts are reused among them. These are the associations that will cause the designers to ensure parts are designed for reuse.

There are four basic ATM machines under consideration, and two of these may be either designed for theft protection or not, yielding six kinds of machines as shown in Fig. 13.3. Protection attributes and functions are shown through multiple inheritance using the *protected ATM machine* class.

There is an equation for the cost of any of these machines:

$$\begin{aligned} \text{Total cost} = {} & \text{withdrawal cost} + \text{installation cost} \\ & + \text{servicing cost} + \text{maintenance cost} \\ & + \text{manufacturing cost} + \text{operating cost} \\ & + \text{security cost} \pm \text{location cost} \, / \, \text{payment} \end{aligned}$$

A cost/payment attribute has been associated with the store location. Having store locations for receipt on ATM machines is a matter of a business arrangement with chains of stores such as convenience stores. The work to negotiate such agreements is planned and scheduled in the build-and-test plan. The negotiation may result in rental payments to the convenient store chain, or in payments by the store chain to the bank for having the attraction of banking in its stores. This part of the planning would normally be developed during concept analysis, as discussed in Chap. 11. As this example has been developed, the opportunity for supplying receipt-only ATM machines is not discovered until later, during subanalysis of the system tier. It becomes an issue requiring resolution by revisiting the build-and-test plan developed in concept analysis and modifying the implementation planning from those earlier steps to include development of new business relationships, implementation of an unanticipated class of machine, and modification to field service plans and implementation.

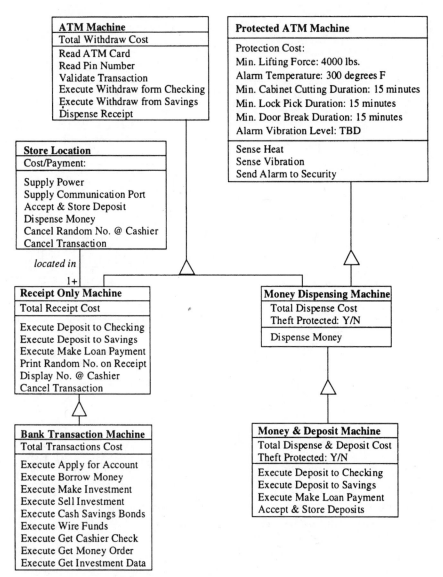

Figure 13.3 Types of ATM machine, modified.

This is an example which requires change control as discoveries are made during engineering to synchronize the planned ongoing work with the impact of the discovery.

Figure 13.4 shows the composition of the machines and how they are interrelated for reuse of parts and field service. The receipt-only

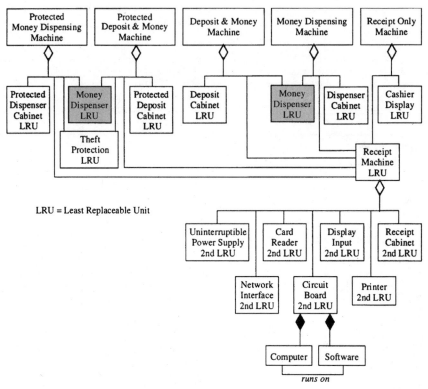

Figure 13.4 ATM machines, parts list, and associations.

machine is built from a receipt machine least-replaceable unit (LRU) and a cashier display LRU. If one of these machines fails, the LRUs are what is replaced in the convenience store, as a unit. All the other four ATM machine types use the receipt machine LRU, secured into their cabinets, for display, computation, network interface, receipt printing, and diagnostics. This minimizes stocking of different parts, and maximizes production runs. Each machine has its own cabinet; the cabinet classes are shown with light shading. The cabinets for the theft-protected machines will be expensive and used only where necessary. All four machines that dispense money use the same money dispenser LRU. In Fig. 13.4 that class is shown twice and is shaded dark so that the reader does not have to deal with lines crossing in the figure. (Some tools do not allow the repetition of a class this way, and the tool tracks crossing association connections without confusion.) The protected machines use the same theft-correction LRU.

The receipt machine LRU, which is used in all four ATM machine types, is built from a power supply, network interface, card reader, cir-

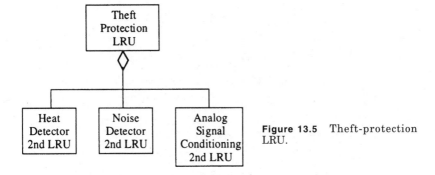

Figure 13.5 Theft-protection LRU.

cuit board, display unit, printer, and cabinet. These seven items are second-level LRUs. They are replacement units when a receipt machine LRU is taken to a repair facility for repair. The circuit board, cabinet, and software will likely require engineering development. The other items can likely be procured from suppliers. The display/input unit may have to be tailored to this product by a vendor. The aggregations in Fig. 13.4 capture not only the parts lists for each kind of ATM machine, but also the reuse architecture of the products. The models capture the engineering creativity in finding a good reuse architecture.

Both protected machines use the same theft-protection LRU shown in Fig. 13.5. The network control and alarm generation are handled by the receipt machine circuit board, which contains the computer and software. Much of the system complexity and response behavior to both the thief and the ATM customer is captured in the software.

Attributes and allocation of behavior. The parts list needs to be augmented with attribute values, and with interconnection diagrams. The attributes are examined first at second LRU level, the LRU level, and then at the ATM receipt machine level. A reasonable set of values are given for cost and for MTBF design goals.

The behavior of the ATM receipt machine is allocated to the parts. Figure 13.6 shows the components with their attribute values, design goals at this stage, and functions. On the basis of the cost attributes, the receipt machine has a cost goal of $1030.

The receipt machine fails if any of these components fails. Under these conditions the reciprocal of the total MTBF is equal to the sum of the reciprocal MTBFs of the components (Blanchard and Fabrycky, 1990, p. 355). The receipt machine MTBF is 5.6 years. The MTBFs assumed are quite long and would require conservatively designed inte-

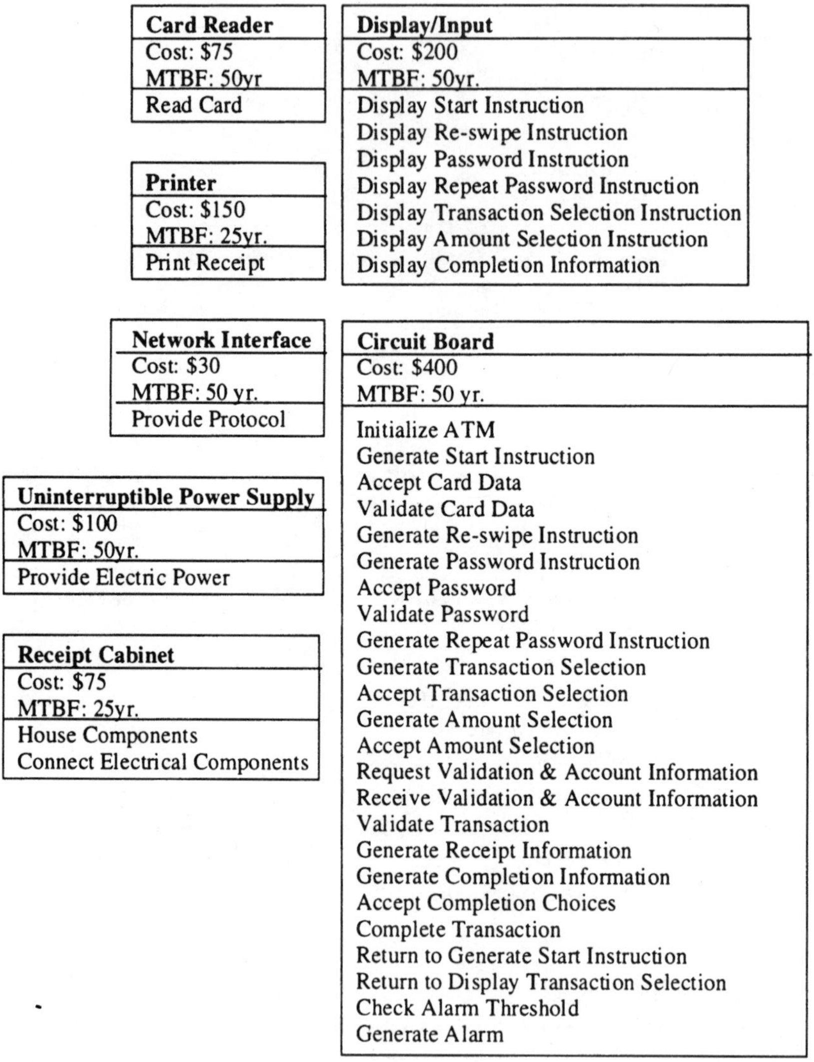

Card Reader
Cost: $75
MTBF: 50yr
Read Card

Printer
Cost: $150
MTBF: 25yr.
Print Receipt

Display/Input
Cost: $200
MTBF: 50yr.
Display Start Instruction
Display Re-swipe Instruction
Display Password Instruction
Display Repeat Password Instruction
Display Transaction Selection Instruction
Display Amount Selection Instruction
Display Completion Information

Network Interface
Cost: $30
MTBF: 50 yr.
Provide Protocol

Uninterruptible Power Supply
Cost: $100
MTBF: 50yr.
Provide Electric Power

Receipt Cabinet
Cost: $75
MTBF: 25yr.
House Components
Connect Electrical Components

Circuit Board
Cost: $400
MTBF: 50 yr.
Initialize ATM
Generate Start Instruction
Accept Card Data
Validate Card Data
Generate Re-swipe Instruction
Generate Password Instruction
Accept Password
Validate Password
Generate Repeat Password Instruction
Generate Transaction Selection
Accept Transaction Selection
Generate Amount Selection
Accept Amount Selection
Request Validation & Account Information
Receive Validation & Account Information
Validate Transaction
Generate Receipt Information
Generate Completion Information
Accept Completion Choices
Complete Transaction
Return to Generate Start Instruction
Return to Display Transaction Selection
Check Alarm Threshold
Generate Alarm

Figure 13.6 The components as objects with attributes and functions.

grated circuits, very high-quality electrical connectors on the cabinet, and a very high-quality printer. Printer life in years is dependent on the number of receipts printed in that time because failure is a result of mechanical wear. The assumption given above corresponds to about a million receipts between failures. The number of field service personnel and the cost of field service are predicated on the machine reliability.

Figure 13.7 shows the functions and attributes of the least-replaceable units.

Theft Protection	Cashier Display	Money Dispenser
Cost: $300	Cost: $70	Cost: $2000
MTBF: 5yr.	MTBF: 50yr.	MTBF: 3yr.
Sense Noise	Display Number	Dispense Money
Sense Vibration	OK Transaction	

Protected Dispenser Cabinet	Protected Deposit Cabinet
Cost: $6000	Cost: $6500
MTBF: 25yr.	MTBF: 25yr.
House Components	House Components
Connect Electrical Components	Connect Electrical Components

Dispenser Cabinet	Deposit Cabinet
Cost: $1200	Cost: $1600
MTBF: 25yr.	MTBF: 25yr.
House Components	House Components
Connect Electrical Components	Connect Electrical Components

Figure 13.7 LRU objects.

Protected Deposit & Money Machine	Protected Money Dispensing Machine	Deposit & Money Machine	Money Dispensing Machine
Mfg. Cost: $9830	Mfg. Cost; $9,330	Mfg. Cost: $4630	Mfg. Cost: $4230
MTBF: 1.3yr.	MTBF: 1.3yr.	MTBF: 1.8yr.	MTBF: 1.8yr.

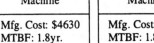

Receipt Dispensing Machine
Mfg. Cost; $1.100
MTBF: 5.1yr.

Figure 13.8 The five ATM machines.

The attributes simply sum up the parts tree. The cost to manufacture is added. MTBF follows a sum of reciprocals law. When the parts tree is captured in a tool, the summations are readily automated. This can be done with a modeling tool that captures all the models or with a spreadsheet.

When the attributes are summed to the ATM machines, the results of Fig. 13.8 are obtained

Hardware interconnection. When the behavior has been defined as done here, the allocation of functions to components establishes many

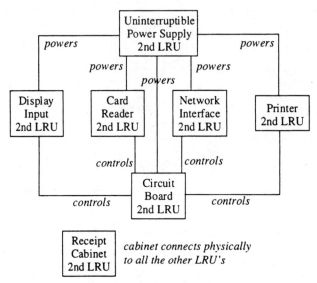

Figure 13.9 Interconnection diagram.

of the interconnections, those between active objects that exchange input/outputs. Figure 13.9 shows the interfaces.

Software components.   The software components are developed in Chap. 14 as an example of the handoff from systems engineering to software engineering and the design of components based on system models. A handoff of this nature may occur in any of the tiers of development when a system, subsystem, or component is to be supplied by a business partner or a supplier company.

13.4   Exercises

1. Analyze installation and field service for the ATM machines:
   a. Apply the six core steps to the analysis.
   b. Compare results with the assumed results in Chap. 13.
2. Model the subsystems of a computer:
   a. Are these all produced by a single vendor?
   b. Which systems will be designed more fully by the computer manufacturer? Why?
3. Model the subsystems of a hospital and their relationship to each other.
4. Consider a communications systems provider. Is the information needed by the provider about a satellite the same as the information needed by the satellite manufacturer?

5. In what roles is a satellite viewed by
   a. Antenna designers?
   b. Communications vendors?
   c. Rocket launchers?
   d. The military?
   e. Satellite manufacturers?

13.5 References

Blanchard, B. F., and W. Fabrycky, 1990: *Systems Engineering and Analysis,* 2d ed., Englewood Cliffs, N.J.: Prentice-Hall.

Woodson, E. W., 1981: *Human Factors Design Handbook.* New York: McGraw-Hill.

14

Handoff

14.1 What Handoff Is

Handoff is the transition between the system design work and the design work performed by individual engineering disciplines, or by suppliers. The systems engineering information, specification, developed at the higher tiers must be delivered to the specialty engineers in a rigorous and understandable format. The disciplines must also be able to feed information back into the systems engineering domain so that estimates of total system performance can be refined as parts of the design and worked through to implementation

Within the design process for large systems, handoff occurs at different tiers of hierarchy. Business rarely decides to attempt to develop all the components of a major system. Outsourcing is a prominent aspect of modern system development. Instead, businesses choose certain aspects of the system design in which they will specialize. These aspects of the system design will be pursued further than those aspects which are contracted to suppliers, purchased from vendors, or provided by business partners. It may be a system, subsystem, or component that is developed and supplied externally. The outside vendors, suppliers, and partners need to do the same rigorous engineering as the initiating engineering organization, but they receive systems engineering information and specifications as a handoff from the initiating engineering organization.

Considering the case of the ATM system, many of the hardware elements are likely to be sourced from external vendors. It would be unrealistic to assume that the display unit LRU or the uninterruptible power supply (UPS) LRU are going to be developed by the same company that is developing the ATM system. The engineering skill and knowledge required by these tasks is too disparate. These are also components which are readily available in the commercial marketplace, making it hard to develop them internally with cost competitiveness.

It is more likely that the developer of the ATM system will choose to design the software which drives the system and the cabinetry which houses the ATM machine. Each of these are not already available in the marketplace. Each also offers the company the potential for providing a discriminator that will enhance one or more of the effectiveness measures. In every system designed, the companies must make similar choices about the scope of their expertise and at what level handoff should occur.

For the sourced components, then, handoff occurs at the component tier. For the network subsystem and the backend information-processing system, other businesses supply entire subsystems at the subsystem tier. For the components that are developed internally, several more tiers of design can occur before handoff occurs. Even when the components are sourced, companies are starting to move away from a handoff based primarily on text shipped to a different organization. Instead, the system team contains members from all the organizations and all the disciplines involved. Design information, including models, is shared among teams that cross both organizational and discipline boundaries. This has the predictable result of reduced errors and miscommunication and a higher likelihood of maximizing the effectiveness measures.

This chapter focuses on the handoff between the systems engineering discipline and the specialty disciplines which will design and specify the low-level components from which the system will be composed. It also discusses some of the continuing coordination needs between the systems engineers and the specialty engineers.

Two handoffs are studied in this chapter, each to a software discipline. The handoff to database engineering and to user interface engineering will each be examined. Before we can look at the handoff, however, we need to take the subsystems down another level of design. This level will establish the appropriate context for handing off the design.

14.2 Context for Handoff

In Chap. 13 we already followed an example of the core technical process applied to the subsystems context. Rather than repeat that here, we simply present the models of the ATM design taken to the next level of detail.

Figure 14.1 divides the ATM into three major structural portions with a few supporting pieces.

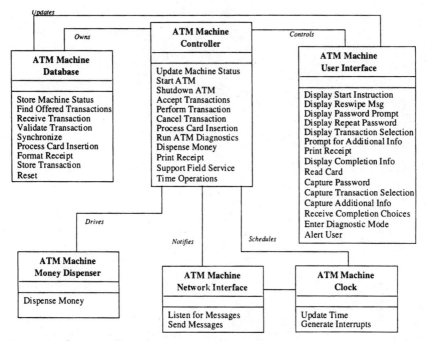

Figure 14.1 Structure diagram for ATM software architecture.

Figure 14.2 gives the behavioral description of the ATM machine's software. The main allocation of requirements and functions in this behavior lie within the *normal, maintenance,* and *testing* operations. The handoff to the engineers in charge of the user interface and database pieces will be examined in the context of the normal operation block. In actual design, of course, these pieces need to be specified and handed off for all phases of operation.

14.3   ATM Handoff-User Interface

A fair amount of information about the user interface has already been specified in the earlier tiers of design development. In any reasonable-sized software system, the user interface design and implementation will have far-reaching consequences for the development of the rest of the system. Of the total amount of software in many large projects, 50 to 80 percent is dedicated to driving the user interface (Brown, 1988).

This being the case, it is extremely important that the user interface be handled with special care. It cannot be considered as an afterthought, something to walk through together after the "real" system

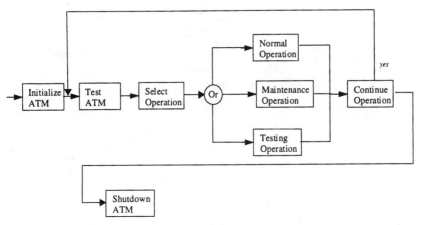

Figure 14.2 View of ATM machine software behavior.

is designed and built. If we revisit the behavior for the ATM from Chap. 12 and consider how many of the behavior elements involve the user interface, we see that well over half of the behavior is directly affected by the interface. Figure 14.3 shows this by shading the elements of the behavior which affect the user interface. Whatever choices are made in designing the user interface are likely, therefore, to directly impact many of the other components of the systems.

14.3.1 Assess available information

As with the other levels of detail, at separation a similar core process is applied. We begin, once again, by gathering all the relevant available information. We start with the models developed thus far.

Models. Figure 14.3 provides the executable specification for the behavior needed from the user interface.

A final decision has not yet been made about what transactions are to be offered through the ATM network (see Fig. 11.10), and the ensuing discussion leads to an initial set of transactions to implement. The analysis in making this decision highlights the possibility that it will change as the system evolves, perhaps not in the initial implementation, but as an evolutionary growth of the system. The impact that this has on the user interface and other components is to decide to use a flexible approach which can accommodate requirement changes of this sort easily.

Scenarios of ATM usage can be derived from looking at the behavior of the bank customer, as shown in Fig. 12.5.

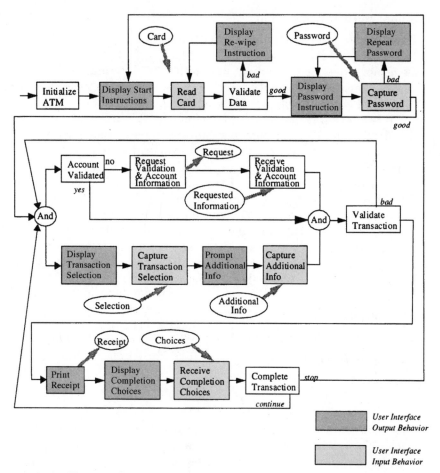

Figure 14.3 User interface–related behavior of ATM machine.

Effectiveness measures. Some of the effectiveness measures are relevant to the user interface; in particular is EM6: "Customers shall prefer to use the ATM system over the bank tellers." This measure is addressed in part by the physical locations of machines within the ATM system. New effectiveness measures were developed at the previous tier of design which translate the original measure into rigorous and verifiable effectiveness measures for the user interface. On the basis of a valid survey, 80 percent of participants on their first use shall

- Find the information displays self-explanatory
- Follow the sequence of user actions successfully
- Make their choices without error

- Complete their transactions
- Express satisfaction in using the ATM machine

Domain knowledge. Especially at handoff, "new" information becomes available. This new information comes in the form of professional experience and education of engineers skilled in a particular discipline.

When the design is handed over from one discipline to another, often necessary changes to the design or requirements are quickly identified. In this case a requirement to adhere to the Americans with Disabilities Act (ADA) is well known by the human factors community. This places new constraints on the way the ATM user interface is designed. For instance, the interface may be required to be Braille-equipped. For the purposes of this example, we will ignore this new requirement to keep the example simple. The way to manage changes such as this with a change adjudication process are discussed elsewhere. Coming out of the change adjudication process will be the accepted set of available information. The three parallel core steps can now be pursued.

14.3.2 Parallel design steps

In the core process the parallel design steps are

1. Define effectiveness measures.
2. Create behavior model.
3. Create structure model.

Similar design work occurs in separation, but the design steps begin to change so as to transition the information into the form needed by the specialty engineering groups.

For the user interface, one of the additional models that needs to be developed is the user's mental model (McGraw, 1992). This model extends the customer model developed in the earlier tiers. The customer models developed so far tell how the customer behaves, what responses are desired from the customer, and what stimulations are given to the customer. These are termed the *behaviors* in systems engineering terms or *work processes* in user interface terms. They also include the structure of the ATM machine context as it relates to the user. Human factors engineering must take into account these work processes and structure but must augment them with the mental model of how the users view the world. If the end design of the user interface is not consistent with the users' mental models, then additional training must be planned to introduce the concept of operation. For the ATM example, the effectiveness measures require that the user interface design match the users' mental models in order to meet EM6. EM6 states that 80 percent of users will successfully use the ATM on their first attempt; thus no training time is provided for.

In the case of the ATM the mental model is fairly easy to discern. The behaviors expected of the ATM user are the same as the existing behaviors of the same user at a bank teller window. Only the actual mechanics of the transaction change. From the user interface design standpoint, one of the challenges is to match the user interface to the process of an actual bank teller. Other parts of the mental model of the users concern the degree of computer experience expected. Since this is to be deployed for the general public, a relatively low experience base is assumed. Users will be assumed to have experience with calculators and simple push-button interfaces. We must not neglect the smaller percentage of computer-literate users. They could be turned off by an interface that is overly user-friendly.

With all this in mind, we begin to develop the more detailed behavior of the user interface. Figure 14.4 gives a behavior for the first piece of the user interface. This behavior takes into account the possibility that the ATM may have a failure of some sort and need to display a message different from the normal message. It also provides a looping mechanism to output more information than can fit on a single screen.

Similar lower-level behaviors need to be developed for each of the user interface–related blocks in Fig. 14.3.

In parallel with the development of the behaviors, the structure of the user interface needs to be developed. Figure 14.5 gives the OMT diagram of the user interface. It consists primarily of the input buttons, the output windows for the screen, and the controller class. The input devices are broken into two subclasses since it is likely that they

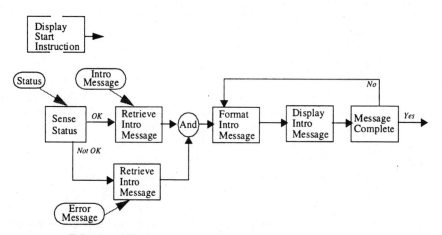

Figure 14.4 Behavior of display start instruction.

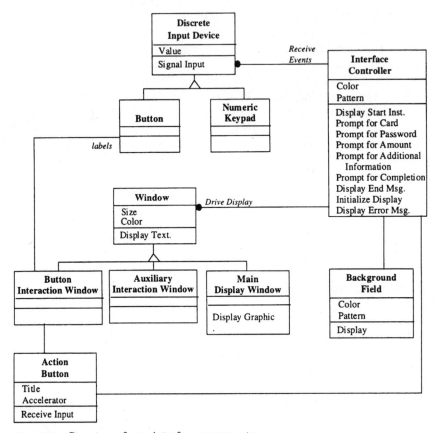

Figure 14.5 Structure of user interface components.

will be sourced as separate items. The output areas are similarly subclassed. Here the distinction between the subclasses is not physical. They will each be rendered on the same physical display device. The difference is semantic, with each window class performing a different role in the logical design of the user interface. These two class hierarchies are associated by an interface controller class. A great deal of the behavior is mapped onto this controller class. OMT diagrams with this general format are relatively common for single-tasking user interfaces. This model also will mesh well with the user's mental model of interacting with a single bank teller. In this case the interface controller performs the role of being the single interaction point.

Once the behaviors are all modeled and the structure definitions are set, we are ready for the final parallel design step in handoff to user interface engineers. The user interface now needs to be mocked up. Multiple versions of the interface with variations on the operating concept are often mocked up.

Mockups extend the executability of the models from a systems engineering simulation to something that can be shown to the various stakeholders for confirmation that the system behavior is what they expected. Frequently, despite the fact that rigorous systems engineering discipline may have been followed, changes are introduced at this point. Features that were not thought of are added to the work scope. Others, that were planned, are removed or changed. Of course, all the requests for change have to be dealt with using the change management process.

Figures 14.6 and 14.7 show the mocked-up screen displays.

The displays shown in Figs. 14.6 and 14.7 are easily put together using any of the commercially available screen layout tools such as Xdesigner in the Unix environment or Visual Basic on the PC plat-

Figure 14.6 User interface mockup displaying the start instruction.

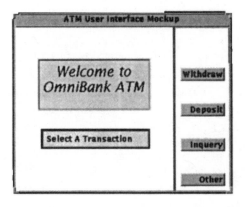

Figure 14.7 User interface mockup prompting for a transaction selection.

form. By hooking the mockup to the executable behavior models, it can be used to run scenarios through the entire simulation as the interior models are developed.

The multiple versions of the mockups are taken forward to the next core step for trade-off analysis and selection on the basis of the verified user preferences from surveys and interviews conducted with the intended users.

Mockups of this nature serve multiple roles in a project. They provide early validation of the systems operating concept by exposing users to a working model. They also form the basis for development of the actual product. The tools used to develop the mockup produce the skeleton programming code in a variety of languages. Figure 14.8 gives a sample of what this code looks like.

14.4   Separation to Database

The handoff to database engineering also follows the core engineering process. As always, the first step is to assess the available information. The context for the portion of the system being designed is especially important to consider. In this case the system being designed is the ATM machine. The rest of the ATM system lies within the context for this design. The impact this has is that the majority of database work lies within the context. The database within the machine is transient in nature, storing a short-term log of transactions which are waiting to be committed to the main ATM system database. It will also be used to store the sequence of transactions that are allowable for the current user. This usage of the database requires coordination between the chief software architect and the database engineer.

14.4.1   Available database information

From the initial information develop in the ATM system context analysis:

11.2. The ATM system shall communicate the transactions it captures to the banks.

11.3. The ATM system shall accept transactions after reading a cash card and receiving a valid PIN number from a system user.

11.4. The ATM system shall execute only those transactions for which validation is received from the bank.

11.6. The ATM system shall print receipts for the transactions executed.

```
...
Widget background_field = (Widget) NULL;
Widget main_display_window = (Widget) NULL;
Widget auxillary_interaction_window = (Widget) NULL;
Widget button_interaction_window = (Widget) NULL;
...
void create_shell (Display *display, char *app_name, int app_argc,
        char **app_argv)
{
   Widget children[4];       /* Children to manage */
   Arg al[64];                      /* Arg List */
   register int ac = 0;             /* Arg Count */
   ...
   XtSetArg(al[ac], XmNtitle, "ATM User Interface Mockup"); ac++;
   XtSetArg(al[ac], XmNargc, app_argc); ac++;
   XtSetArg(al[ac], XmNargv, app_argv); ac++;
   widget0 = XtAppCreateShell ( app_name, "ATM_prototype", appli-
        cationShellWidgetClass, display, al, ac );
      ac = 0;
       ...
   XtSetArg(al[ac], XmNspacing, 30); ac++;
   XtSetArg(al[ac], XmNmarginWidth, 5); ac++;
   XtSetArg(al[ac], XmNmarginHeight, 5); ac++;
   XtSetArg(al[ac], XmNentryAlignment, XmALIGNMENT_END); ac++;
   XtSetArg(al[ac], XmNentryVerticalAlignment,
        XmALIGNMENT_BASELINE_BOTTOM); ac++;
   button_interaction_window = XmCreateRowColumn ( widget2, "but-
        ton interaction window", al, ac );
   ...
   act_button1 = XmCreatePushButton ( button_interaction_window
        "Action Button 1", al, ac );
       ...
   children[ac++] = background_field;
   children[ac++] = main_display_window;
   children[ac++] = auxiallary_interaction_window
   XtManageChildren(children, ac);
      ac = 0;
   XtAddCallback(act_button1,XmNactivateCallback,
        interface_controler.mainloop, ACT_BUTTON,1);
       ...
   children[ac++] = act_button1;
       ...
}

int main (int argc, char **argv)
{
   XtToolkitInitialize ();
   app_context = XtCreateApplicationContext ();
   display = XtOpenDisplay (app_context, NULL, argv[0],
        "ATM_prototype", NULL, 0, &argc, argv);
   create_shell ( display, argv[0], argc, argv );
   XtRealizeWidget (widget0);
   XtAppMainLoop (app_context);
     exit (0);
}
```

Figure 14.8 Fragments of executable code produced by user interface mockup tool.

Figure 12.13 gives the context for the ATM. This serves to frame the context for the database used within the ATM machine. Figure 14.1 refines that information, showing the database in the context of the rest of the ATM machine software.

Other available information is the knowledge of the partitioning of behavior between the ATM and the transaction concentrator. This was not detailed previously in the example but is assumed here. In short, the database internal to the machine is responsible for tracking short-term knowledge. It must be able to recover its own state from any exception conditions that arise. It also has to ensure that the transaction concentrator has logged any transaction that it performs. The concentrator is responsible for long-term logging of transactions and for printing all the reports required of the system. We also have available any of the other models that are developed for other parts of the system. These can be called on as needed, for clarification or possibly for introduction of change that the database subsystem requires.

As always, we proceed to the parallel design steps.

14.4.2   Behavior and structure of ATM database

Database design requires both structural modeling and behavioral modeling. It also has its own set of measurement criteria or effectiveness measures. One of the advantages that arise from designing with executable models is that the implementation is separated from the design. Thus, if, as is likely in this case, the prudent approach is to implement the database directly within a programming language, then the design can be transformed into code directly. If, on the other hand, the design calls for more highly crafted database mechanisms, the design can be transformed into a schema for use with a commercial database management system. The portion of the database design that lies within the transaction coordinator is likely to need this level of sophistication. The same design approach is employed in each case, however, with the final implementation choice postponed until the design is complete. The choice can then be made by weighing all the factors in the design.

Behavior.   Figure 14.9 gives the normal processing associated with the ATM machine database.

This behavior lies within the normal operations context presented in Fig. 14.2. Looking at this behavior, we can see that the database behavior is a linear path through a sequence of functions, with one iterative section. With the use of graphic models to view, and construct, the design of the database has made this attribute of the design plainly apparent. With the behavior laid out, we can now proceed to the database structure.

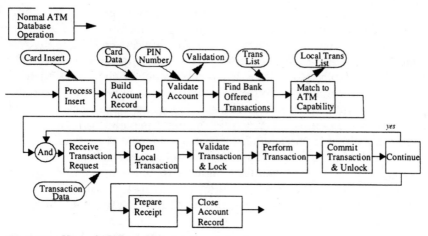

Figure 14.9   View of ATM machine database behavior.

Structure.   In designing the structure of the database, we can reflect
back on the behavior for identification of the necessary objects. Some of
the database objects will be used to store transaction-related data.
Other items will be needed to store data which is internal to the work-
ings of the system. The inputs and outputs to the process steps are
used to identify candidate items for inclusion in the database, as are
the names of the process steps. In this way the database engineer transforms the requirements given in the form of a behavior model into the
necessary structure definition. A listing of these includes

- Account
- Transaction
- Bank
- Lock
- Receipt
- Card
- PIN number

These are all candidates for representation in the database. Further
engineering analysis leads us to eliminate some of the candidates and
add others. *Card* and *PIN number* are both eliminated because they
are transitory with respect to this database. When the central ATM
system database is designed, these will be reconsidered. *Bank* is also
eliminated since there are no relevant characteristics associated with
it. *Receipt* requires more consideration. It could be made a part of the
design or could be eliminated depending on what other choices are

made. This is a decision left to database engineering experience and knowledge and cannot be based on methodology.

In our sample design we have chosen to eliminate *receipt* in favor of keeping *transaction,* which we feel more accurately names database information. *Account* and *lock* are also kept, each for a different reason. *Account* has identifying information which is needed for the duration of the database entries. *Lock* is more of a traditional database element which might be provided as part of the implementation choice or need to be modeled. In our case we choose to model it.

Beyond the initial candidates we have added a few classes. We need a class to store the information relating to the available operations that a bank offers. We also have added a class which houses the database control behavior and information. Figure 14.10 gives the OMT diagram of our design.

As with the user interface engineering, we can build this design using interactive design tools. These tools can then turn the design around into an implementation. This generation of the implementation, or at least of its structural elements, ensures that the design is accurately transformed. As with the transition between tiers of systems engineering hierarchy, the automation of the handoff eliminates the chance for introduction of error. Figure 14.11 gives one of the possible code projections from the OTM model. The same information could just

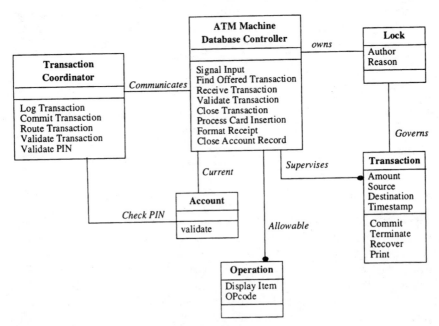

Figure 14.10   View of ATM machine database structure.

```
// DECLARATIONS FOR OMT MODULE atm
class Transaction_Coordinator;
class ATM_Machine_Database_Control;
class Account;
class Lock;
class Transaction;
class Operation;

class ATM_Machine_Database_Control
{
 public:
  void Recover_State ();
  void Find_Offered_Transaction ();
  void Receive_Transaction ();
  void Validate_Transaction ();
  void Close_Transaction ();
  void Process_Card_Insertion ();
  void Format_Receipt ();
  void Close_Account_Record ();
 protected:
  Account* ptrAccount;
  Set<Operation*> ptrOperation;
  Set<Transaction*> ptrTransaction;
  Lock* ptrLock;
  Transaction_Coordinator* ptrTransaction_Coordinator;
};

class Account
{
 public:
  void validate ();
 protected:
  ATM_Machine_Database_Control* ptrATM_Machine_Database_Control;
  Transaction_Coordinator* ptrTransaction_Coordinator;
};

class Transaction
{
 public:
  void Commit ();
  void Terminate ();
  void Recover ();
  void Print ();
 protected:
  void* Amount;
  void* Source;
  void* Destination;
  void* Timestamp;
  ATM_Machine_Database_Control* ptrATM_Machine_Database_Control;
  Lock* ptrLock;
};

class Operation
{
 protected:
  void* Display_Item;
  void* OPcode;
  ATM_Machine_Database_Control* ptrATM_Machine_Database_Control;
};
```

Figure 14.11 Automatically generated C++ database declarations.

as easily have been translated into code for implementation with the SQL (Structured Query Language) database management system.

14.5 Handoff

Handoff is one of the critical design points for any system. The requirements for each of the components must be clearly and unambiguously conveyed to the specialty engineers. As the design is passed along, the basic core technical process continues to be employed. It is also augmented with modeling techniques which are peculiar to the specialty. We have looked at only two handoffs in this chapter. In practice, there would be tens to hundreds of handoffs to a variety of specialties, even in a system of modest size such as the ATM system. Each of these needs to be handled with care and diligence.

14.6 Exercises

1. Analyze handoff to the engineering of field service and installation for ATM machines (a subset of the whole system to limit problem scope).
   a. Select useful models from the exercises of Chap. 13.
   b. Apply the six core steps and extend as needed the results of Chap. 13 to establish how installation and field service can become a competitive income-producing operation.
   c. Define the parts of the ATM machines that are involved and the kinds of information which must be supplied.
   d. Define the major elements of training required.
   e. Define repair, resale, and disposal activities.
2. Define the handoff points for the components of a computer.
3. What information is required to hand off the design of a chiller for a water cooler? How should it be presented?
4. Systems are often synthesized for existing components. How does this affect handoff?
5. What factors should be considered in determining when handoff should occur in a design?

14.7 References

Brown, C. M. L., 1988: *Human-Computer Interface Design Guidelines*. Norwood, Mass.: Ablex Publishing.

McGraw, K. L., 1992: *Designing and Evaluating User Interfaces for Knowledge-based Systems*. Englewood Cliffs, N.J.: Prentice-Hall.

15

Interface with Acquisition and Management

15.1 Introduction

The preceding chapters describe how to model all kinds of systems: products, services, businesses, processes, and plans. The same modeling techniques were applied to the systems engineering process itself, with emphasis on the technical engineering work. The major behavior models and information models for the systems engineering process are collected together for reader convenience in the last chapter.

In addition to modeling the systems engineering process, the hand-off to engineering design disciplines was described in Chap. 14. This chapter describes the remaining major interface of systems engineering: the interface with acquisition organizations and with management. The usual situation pertains. The cultures, processes, notations, and naming conventions have evolved independently such that the common abstractions and development steps are obscured. This chapter identifies the common abstractions that pertain to the interface with acquisition and management.

15.2 Introduction of Modeling into Business Cultures

The introduction of the modeling of complex systems into businesses for which it is new requires a culture change. Such an introduction can be initiated only if those in charge of setting business goals favor the change. Those in charge must see the change as one which will improve business profitability and can be integrated with the existing culture. In addition, the change must be perceived by the engineers affected as helping them with the goals, schedules, and evaluations which they must meet. This population of engineers includes not just the systems engineers but also all those who receive specifications from them or who participate on integrated teams.

The several existing cultures with which the systems engineering with models must integrate have long independent development histories. This chapter considers two types of businesses and shows how the development of systems with models is related to these traditions. The relationships are close and compatible. However, a first look at the relationships shows substantial differences in notations, the naming of things, and the views of information used. The two business types this chapter considers are the aerospace supplier industry and commercial product/service development businesses.

The aerospace industry responds to the major agencies of government and the acquisition authorities which they have established. The development of aerospace products is controlled by government budgeting and the rules of acquisition authorities. The state of system development and its best practices are summarized in the emerging systems engineering standards (IEEE P1220, 1994; EIA/ANSI, to be released). Some relationships are developed here between the P1220 standard and the six core systems engineering steps used in modeling. The EIA/ANSI standard, scheduled to be released (later this year) develops levels of abstraction higher than those included in P1220.

Commercial product and service development businesses are led and controlled by their board of directors and their management. Sophisticated techniques have been developed over the years in companies and business schools to establish a business strategy which matches products and services to the marketplace to gain competitive advantage. Management adoption and implementation of these strategies drives the systems engineering that is done. The methods, techniques, views of information, and notations used by management for strategy analysis have evolved separately from systems engineering and are different in appearance and naming conventions. However, some of the basic abstractions used by management are identical to those used by systems engineers and engineering teams, because both groups are analyzing product or services and their appeal to customers. It is likely futile to try to establish a single notation and set of views of information to be used by all. Within management circles and also within the systems engineering profession, a plethora of notations and views are in use. It is useful to select a representative modern methodology for strategic business analysis, and extract from it the basic abstractions which are common to strategic business analysis and to systems engineering. This basic understanding can then be used to transform information between business management and systems engineering teams, or to support teams that directly integrate management strategy experts with the product development team. Relationships are developed here between a representative modern methodology for commercial business strategy development (Gale, 1994) and the six core systems engineering steps.

15.3 Commercial Product/Service Development Businesses

These commercial businesses develop their own products and services, manufacture or source the parts/infrastructure, and sell their product lines/services over decades. Occasionally a totally new product or service is developed. More frequently product features are extended or new technology is introduced. There is no financial return to the business for up-front investment in new product until customers voluntarily make purchases according to their evaluation of the best offering available to them. The products range from simple systems to very large, complex systems. Competition and up-front investment in product keep the development processes lean.

A century of developing techniques for business strategy has been integrated into customer value analysis (CVA) (Gale, 1994). Some of these techniques have emerged from the pioneering work of Deming and Juran in the 1950s and its application in Japan and the United States. *Quality function deployment* and *house of quality* methods are now widely applied. Strategic planning at GE in the 1970s and studies by the profit impact of market strategy (PIMS) program demonstrated the importance in understanding related factors such as market share and market-perceived quality and value as seen by customers and prospective customers (Gale, 1994, p. 230). To the tradition of financial reporting, tight financial control, and high manufacturing quality, CVA adds market-perceived quality and value. To organizational function heads with fiefdoms, CVA adds interfunctional teams that understand competitive strategy. Analogous developments have been occurring in the development of systems. To the tradition of defining systems with text requirements, model-based systems engineering adds executable modeling for efficiency and rigor. To the earlier practices of individual engineering fiefdoms, modern engineering practice adds interdisciplinary teams that understand the system requirements and effectiveness measures. The effectiveness measures, domain analysis, and concept analysis of systems engineering are closely related to perceived quality and value in CVA.

Just as there have been many notations and methodologies applied to systems engineering, many nonfinancial measures and representations have been applied to business analysis. Often customer satisfaction, market-perceived quality, productivity, innovation, and technology trajectory are known to be important but are not presented in a way that an interfunctional team can make use of that information. One of the modern systematic presentations of the information is provided by the seven tools of CVA (Gale, 1994, p. 209):

1. Market-perceived quality profile
   - Quality related to that of competitors
   - Quality attributes with importance weights
   - Perceived quality as scored by customers for each attribute
   - Quality ratio of own product score versus competitor's score for each attribute
   - Market-perceived quality ratio as weighted average of attribute quality ratios

   For example, quality attributes for luxury cars could be trouble-free, fuel economy, aesthetics, service, comfort, drivability, rapid acceleration, large and roomy, sales environment, and brand image.

2. Market-perceived price profile
   - Competitive pricing
   - Price satisfaction attributes with importance weights
   - Price satisfaction as scored by customers
   - Relative price ratio of own product score versus competitor's score

   For example, price satisfaction attributes for luxury cars could be purchase price, trade-in allowance, resale price, and finance rates.

3. Value map
   - Relative price ratio (from 2) versus quality ratio (from 1)

4. Won/lost analysis
   - List recent sales efforts and who won or lost
   - Attach explanation

5. Head-to-head
   - Quality ratio of own product score versus competitors for each attribute
   - From 1 (above)

6. Key events timeline
   - List of important events in the marketplace

- Lists time
- Lists who is responsible

7. What/who matrix

- Quality attributes versus responsible organization

Five of these seven tools, 1, 2, 3, 5, and 7, utilize quality attributes or price-satisfaction attributes. These customer attributes correspond directly to the systems engineering effectiveness measures which are used to guide trade-off to find a near optimal design. The weighting functions used in CVA correspond to the weighting functions used to create a single cost function for trade-off. The same basic abstractions drive much of the business strategy analysis and the criteria for finding a near-optimal design for the products that implement the design in the marketplace.

In both CVA and in model-based systems engineering, it is necessary to develop many of these attributes and weights by survey of customers, operators, or others who are knowledgeable. Relative value to the customer in systems engineering is often obtained by performing concept analysis as described in Chap. 11. This provides a quantitative value number for customer-perceived value attributes based on contribution of the product to the profitability of the customer. For the situations in which it applies, quantitative modeling is an approach more rigorous than those described in CVA and yet is completely compatible with CVA. In many situations survey, not analysis, must be applied to get the desired attribute values related to customer preference. Some situations are subtle and require both. For example, a quality attribute or effectiveness measure for high-performance automobiles is rapid acceleration. This quantity can be calculated during specification and design with engineering equations from the attributes of parts such as the torque–revolutions per minute (rpm) curve for the engine, transmission ratio and friction losses, friction between tires and road, and automobile weight. The acceleration achieved can be measured on prototype cars and compared with measurements on competitors' cars. One automobile company found that their automobile had acceleration superior to that of its chief competitor but still fell behind in customer scoring of this quantity. Further analysis showed that the competitor car responded to rapid throttle advance with a slight pause, and then with a small backward flexure of the seat when acceleration began. Customers responded to the feeling of acceleration, not to the absolute fact.

Confirmation of the attribute values is often obtained as early as possible with customer survey of early product prototypes or service offerings. Examples include test marketing of long-life lightbulbs, the

GE appliance facility in Louisville appliance park for customer use of prototype appliances, prototype medical diagnostic equipment in select teaching hospitals, and early trials of cellular phones or home shopping networks. Executable specifications resulting from model-based systems engineering provide opportunity to get this confirmation earlier and at lower cost in many cases.

The optimization features of model-based systems engineering and the application of concept analysis form the interface between systems engineering and strategic management of the business. It is useful and effective to create a direct bridge using effectiveness measures and their weights and concept analysis modeling and surveys. To the extent that this is done, it becomes possible to expand the ideas of teams in the two fields: management and systems engineering. The interfunctional management team and the integrated product development team can merge. At the very early stages of development, management participation on the team is expected to be large. As the development matures and progresses, and as the team grows much larger in size, there is likely to be an increasing engineering and manufacturing presence on the team and a relatively smaller management participation. The effectiveness measures, and the executable models that produce effectiveness measure values, bind management and engineering together in this approach because the effectiveness measures are the same abstractions as the customer value satisfaction attributes and quality attributes. With executable models it is possible to project the views of information wanted by managers or by engineers because the same basic abstractions are important to both.

15.4   Modeling and Aerospace Acquisition

Aerospace businesses must respond to funded contract opportunities as they become available. The system requirements, timing, funding amount, funding rate, funding continuity, schedule, and process requirements of the contracts are largely out of their control. These determinative factors are established by Congress, the executive, and government agencies, and are influenced by the media. This is a highly technical, political, competitive, and social determinative process which considers national advantages and dangers. Systems engineering in this arena generally assumes that there will be a request for proposal (RFP) issued by an acquisition authority to which the business must respond. Typically, that RFP contains a text list of requirements to be met by the design and validated on the completed system. For large, complex systems, the requirements document can be hundreds or more pages in length. Awarded contracts define the requirements to be met, the schedule, the deliverable, the standards to be met, and extensive reviews and documentation required by the acquisition authority.

This acquisition process has resulted in the development of extremely large and complex systems which push state of the art and work under extreme conditions. The best practices of systems engineering have been described and are taught at the Defense Systems Management College (Kockler, 1990), and are appearing in emerging standards (IEEE P1220, 1994; EIA/ANSI, to be released). The acquisition process is under pressure to become more efficient because of the difficulty encountered in continuing to acquire and maintain the increasingly complex systems which are desired with the funding that is available for them.

If one considers the engineering of complex systems to be a valuable jewel, then it is different facets of that single jewel that are viewed from different directions by aerospace systems engineering, by commercial product/service development businesses, and by systems engineering using models and objects. Except for detailed knowledge of particular applications and technologies, the actual technical systems engineering work that needs to be done to develop complex systems is the same for the many types of systems. This can be seen from Fig. 15.1, which shows physical elements from which the system is built. In OMT, this would be a parts tree aggregation.

Standard P1220 provides a standardized set of names for the objects in the successive levels or tiers of decomposition/synthesis of the system. It defines a *part* as the lowest element of a physical or system architecture, specification tree, or system breakdown structure that does not need to be partitioned further (e.g., bolt, nut, bracket, semiconductor, computer software unit). This is a typical example of the parts tree or aggregation tree for the system in an OMT model.

Three very important concepts apply to Fig. 15.1:

1. What constitutes a system, product, subsystem, assembly, component, subcomponent, subassembly, or part is relative to the business dealing with it.

2. The systems engineering process applied at any of these tiers of decomposition is basically the same, a core process applied repeatedly.

3. The requirements that defined the system came from application of the systems engineering process at a higher level of decomposition, from the tier above.

15.4.1 Relativity of systems: Products

At any tier of decomposition of the system: product, subsystem, etc., any of these physical elements can be sourced from a subcontractor.

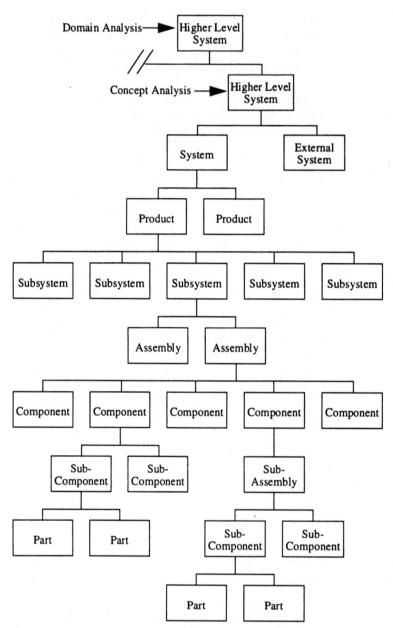

Figure 15.1 Typical P1220 system-part breakdown.

The product, subsystem, or component for which the subcontractor agrees to supply becomes the system so far as the contractor is concerned. What is the "system" is relative to what you agree to design and supply. *Systems* are systems of systems supported by an extremely large vendor network. The vendor receives a description of what is wanted and its requirements, and supplies objects that meet what is wanted, often built to a proprietary design of the subcontractor. The requirements can be supplied in several forms as text "shall" statements; as complete narrative descriptions of the excitations, responses, performance, and constraints; and as executable models of the excitations, responses, performance, constraints, and structure.

15.4.2   A core technical systems engineering process

A fully useful systems engineering process is applicable at all tiers of the contractor/subcontractor network. It is able to define fully both what a system is to do and how the system is to be built. It is able to produce both requirements and a near-optimal design solution. It must consider the systems engineering of the product, along with its integration, distribution, support, and disposal; needed product training; product test; and product manufacture.

If the process is model-based, then the process description must define the models to be used, the ordering of their use, and what they capture and transform.

15.4.3   Requirements come from the tier above

The requirements that appear in a request for proposal or a contract come from systems engineering applied at the tier above. There are aerospace businesses, often called *system integrators,* which deal primarily with the high-level generation of requirements and the coordination of subcontractors. Many other kinds of businesses, such as commercial product and service developers, do not respond to a request for proposal because they develop internally the product/service concept, its implementation as a product line over time, and how to modularize it for high levels of reuse, ease of evolution, and compatibility with earlier releases. They often outsource the majority of the product elements or service infrastructure. They control the requirements they present to their suppliers to their own internal or industry-agreed standards. From the viewpoint of this kind of business, the systems engineering process does not begin with an RFP and analysis of requirements from the RFP or a contract; it begins with analysis of the market. Descriptions of systems engineering using models takes a

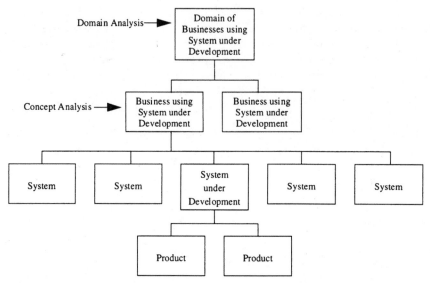

Figure 15.2 Renaming of P1220 system-part breakdown.

similar point of view. This results in two tiers of development or de-composition above system under development as shown in Fig. 15.2.

The business which purchases and uses the system will also use many other systems that must all work together. Concept analysis (Chap. 11) models the business using the system under study to es-tablish the value of that system to the business and the operators and users of the system. This may be done for a single point of time or over a period of time such as a decade to understand product evolu-tion. Domain analysis extends this to a domain of businesses using the system under development.

Very often it is desirable to sell the system to more than a single type of business. This goal makes it desirable to partition the system such that the system and the elements of the system match the differ-ent businesses' uses. This is done by domain analysis, which applies the techniques of modeling to a collection of businesses using the product. Functionality and modularity that satisfy multiple business-es are abstracted from the analysis. This is design for reuse.

A supplier business responding to an RFP often need not be con-cerned with the business and domain levels of decomposition. If there are problems with the requirements received or if it is desirable to market the resulting product to businesses other than the contractor issuing the RFP, it may be important to analyze these tiers.

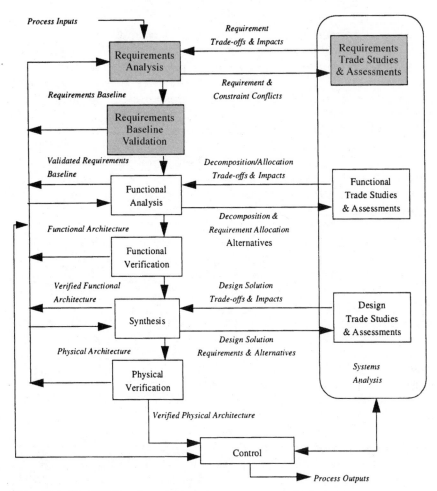

Figure 15.3   The P1220 systems engineering process.

15.4.4   P1220 systems engineering process

Figure 15.3 shows the process as described in the P1220 standard.

The P1220 standard and its detailed description of the work steps to be done does not assume the existence of an RFP with a text requirements document. Rather, the P1220 description of requirements analysis, requirements trade studies and assessments, and requirements baseline validation are a prescription for developing the requirements from information about the business, operators, and users who will utilize the system under development. This prescription can be used at the domain and concept/business levels of decomposition as well as at the lower tiers discussed in P1220. However, the partitioning of the systems engineering process differs from that used in Chap. 4. The equivalence is quite simple. The application of the six core technical modeling steps to the context of an object is equivalent to the shaded requirements-related steps. A second application of the six core technical modeling steps to the object itself is equivalent to the nonshaded steps. The same modeling process is applied twice, once to the context of the object, then to the object itself.

From the viewpoint of modeling, the requirements for a particular subject system are created by applying the six core technical steps to a domain of businesses using the subject system, or to a particular targeted business using the subject system and to the context of the subject system. The information generated is not just the requirements for the system but a context description and a partitioning that is near-optimal for a product line, for evolution of the subject system over time through a succession of releases, and for high levels of reuse. When this work is done by one organization and then the requirements are used to contract further development with other organizations, an RFP or RFPs must be written using the requirements. This is frequently the situation in the aerospace industry. In much of the commercial world a commercial product/service development company does all this work and produces requirements for the vendor network that supports it. In all cases the requirements may be in the form of text "shall" statements, narrative operations concepts, executable models, or a combination of these.

15.5 Summary

The full analysis of a system to be developed, the subject system, involves systems engineering at all the levels from domain to parts. All this work is done and controlled by commercial product/service development businesses. This work is typically partitioned among several businesses in the aerospace industry with requirements embedded in an RFP used to transfer information and contract responsibility among the organizations.

The management techniques used by commercial businesses rely heavily on quality attributes, price satisfaction attributes, and associated weighting functions. These quantities correspond directly to the effectiveness measures and the weights for a design cost function that are essential to trade-off in systems engineering. The points of view and the assigned teams can be unified by recognizing and using these common abstractions. The quality attributes and price-satisfaction attributes are the major items of information for the interface between management business strategy and the engineering of complex products and services.

The viewpoint of engineering with models and objects and the viewpoint of standard P1220 are very similar in terms of description of the detailed work steps. The major difference lies in how the steps are partitioned in the process description. From the modeling standpoint, it is useful to describe the process in a manner that shows the repeated use of a few different models. Thus the description is a single repeated core technical process of six modeling steps which is applied first to the context of an object to generate requirements and then to the object itself to generate system design. This partitioning is consistent with high levels of abstraction and with what occurs in commercial product/service development businesses. P1220 does not partition the process in this fashion. Rather, it partitions the process into requirements analysis, functional analysis and synthesis supported by trade studies, and assessments which are grouped together, generalized, as systems analysis. The partitioning of the systems engineering process with a separate partition for requirements analysis matches supplier businesses which receive requirements in an RFP from an initiating organization. The interface between the businesses responding to the RFP and the initiating organization can be bridged by augmenting the text requirements of the RFP and the text-based proposal responses with executable models. The information transfer is made more rigorous and less prone to errors of interpretation. The work can be performed in accordance with the best practices proven through use and described in standards such as P1220. After contract award, it is possible to demonstrate the progress being made by executing the models as well as by providing documentation for review.

15.6 Exercises

1. Create examples of the seven tools of customer value analysis for the ATM system.
   a. Consider the banks that own the system, the bank employees who work with it, and the customers who use it.
   b. Compare quality attributes and value attributes with effectiveness measures for the ATM machine.
2. Map the detailed steps that decompose requirements analysis, functional analysis, synthesis, validation, and systems analysis onto the six core steps applied to context of the object under development and to the object under development.
3. If the RFP-based acquisition system works to produce complex systems which push the state of the art, why does it need to change?
4. In what way(s) does the six-step core technical process differ from the emerging standards? How are they alike?

15.7   References

EIA/ANSI, (to be released): *EIA Interim Standard Systems Engineering.* Arlington, Va.: Electronic Industries Association.

Gale, B. T., 1994: *Managing customer value: Creating Quality and Service that Customers Can See.* New York: The Free Press.

IEEE P1220, 1994 (Feb.): IEEF *Trial-Use Standard for Application and Management of the Systems Engineering Process.* New York: Institute of Electrical and Electronic Engineers.

Kockler, F. R. (Defense Systems Management College), 1990: *Systems Engineering Management Guide.* Washington, D.C.: U.S. Government Printing Office, 000802001202-5.

16

Choosing Methodology

16.1 Tailoring Metaprocess to Methodology

This chapter focuses on the alternatives that exist in modeling systems. The alternatives and tailorability of the systems engineering metaprocess are very broad. Yet a team developing a large, complex system needs to perform its work efficiently with high levels of information exchange among the large numbers of team members. The team must proceed with a consistent set of engineering steps, views of information, notations for that information, and reviews of progress. The team needs to work with a methodology that they can apply efficiently. The metaprocess must be tailored and particularized for the teams.

Although the engineering steps and notations presented in this book can be used directly as a pattern for a methodology, in many cases it will be most profitable to fit the methodology to the existing culture and experience of the workforce. The workforce may be trained in aerospace-style systems engineering, in one of the forms of object-oriented software development, in the structured analysis type of software development, or some other tradition. A near-optimal solution to this process system problem is to match the proven best practices of systems engineering to existing culture, because training is very expensive. Some heuristics for tailoring are

Utilize proven best practices as incorporated in the core technical process and described detail in texts (Blanchard and Fabrycky, 1990).

Decide how the system development will be partitioned among the teams:

- By a system parts list, which emphasizes subsystems to components
- By functional groupings, which emphasizes similar functions

- By partitioning the context into weakly interacting regions, which emphasizes response to excitation without predetermining functional groupings or decomposition into parts

Select the views of information to be used and the notation for the views:

- The views must span the work to be done.
- The team members must be trained to understand and work with the views.
- Training costs and errors from misunderstanding will be minimized if the workforce has experience with most of the views and notations selected.

Tailor the assignment and sequencing of engineering steps to the workforce and the application:

- In some organizations there is a long-term culture of some groups performing analysis of text requirements, behavior, and structure; and separate groups doing performance analysis.
- Choose to either partition the core technical process among teams, or to have teams execute the whole core technical process on their assigned partition of the system.
- Either encourage the teams to use the concurrency among the core engineering steps creatively, or give them a recommended sequence of development for those concurrent steps.
- In some applications the objects are well known in advance, and creating structure models first makes sense.
- In other applications functionality and excitation behavior are known most thoroughly, and creating behavior models first makes sense.
- Sometimes the effectiveness measures have either been well defined so they can be accepted early, or they badly need definition to guide the development and teams so that doing effectiveness measures first makes sense.

Incorporate a well-defined process for handling the unexpected discoveries made by the team during development and for handling the late discoveries made by sponsors and then required of the development.

- The discoveries will interrupt the ongoing systems engineering work at any point and send it back to some other point.
- An instituted process and supporting organizational structure is required to handle the discoveries.

16.2   Best Practices and Views of Information

As had been shown in this book, systems engineering has its own best practices, which have been refined for many decades. Several of these best practices have a great impact on the information generated, on the views of information which are used in modeling, and on process steps which are critical to any methodology used for systems engineering. Among these best practices are

1. Hierarchical development in tiers inclusive of domain analysis, concept analysis, system analysis, subsystem analysis, sub-subsystem analysis, and so on down to component analysis. It may be top–down (decomposition) or bottom–up (synthesis).

2. Specification of what a system is to do, including its behavior, separate from how it is to be built, leaving design to design engineering teams. This enforces separation of behavior models from structure models.

3. Creation of trade-off criteria and use of a trade-off process step to find a near-optimal system solution from a multitude of possible solutions. This is made efficient by using alternative mappings of behavior onto structures of alternative sets of components to develop a set of alternative designs for evaluation. Separate models of behavior and structure are needed to make this practice efficient.

4. Creation or refinement of an implementation plan at each tier of development.

16.3   Views of Information in Systems Engineering

The two primary views of information are those of structure and behavior. They are kept separate as views for purposes of specification and trade-off. They are merged by the allocation or mapping of behavior onto the structure for a complete model of the system, subsystem, or component. Figure 16.1 shows this separation and the mapping. There remains the issue of what are the possible views of behavior and of structure.

16.3.1   Possible views of structure

Description of structure requires aggregation or parts list, interconnection, and classification, all annotated with number. This results in a primary view of structure and six subsidiary partial views:

1. Aggregation, interconnections, and classification; subsidiary partial views:

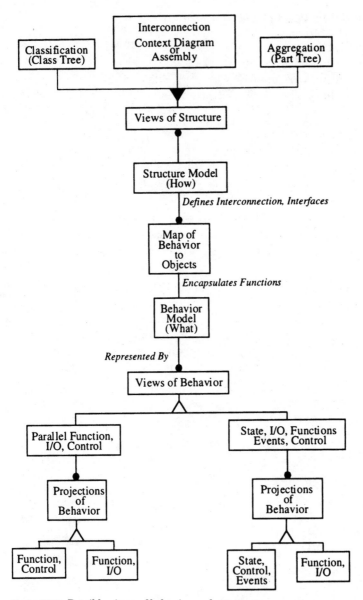

Figure 16.1 Possible views of behavior and structure.

1.1. Aggregation or parts list
1.2. Interconnection
1.3. Classification
1.4. Aggregation with interconnection
1.5. Aggregation with classification
1.6. Interconnection with classification

16.3.2 Possible views of behavior

Description of behavior requires function, control (ordering of functions), and input/output. There are also two ways of representing concurrent functions; more than one function is executing at a given time, the predominant situation in large systems. One can describe what is occurring at a given time and call it *state,* or one can describe the functions as *parallel functions.* This results in two primary choices in views of behavior, each of which has subsidiary partial views.

1. Parallel function, control, and input/output
   1.1. Parallel function and control
   1.2. Parallel function and input/output
   1.3. Input/output and control
2. State, control, events, function, and input/output
   2.1. State, control, and events
   2.2. Function and input/output

Views of behavior and notations.   These views are collections of information which can be represented with many different graphic or text notations. Some of the popular notations are listed below.

1. Parallel function, control, and input/output—behavior diagrams
   1.1. Parallel function and control—functional flow block diagrams
   1.2. Parallel function and input/output—activity charts, data flow diagrams, N-squared diagrams
   1.3. Input/output and control—control flow diagrams
2. State, control, events, function, and input/output—example not known
   2.1. State, control, and events—statecharts
   2.2. Function and input/output—activity charts, data-flow diagrams, N-squared charts

All of these possible views of behavior, with one exception, are in use and are supported with tools. The exception is 2 (above)—state, control, events, function, and input/output—which would be difficult to represent in a single diagram. Systems engineering tools tend to neglect structure 1.3, classification. Software engineering tools tend to neglect the primary behavior views based on parallel function and to emphasize state.

Statecharts rather than state transition diagrams are included in behavior 2.1 because state transition diagrams are limited in their ability to model real systems and are not hierarchical. Statecharts have removed those limitations. In addition there is a close relationship between functional flow block diagrams and statecharts.

The IDEF notations have not been included in this discussion because they now lack some elements that are needed for executability.

In systems engineering intrinsic sequences of functions may be made concurrent by pipelining, and intrinsically concurrent and independent functions may be serialized for performance reasons. These transformations preserve what the system does and optimize performance. They change the states, so that the state pictures must be transformed also.

16.3.3 Equivalences: statechart and functional flow block diagrams

Statecharts (Harel, 1987) have the advantages of being hierarchical, of having a well-defined relationship with functions, and of defining AND states that reduce the problem of state explosion. State explosion occurs when one considers problems such as five elevators serving 30 floors of a building. The total number of different simultaneous functions and conditions, up–down, stopped, floor, for the system of five elevators is too large to serve as a useful representation of the problem. Statecharts have been integrated into some software engineering methodologies (Rumbaugh et al., 1991), (Selic et al., 1994).

As is generally the case with different languages, there will be certain expressions which can be written in one of the languages with no equivalent in the other. In spite of this fact, it is often the case that a significant span of modeling can be written in both languages with translation between the two. This is the case for FFBDs and statecharts.

Statecharts represent states as shown in Fig. 16.2.

Functions in FFBDs correspond to activities in statecharts. Sequence

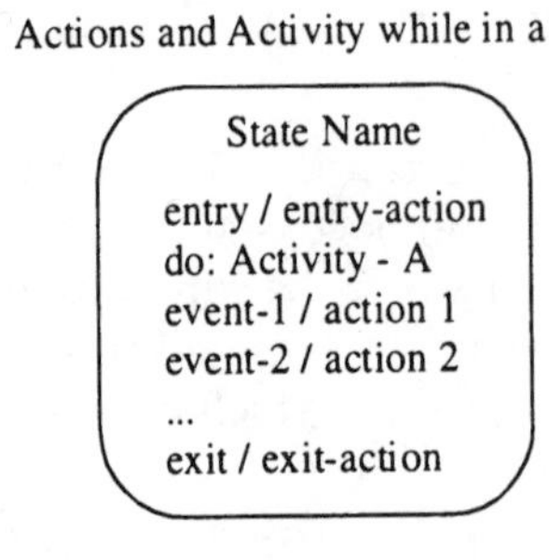

Actions and Activity while in a State

State Name

entry / entry-action
do: Activity - A
event-1 / action 1
event-2 / action 2
...
exit / exit-action

Figure 16.2 States in statecharts.

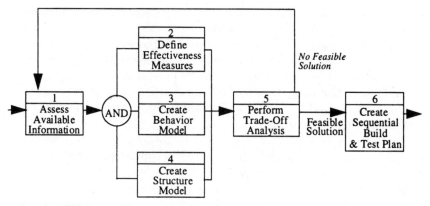

Figure 16.3 FFBD view of core technical steps.

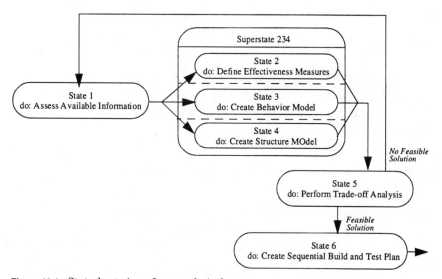

Figure 16.4 Statechart view of core technical steps.

in FFBDs results in sequential states in statecharts. A selection in FFBDs corresponds to transition to states with corresponding activities in statecharts. Concurrency in FFBDs, AND, corresponds to AND states in statecharts. This can be shown by comparing the core technical steps in FFBD notation and statechart notation (see Figs. 16.3 and 16.4).

16.4   Some Methodology Problems and Differences

The fact that different methodologies can express what needs to be expressed in their respective notations is not sufficient for them to be applied in the same engineering discipline. Object modeling technique (OMT), for example, uses statecharts, data-flow diagrams, and the needed structural associations (Rumbaugh et al., 1991). However, OMT does not apply its process to a hierarchy of tiers to deal with domain analysis through component specification. The process of OMT omits three of the core steps shown in Fig. 16.3. It does not formalize core steps 2, 5, and 6. It does not combine statecharts and data-flow diagrams into an executable behavior.

Real-time object-oriented modeling technique (ROOM) also uses statecharts (Selic et al., 1994, pp. 484–486). However, ROOM does not use the AND state construction which captures concurrency. Large, complex systems have tremendous concurrency at their top level. Best practice in systems engineering captures this concurrency independently of structure, and then allocates it to different possible structures.

In selecting a methodology and tool support for modeling in systems engineering, it is essential that the language and notation can capture the systems engineering information. It is equally important that the methodology contain all the steps needed for executing best systems engineering practices.

One of the best practices which needs further comment is control of change when the unexpected is discovered, as always happens in developing large, complex systems.

16.5 Discovery and the Change Control Process

In real applications the forward process is never followed without interruption because customers discover that requirements must change, engineers discover technical problems, and management discovers need for funding and schedule changes. These changes cause the engineering work to be interrupted at some step of the process. They force an assessment of impact of the discovery, and work is resumed at some different step in the process. Since the work is interrupted at any step and may resume at any other step, these impacts cannot be described in a work flow diagram.

The real engineering work conditions can be rigorously described. The change control process describes identification of the need for change, change impact assessment, change authorization, change planning, change execution, and process improvement based on analysis of change causes.

The word *discovery* is used here rather than *error report* or *bug report* because it is very valuable to find these unknown issues as early as possible to minimize development cost and to use the discoveries as the precious information that can improve the process.

Although all large programs experience imposed change and discovery, the published life-cycle models do not model the critically important change management process. The waterfall life cycle (Royce, 1987) does not show all the potential feedback loops among phases because those loops can begin anywhere and end anywhere. The spiral model (Boehm, 1986) does not describe the criteria and issues which are drivers for the successive product prototypes, releases, and partial builds.

16.5.1 The change control process description

The change process begins when someone discovers issues that demand a change in the project. This discovery may be made at any level of authority. The discovery may cause the project to interrupt work at any step of the engineering process and to go to any other step.

The change process is shown in Fig. 16.5.

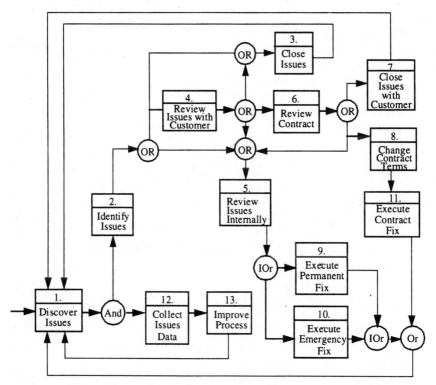

Figure 16.5 FFBD view of the change control process.

There are two major branches to the set of change process functions. The upper branch describes the set of tasks which resolve the issues by making changes to the analysis, design, and implementation of the system being built. The lower branch describes the set of tasks which report the changes, track the changes to cause, and alter the engineering and manufacturing processes in use so that the occurrence of a detected type of issue is reduced. The lower branch uses the occurrence-of-issue discovery to improve the engineering and manufacturing processes. Its purpose is to reduce variance in the engineering and manufacturing processes. It is a critical aspect of quality analysis. Too often the person who discovers and reports issues early is punished rather than rewarded, and the discoveries are not used to improve the business.

16.5.2   Change to the system: upper branch

Figure 16.5 shows that the first step for system improvement (step 2) is to identify and analyze the issues. The analysis produces a description of the issue, a technical analysis of the impact of the issue, and a category and priority for the issue. For large, complex programs there will be many open issues at any point of time. Subsequently any of three actions is taken: first the issue is closed (step 3), second the issue is reviewed internally (step 5), or third the issue is reviewed (step 4) with the customer or with marketing if it affects contract terms or if it impacts the acceptance of the product by customers in the marketplace.

Tasks 4 and 6 of Fig. 16.5 imply review not only of a formal contract with a customer but also of the less-formal requirements and understanding between engineering and marketing functions. This type of understanding is critical for commercial business which make no sales if their new products do not fit the marketplace. In both situations it is essential to

- Describe the issue to the customer or marketing in language they understand.
- Analyze the impact of the issue with the customer or marketing.
- Listen to customers or marketing evaluate impact, which may be foreign to the engineers, in their own language, which may also be foreign to the engineers.
- Set priorities if there are multiple issues.
- Categorize the issues as unimportant, as not really affecting contract (hence internal), or as affecting the contract.

For those issues that affect contract, there is a contract review (step 6) in Fig. 16.5, which must detail a plan, a change proposal, to fix the issues with associated cost and schedule. That plan must be reviewed by customers, marketing, and management. There must be an agreement on how the issues are to be resolved. The proposed changes and schedule may be accepted as a contract change, may be downgraded as an internal issue to be corrected without change to budget and schedule, or may be judged not to be worth the time, risk, and effort to fix. Accordingly, Fig. 16.5 shows branching from step 6 to steps 5, 7, and 8.

Internal review (step 5) is very similar to review with the customer (step 4). In this case it is carried out within the project. The size of the project dictates how formally such reviews are conducted and how the power of decision is allocated in the organization. Very large projects with hundreds to thousands of workers require much more formality and carefully assigned boards and responsibility than do small projects with only a handful of staff.

During the internal review (step 5), the project plans the permanent fix (step 9). In some cases it is necessary to execute an emergency fix (step 10). Because this may have to occur very rapidly, quick procedures may be put in place to make sure that the identification of the issue and review/authority to make a fix (steps 2 and 5) occur without delay. This is particularly true for modifications to systems requiring high availability that are in use and in the maintenance phase.

If the contract terms must be changed, then system development continues on the basis of the change, and the discovery of issues is continuous.

16.5.3 Process improvement

The early discovery of issues reduces the risk of the project going over cost, missing delivery time, and missing the market needs. These discoveries can be used to improve the engineering and manufacturing processes so that fewer issues will be discovered in the future. To accomplish this, it is necessary to collect the issues data (step 12), and then analyze and use that information to define and implement process improvements (step 13).

In step 12 it is necessary to collect and report the status of issues to understand the frequency of testing and review, the frequency of issue discovery, and how well the issue resolution process is working. These data also give a picture of how well the project is proceeding toward a robust, validated integration. It is also necessary to track the issues to their cause and collect that cause data. The cost of rectifying the issue needs to be collect and associated with the cause of the issue. This information is essential to prioritizing which parts of the engineering and manufacturing process should be targeted for improvement to gain the most in efficiency of the work and reduce cost and risk.

To implement process improvement, it is necessary to identify process deficiencies, prioritize the importance of the deficiencies, create a plan to improve the process, compare cost of the improvement with the cost of the issues, and then execute the cost-effective plans.

Real projects always make discoveries and encounter issues as described above. A life-cycle model which depicts what really happens on projects must include a change control process similar to the one just described. The implementation of a change control process may be very formal and complex for large projects or simple and less formal for small projects.

Unless staff are rewarded for discovering and rectifying issues as early as possible, issues will be uncovered late when they are expensive. Unless the information obtained as a result of the discoveries is used to improve the engineering and manufacturing processes, productivity will lag. Process improvement must be funded and rewarded.

16.6   Concluding Remarks

Systems engineering, as defined in the introduction, is an art. It requires training, experience, and creativity to work efficiently through the large solution space of systems problems (an NP-complete class of problems). The solutions are a near-optimal application of available resources and scientific understanding to meet the needs of people.

The modeling described in this book is a technique that uses the laws of science and logic to capture the system information once rigorously, and then to transform and express it in the views needed by all the stakeholders to the system problem. The transformations are essential because the stakeholders have very different backgrounds, information needs, and training.

The modeling is not a substitute for training, experience, and creativity. If applied blindly, the modeling will lead to unnecessarily large models which do not converge rapidly to a near-optimal solution. It is important to apply the modeling with well-developed heuristics such as the technical systems engineering process of six core steps. The core steps must be applied creatively to discover the unexpected and highly valuable solutions that have greatest value and lowest cost. They must be applied creatively to find a solution rapidly by discarding engineering directions that will not be useful, yet without missing the discovery of highly valuable solutions. Discovery is the heart of the art of engineering.

Discovery is the finding of unexpected valuable solutions and also unexpected and important issues. The forward work may be interrupted at any time by the discovery of an issue that requires looping back to earlier stages of work for resolution. Thus there is a change control process in parallel with the technical systems engineering process. It is critical. It is the feedback that stabilizes the process and ensures convergence. Some recommendations:

- Institutionalize proven best practices.

- Use modeling as extensively as the applications, organization culture, management support, and investment realities allow.

- Tailor a good systems engineering metaprocess to a methodology for your organization.

- Include both a technical engineering process and a change control process.

- Introduce new process, training, or tools first on projects of modest size and relatively short duration to prove what works quickly. Then scale up.

Systems engineering requires a rich and broad perspective. It is a compound of art, training, experience, creativity, scientific understanding, awareness of technology, and discovery—applied to meet the needs of people individually, as nations and as a world. Meeting needs is exciting. Discovery is exciting. The authors wish you exciting careers.

16.7 Exercises

1. Describe the methodologies for capturing structure information. Are there elements of structure which they fail to capture?

2. Describe the relationship of data-flow diagrams to statecharts.

3. Model the impact of a requirement that the ATM system be able to process loan requests.

4. How do the core steps minimize design change?

5. Describe the impact of change control on quality.

16.8 References

Blanchard, B. F., and W. Fabrycky, 1990: *Systems Engineering and Analysis,* 2d ed., Englewood Cliffs, N.J.: Prentice-Hall.

Boehm, B. W., 1986: A spiral model of software development and enhancement. *ACM Sigsoft Eng. Notes* **11**(4), 22–42.

Harel, D., 1987: Statecharts: A visual formalism for complex systems. *Sci. Comput. Program.* **8,** 231–274.

Royce, W. W., 1987: Management of the development of large software systems: Concepts and techniques. *Proc. ICSE,* vol. 9. New York: IEEE Computer Society Press.

Rumbaugh, J., M. Blaha, W. J. Premerlani, F. Eddy, and W. Lorensen, 1991: *Object-Oriented Modeling and Design.* Englewood Cliffs, N.J.: Prentice-Hall.

Selic, B., G. Gullekson, and P. T. Ward, 1994: *Real-Time Object-Oriented Modeling.* New York: Wiley.

A Collection of Process and Information Models

For the convenience of readers, the major process and information models distributed throughout the book are collected here (Figs. 17.1 to 17.23) in one place for ready reference.

1. Part list or aggregation ◊
2. Classification or generalization/specialization △
3. Assembly or association ───────
4. Context (next nearest neighbors) or association ───────
5. Multiplicity or number ● zero or more ○ one or more   annotation
6. Classes of objects
7. Instances of objects
8. Attributes of objects - weight, size...
9. Functions or operations of objects

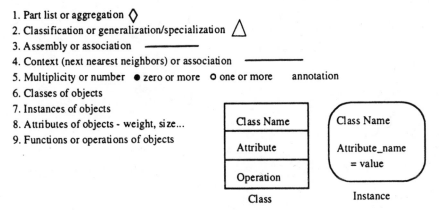

Figure 17.1 Semantics and symbols for executable structure.

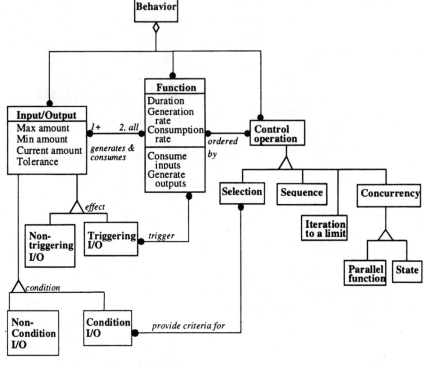

Figure 17.2   Information model for behavior.

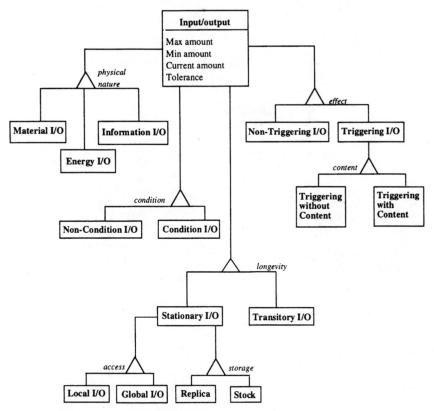

Figure 17.3   Information model for input/output.

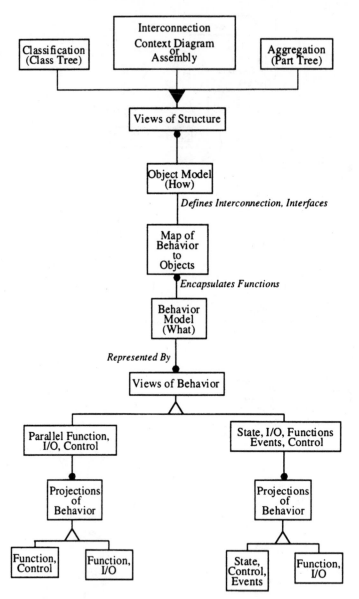

Figure 17.4 Behavior-and-structure information model.

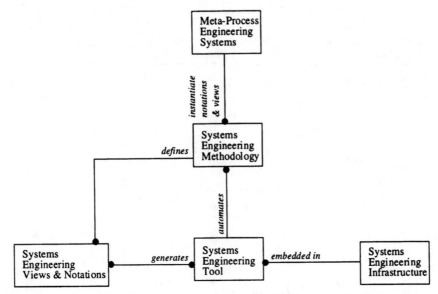

Figure 17.5 Associations between metaprocess, methodology, tools, and infrastructure.

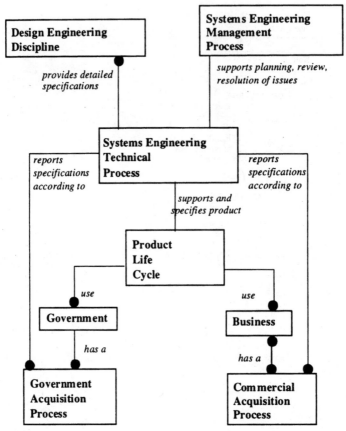

Figure 17.6   Associations between process, product life cycle, and acquisition.

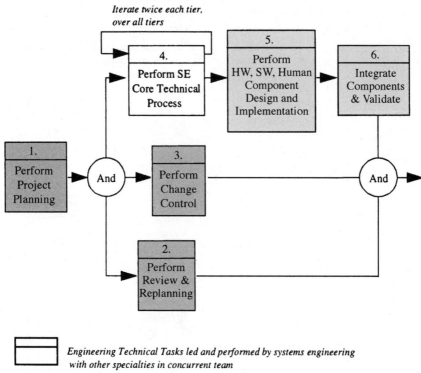

Figure 17.7   Model for the systems engineering process.

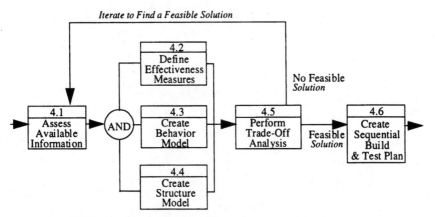

Figure 17.8   FFBD view for the systems engineering core technical process.

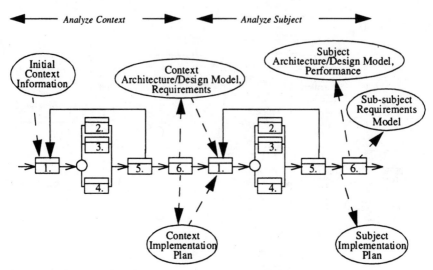

Figure 17.9 Sequential application of core technical process to context and subject.

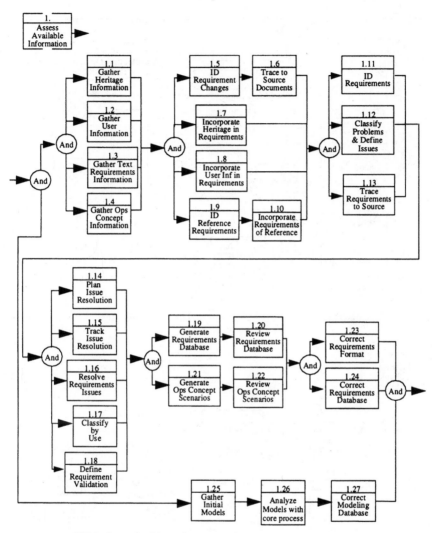

Figure 17.10   FFBD decomposition of core step 1.

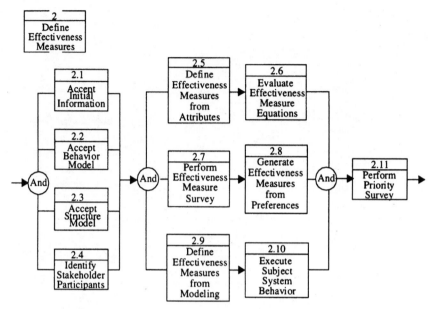

Figure 17.11   FFBD view of defining effectiveness measures, core step 2.

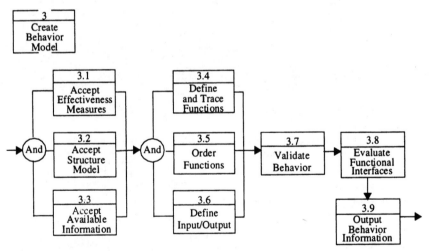

Figure 17.12   FFBD view of core step 3.

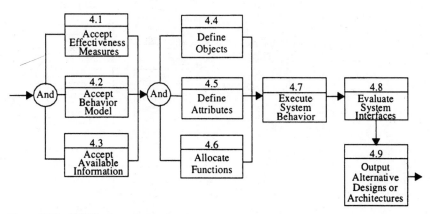

Figure 17.13 FFBD view of core step 4.

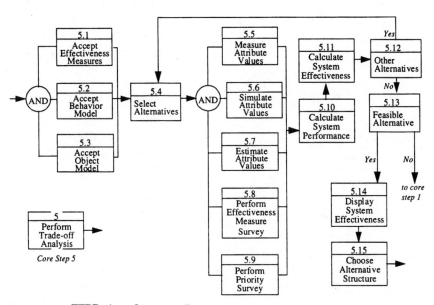

Figure 17.14 FFBD view of core step 5.

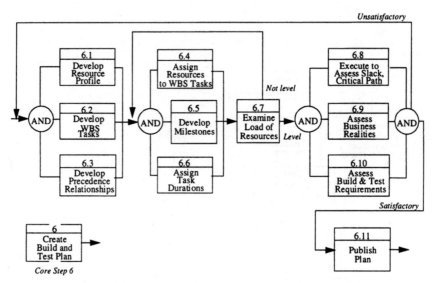

Figure 17.15   FFBD view of core step 6.

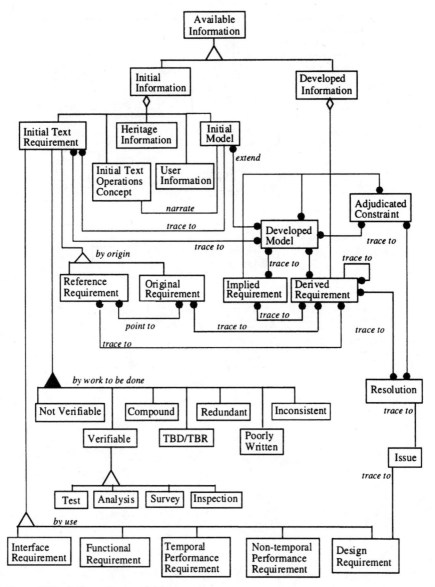

Figure 17.16 Information model for requirements.

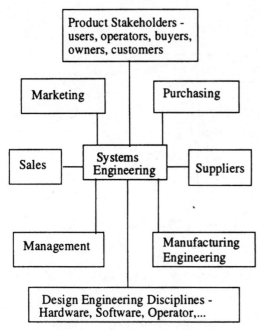

Figure 17.17 Context for systems engineering.

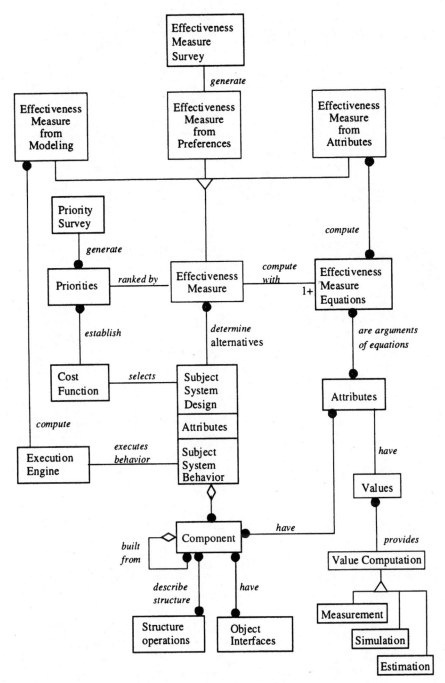

Figure 17.18   Information model for creating effectiveness measures.

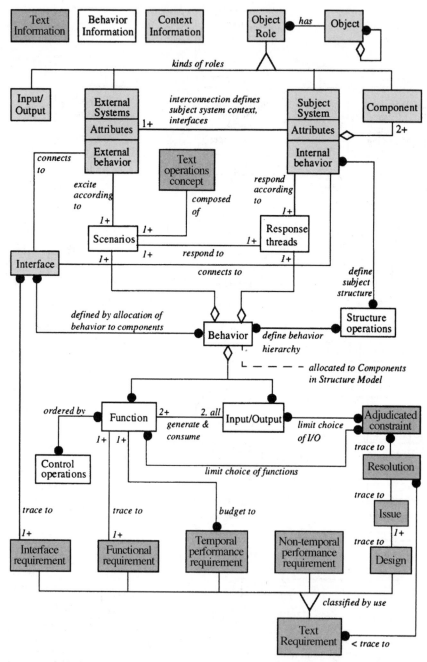

Figure 17.19 Information model for text requirements, behavior, and context.

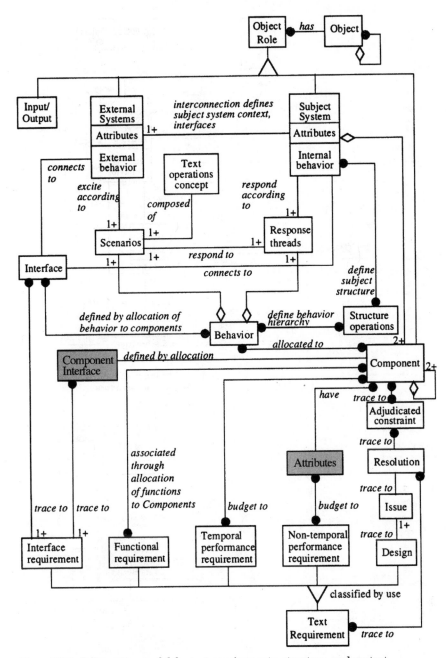

Figure 17.20 Information model for text requirements, structure, and context.

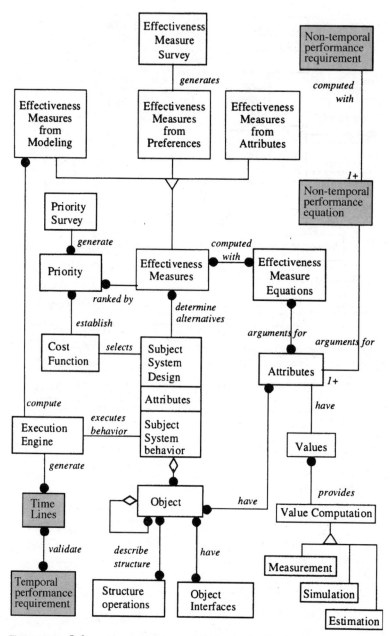

Figure 17.21   Information model for performing tradeoff analysis.

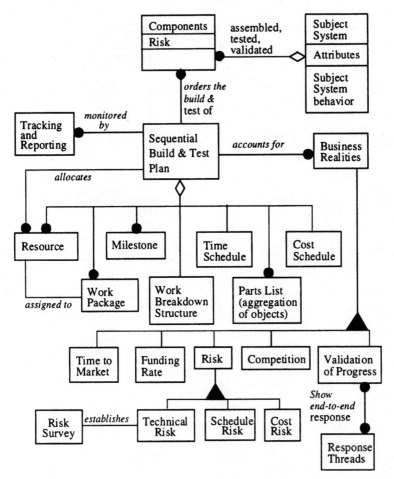

Figure 17.22   Information model for core step 6.

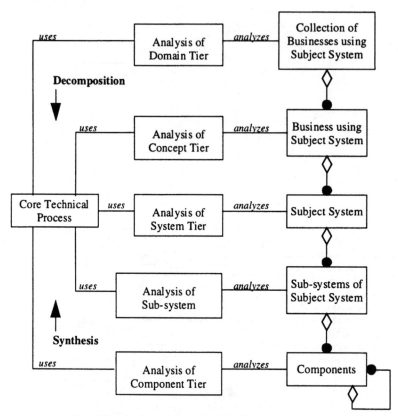

Figure 17.23 Tiers of analysis and decomposition/synthesis.

Index

ABOUT THE AUTHORS

DAVID W. OLIVER, PH.D., is a consultant who has performed research and development in systems engineering, software engineering, factory automation, microwaves, material science, semiconductor processing, and high-frequency ultrasound. He managed the factory automation, computer science, and technology transition from the General Electric Corporate Research and Development Center to all General Electric departments.

TIMOTHY P. KELLIHER develops methodologies and tools for human-computer interfaces (HCI), systems understanding, and Internet-based applications. He works at the General Electric Corporate Research and Development Center.

JAMES G. KEEGAN, JR., is a technical editor and writer whose documentation firm produces technical publications for a wide range of applications and audiences.